Algrove Publishing Limited
1090 Morrison Drive
Ottawa, Ontario
Canada K2H 1C2

Canadian Cataloguing in Publication Data

Main entry under title:

　　Popular mechanics shop notes for ...

(Classic reprint series)
Includes indexes.
Originally published: Chicago : Popular Mechanics Co., 1905-
"Compiled from the "Shop notes" department of Popular mechanics
　　magazine, and "Written so you can understand it;" tells easy
　　ways to do hard things" --Added t.p., v. 1.
Cover title.
Contents: v. 23. 1927.
ISBN 1-894572-29-7 (v. 23)

　　1. Do-it-yourself work. 2. Industrial arts. 3. Bricolage. 4. Métiers. I. Title: Shop notes for ... . II. Series: Classic reprint series (Ottawa, Ont.)

TJ1160.P66 1999   600   C99-900763-7

Printed in Canada
#10401

Publisher's Note

Virtually every woodworking magazine in the English-speaking world has a shop notes section and has published an accumulation of them in book form. This was all started in 1905 with the first annual issue of *Popular Mechanics Shop Notes*, a compilation of advice on jigs, fixtures, methods of work, processes and projects. The earlier issues focussed primarily on metalworking, but with tips for a variety of other trades liberally sprinkled throughout. As years went by, the contents shifted more and more to woodworking and handyman projects. Each book is profusely illustrated. The line drawings of the earlier issues were supplanted by superb engravings until photographs started to creep in during the 1920s. Each year has its charm but all issues share the attribute of being clear, concise and widely informative.

Leonard G. Lee, Publisher
Ottawa
September, 1999

WARNING

This is a reprint of a book compiled in the early 1900s. The book describes what was recommended to be done in accordance with the knowledge of the day.

It would be advisable to treat all corrosive, explosive and toxic materials with much greater caution than is indicated here, particularly any materials that come in contact with the body.

Similarly, some of the recommended projects were dangerous then and remain so now. All of this material should be regarded with a judicious eye and necessary precautions taken.

Popular Mechanics Building

Devoted exclusively to the publishing and distributing of Popular Mechanics Magazine and books of interest to everyone. It contains presses that turn out the equal of 35,000 magazines and books each working day.

Popular Mechanics Press

Publishes books in the same clear, concise language as is used in Popular Mechanics Magazine. Books now ready for delivery that will be of value to:

Machine Operators	Automobile Mechanics	Contractors
Shop Foremen	Electricians	Farmers
Machinists	Carpenters	Mechanical Engineers
Shop Owners	Photographers	Railroad Mechanics
Factory Superintendents	Draftsmen	Foundry Workers
Inventors	Welders	Painters and Decorators
Patternmakers	Plumbers	Steam Fitters
Merchants	Marine Engineers	Laboratory Workers
Scientists	Teachers	Sheet Metal Workers
Vulcanizers	Tool Makers	Boys mechanically inclined

—in fact, for everyone who has the slightest mechanical instinct, including women.

All Popular Mechanics literature is "Written so you can understand it."
Complete illustrated catalog of books free upon request.

Popular Mechanics Press, Room 107 Popular Mechanics Building, Chicago, Ill.

Printed in U. S. A.

POPULAR MECHANICS

SHOP NOTES

FOR 1927

VOLUME XXIII

WITH 374 ILLUSTRATIONS

———

POPULAR MECHANICS PRESS
CHICAGO

THE wide range of subjects covered in this 1927 issue of Shop Notes is indicated by the following partial list. Most readers will probably be interested in some of these, and many will derive benefit from all the 479 articles.

AUTOMOBILE REPAIRING	IRRIGATION CANALS
BATTERY WORKER	JEWELER
BRASS WORKER	LATHE WORK
BUILDER	LUBRICATING
CARPENTER	MACHINE REPAIRING
CLEANING	MECHANICAL DRAWING
CONCRETE WORKING	PAINTING
DAIRYMAN	PLANER WORK
DECORATING	PLUMBING
DRAFTING	POLISHING
DRAINAGE	RAILROADING
DRILLING METHODS	REPAIRMAN
ELECTRICITY	SHEET METAL WORKER
ELECTROPLATING	SHOP MANAGEMENT
FARMING	SOLDERING
FILING	STORAGE BATTERIES
FURNITURE MAKING	TOOL MAKER
GARDENING	VENTILATION
GARAGE OWNER	WELDING
GLAZIER	WINDOW TRIMMING
GRINDER WORK	WIRE WORKING
HOME MECHANICS	WOOD TURNING

Complete Index, Page 205

Shop Notes

A Jigsaw for a Dollar

By M. ORDAHL

WANTING a jigsaw for his shop, but not having the wherewithal at the moment to buy one, a mechanic set out to improvise one. After thinking the matter of a suitable mechanism over for some time. he decided that the easiest thing from which to make it was an old sewing machine. Half an hour's search of the secondhand stores in the neighborhood resulted in his parting with a dollar and acquiring an old head, the insides of which were all present and in good order.

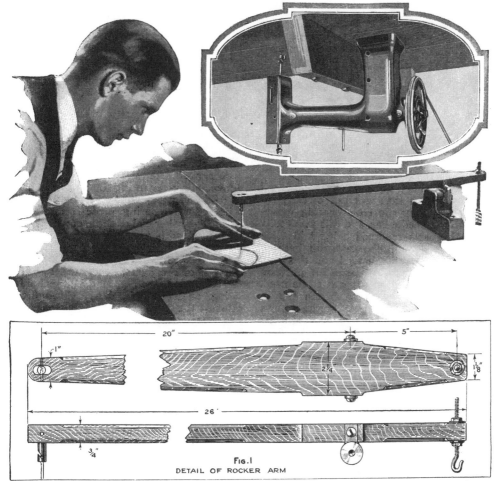

Fig.1
DETAIL OF ROCKER ARM

A Jigsaw Made from an Old Sewing-Machine Head; Insert, the Head in Position under the Bench; Below, the Rocker Arm

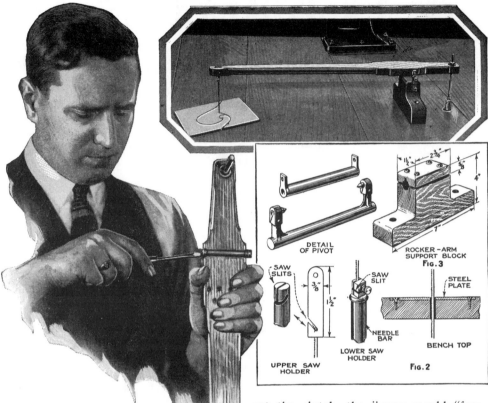

Above, Top View of the Completed Machine; Left, Fastening the Pivot; Right, Details of the Various Parts

The first thing done was to remove all the mechanism that was not directly involved in giving the reciprocating movement to the needle bar, and this was easily done, the parts removed being laid aside for the moment. The cast-iron base of the head was then removed and the head turned upside down and placed in position under the bench where it was to be used. Holes were drilled in the bench top to correspond to the position of the screws that formerly held the base, the old holes in the head tapped out to fit ¼-in. capscrews, and the head fastened in place. The heads of the capscrews were counterbored into the bench top so as not to interfere with the work, and a small hole was drilled in the top of the bench in line with the end of the needle bar.

As the saw was to be driven from a small motor mounted on the base of the bench, the flywheel was removed from the sewing machine and grooved for a ¼-in. round belt. There was plenty of stock for this. Incidentally, the wheel had a small clutch that was used when winding bobbins, and this worked in very nicely, as, by throwing

out the clutch, the jigsaw would "freewheel" while the motor was in use for other purposes.

A rocker arm was next made to the dimensions given in Fig. 1. This was made of oak, and was provided at one end with a hook for the spring, made from a ¼-in. bolt. The other end of the arm was slotted and fitted with a saw holder. This was made from a short piece of ⅜-in. cold-rolled steel, slit with the hacksaw to admit the end of the jigsaw blade and to catch the blade pins (see Fig. 2). The saw holder swings on a brass pin, driven through the sides of the arm. Upon looking over the parts taken from the underside of the sewing-machine head, a pivot and pivoted shaft were found, which, with a few minutes' work, were adapted to form a pivot for the rocker arm. One of the parts had two lugs that were cut off to length, drilled for small wood screws and fastened to the rocker arm. The other part had two adjusting-screw centers and was fitted into a support block, made as shown in Fig. 3. This, in turn, was bolted to the top of the bench and the arm slipped into place and adjusted by means of the pivot screws. Directly below the hook on the rear end of the arm, a hole was bored in the bench, and a spring (taken from an old bed spring) hooked on, passed through the hole and held in place by means of a short piece of ¼-in. rod through the end.

It was only found necessary to cut a cross slit in the end of the needle bar in the head to adapt it to holding the saws. The top of the bench was recessed to take a sheet-steel plate, through which the saw passed, and the saw was complete.

The motor driving the saw has a speed of 1,750 r. p. m. The grooved wheel on the saw is approximately 5½ in. in diameter, and a 3-in. pulley on the motor will run the saw at a satisfactory speed.

Washing Auto Windows

For washing automobile windows that have become covered with oil, dirt or dust, the following formula will be found excellent: 1 gal. water, ½ cup alcohol, ½ cup ammonia, and 1 tablespoon salt. The water, of course, serves its usual function as a cleanser, the alcohol aids in drying and saves a lot of rubbing, and the ammonia and salt cut the grease and fix the luster on the glass. This is splendid for general window washing also, and to give a high luster to fine cut glass.

Improving the Crowbar

Crowbars of the usual type can be greatly improved by providing a handle at one end, as shown in the photo. This prevents blistering of the hands and the bar can be manipulated more conveniently. To make this handle, one end of the bar is split with a hacksaw and the halves rounded to form the sides and handle. A short piece of pipe is slipped over the ends just before they are bent together.

Non-Blistering Handle on Crowbar Increases Ease of Manipulation

A 5½-ft. bar has been found most convenient for farm work, and for chopping through ice, frozen ground, etc.

Building Tapering Brick Pilasters

Building tapering brick pilasters seemed a difficult job, but proved quite easy with the aid of the guides shown in the photo. Two lengths of 1 by 3-in. stock were

Guide for Erecting Tapering Brick Pilasters Saves Time

cut to the required height. These were braced by smaller crosspieces, and wires were used to hold the sides together. The pilasters were then built up inside. This method proved timesaving and enabled the builder to make all the pilasters alike. —E. J. Veronda, South Pasadena, Calif.

Relief for "Burning" Feet

Workmen in machine shops and garages will find relief from "burning" or "scalding" feet, if they cut an inner sole for their shoes from ordinary cork gasket or packing material. After cutting the cork to fit, it is securely fastened in the shoes by shellacking the bottom side of the cork and applying a light coat along the middle of the sole. If the size of the shoe permits, make these inner soles of two thicknesses of cork.

¶When making ring gauges, always leave a thin collar on each end of the hole, so that any bell-mouthing in lapping can be ground off.

Paint-Pot Hanger

Nearly all paint-pot hangers are arranged for use on a ladder, or to attach to some place on the wall which is suited

Simple Paint-Pot Hanger for Shingled Walls

for the purpose. The one shown in the illustration is designed for use when painting a shingled house. It consists of a piece of hardwood, 6 or 8 in. long, with a hook in one end, from which the pot is suspended, and a long strap hinge screwed to the other, as shown. The upper end of the hinge is left in normal condition, but the lower end should be filed down to a sharp point and bent away from the stick at right angles. The method of using this hanger is evident from the illustration. The weight of the paint pot will force the pointed end of the hinge into the wood.—L. B. Robbins, Harwich, Massachusetts.

Emergency Water Supply for Washroom

A break in the water pipe supplying the men's washroom made some repair necessary as it was near quitting time and scores of men would demand water for cleaning up. As the break could not be fixed at once, the pipe was uncoupled and plugged on the washroom side of the break with a hardwood plug and a garden hose attached to one of the faucets in the washroom and run to a sprinkling hydrant outside. Then, by opening this particular faucet and turning on the hydrant, water was forced backward into the faucet under high pressure and a fair pressure was obtained at each faucet in the washroom.—Harold E. Benson, Boulder, Colorado.

Removing Rust from Tools

Many of the so-called rust removers actually remove the rust from objects but also the finished surface of the metal itself. A derusting process has just been evolved in which acids and alkalies are eliminated, a simple chemical substance being used in a water solution. The substance is ammonium citrate. A tablespoonful of this to ½ pt. of water works very well. The chemical is inexpensive, non-corrosive and gives off no fumes; in fact, it is a very agreeable substance to work with. The tools, instruments, etc., are immersed in the solution overnight. In the morning, the rust will be found to have disappeared, the solution being brown, due to the formation of ferric citrate. But the solution can be used until depleted. The articles are then rinsed in water and oiled. If desired, they can be left overnight in a solution of potassium chromate, then rinsed and dried.

Locking Cabinet Drawers

Cabinet drawers without locks can be made safe by using the method shown in the illustration. The locking device con-

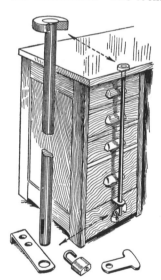

sists of a ⅜-in. iron rod, long enough to pass in front of the drawers, with a collar 1 in. in diameter pressed onto the top end. A ⁹⁄₁₆-in. hole is bored through the top of the cabinet and counterbored about ¼ in. deep so that the collar will be flush with the top when the rod is passed through. The lower end of the rod is slotted to take a sheet-metal latch drilled for insertion of a lock, and is held in a perforated strap countersunk into and screwed to the base, as indicated.—R. L. Hill, Saginaw, Mich.

❡Transparent celluloid, dissolved in acetone, makes a good lacquer for silver.

KINKS FOR THE BUILDER

Easily Made Desk for Foreman on Job

Taping Speaking-Tube Joints Prevents Leakage

Pipes Wired in This Way Don't Vibrate

Portable Street Barricades

Pipe Drains Porch Floor

A Derrick Swung from the Steel Column of a Building under Construction Is Handy for Many Jobs

Simple Wood Vise Attached to Strut for Filing Circular Saws

A Self-Inking Stamp That Can Be Changed Instantly

One day when I had about 50 envelopes that I wished to print with a return ad-

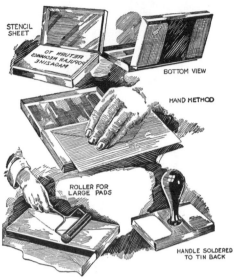

Self-Inking Stamp Made from a Mimeograph-Paper Stencil and an Ordinary Pad

dress, I found a stencil was in place on my mimeograph. Not wanting to remove it for so short a run, I devised the stamp shown in the illustration. It is self-inking, and the lettering can be changed at any time at a cost of about one cent for each new wording. Although I made the stamp to supplement my mimeograph in marking small articles, such as envelopes, bills, receipts, cards, etc., its use is not limited to owners of mimeographs. It will be found most serviceable to all who have numerous small items to be stamped or printed, but do not care to have a great number of rubber stamps made. Stencil sheets may be purchased for 14 cents and less, depending on size. The 14-cent sheet will make ten to fifteen pieces the size of a stamp pad. The typewriting or drawing is done on the stencil before separating it from the backing sheet. Then the backing sheet is torn off, and the stencil cut to the proper size to fit the pad. Sufficient margin is allowed to fold the sheet over the pad; the sheet is stretched tightly over the latter and the ends glued to the bottom. Pads may be bought in the 5 and 10-cent stores. Impressions are made by pressing the paper on the pad firmly. For some purposes, it is expedient to solder a handle to the back of the pad holder, as shown in the drawing,

permitting the device to be used as an ordinary stamp. When very large pads are used, the impression should be made with a small roller.—Lucius Winchester, Norwalk, Conn.

Repairing Broken Triangles

Triangles are easily broken and the draftsman's habits in handling them do not help the situation materially. Fanning ink lines and other practices soon ruin them. Also, in leaning on them, they are sometimes cracked, making it difficult to pick them up when in a flat position. Cracked triangles can be repaired in a very simple and effective manner. Make a solution of 3 parts of alcohol and 4 parts of ether, mixed together well, and apply it to the broken edges, and when more or less warm, press them together, keeping the triangle on a flat surface and using thumbtacks as bracing. Allow the joint to dry for 24 to 36 hours. The triangle will then be as good as new.—L. H. Georger, Buffalo, N. Y.

Telephone Poles Made from Old Water Pipes

The owner of a telephone system found that old, discarded water pipes make good strong telephone poles, which are of special advantage as frequent fires, kindled along the road to clear the brush, will not harm them. The sections of pipe are 25 ft. long and have a piece of round timber driven into the upper end and to this piece the crossarms are bolted. It is necessary to paint these pipes occasionally to prevent deterioration due to rust and if this is done, they will last practically indefinitely.—L. M. Jordan, Vredenburgh, Alabama.

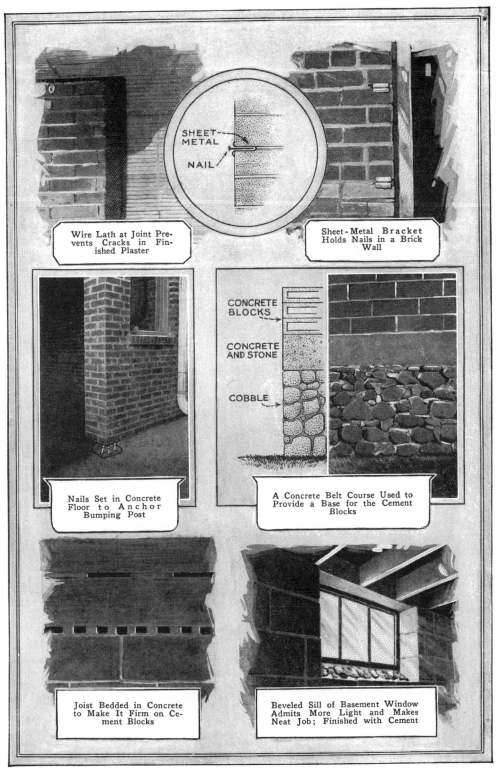

Wire Lath at Joint Prevents Cracks in Finished Plaster

Sheet - Metal Bracket Holds Nails in a Brick Wall

Nails Set in Concrete Floor to Anchor Bumping Post

A Concrete Belt Course Used to Provide a Base for the Cement Blocks

Joist Bedded in Concrete to Make It Firm on Cement Blocks

Beveled Sill of Basement Window Admits More Light and Makes Neat Job; Finished with Cement

Trolley-Operated Concrete Mixer

A novel concrete mixer is being used in San Francisco for paving the street-car tracks. The machine is equipped with

Novel Concrete Mixer That Runs on Street-Car Tracks and Uses Trolley Current

flanged wheels, a trolley pole and a motor, which also runs the mixing drum. A swinging spout, about 10 ft. in length, is suspended ahead of the mixer. The outfit is run on one of the tracks while pouring the paving base for the other. As it is used only at night, the mixer is run off the tracks and parked during the day.

Oiling Spring-Perch Nuts

Late-model Ford cars are fitted with conical nuts on the front-spring perches, which keep the front ends of the radius rod to the axle. When tightening these nuts, they often stop between openings for cotter pins and it is difficult to draw them to the next one. As it is hardly practical to grind off the conical end of the nuts to allow them to be turned on farther, they should be backed off several turns and oil applied to the ends. The oil reduces the friction and usually allows the nut to be turned to the next opening for the cotter pin without trouble.—E. T. Gunderson, Humboldt, Iowa.

Marking Trunks

Hunting for a particular trunk among a whole carload of them, or in a baggage room, means a loss of time when one is in a hurry. To avoid this, paint a wide stripe of any bright color all around the trunk on the sides and also across the top and bottom. This makes it visible at all times, no matter in what position the trunk is placed, and it can be picked out of a lot of similar-looking trunks at a glance. The stripe should be painted neatly and be from 3 to 5 in. wide.—H. R. Wallin, Galveston, Tex.

Raising Vertical Piping

For raising heavy vertical pipe, such as pump piping, columns to high water tanks, etc., the device shown in the illustration has been found very effective. It consists of a tripod of 3 by 4-in. wood with a 1-in. bolt through the top from which a short chain is hung. Attached to the end of this chain is a clamp made of two pieces of ½ by 1½-in. strap iron, bent to the shape indicated and held in place by two bolts, to one of which the chain is attached. A lever fulcrumed on a stand, as shown, has a similar chain and clamp attached to its short end. In use, the clamps are fastened around the piping with a sliding fit, so that, when the long lever arm is pressed down, the lower clamp locks the piping and raises it several inches, while the upper clamp grips and holds it when the lever is raised for a new purchase. Pipe may be lowered with the same device by raising the clamps with the hands as the strokes are made and riding the lever upward. The device is also an efficient post puller.—L. M. Jordan. Vredenburgh, Ala.

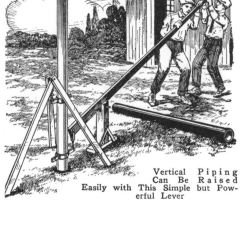

Vertical Piping Can Be Raised Easily with This Simple but Powerful Lever

¶Before painting window sash, rub a cloth soaked in kerosene over the glass.

Building Plaster Apron for Bathtub

Setting China Soap Dishes; Copper Nails Hold Mortar

Wood Jack for Holding Doors While Planing Edges

Handy Package Receivers Built in Front-Porch Wall

Left, a Telephone Niche, and Right, the Method of Framing It

Convenient Gasoline Drum

A farmer who believes in having everything convenient, built a substantial platform just outside of his garage for a 50-

Elevated Gasoline Tank near Garage Facilitates Filling of Auto Tank

gal. gasoline drum and attached a 5-ft. length of hose to the faucet. The free end is fitted with a small tin cylinder in which is set a strainer of cloth, screen and chamois, to keep out foreign matter.

Operating Small Machinery with Speedometer Parts

When operating small machinery such as laboratory equipment or moving window displays, it is sometimes desired to have the source of power at a distance, to provide a speed reduction or to transmit power at an angle. Where the power under consideration is small, an old speedometer swivel joint and flex-

ible shaft, which can be purchased for a small sum at an auto-wrecking house, will often solve the problem. The gear reduction in these swivel joints is 2½ to 1, and they need no attention as they are grease-packed. The spur-gear wheel is made of fiber and is easily converted into a grooved pulley. The flexible shaft is perfectly satisfactory for transmitting small power, and can be bent in any direction and located where it is impossible to place motors or belts. Another inexpensive ready-made gear reduction is to be found in the small emery grinding wheels which clamp to a bench or table and are crank-operated. They are generally accurately made and can be converted into a speed-changing device with little trouble.

Cutting Spirals

Cutting a spiral or, more correctly, a helix, usually calls for expensive machinery. To do such a job accurately without this equipment is practically impossible, but if the spirals need not be absolutely accurate they can be cut by simpler methods. In the photo is shown a method of cutting a spirally grooved roller in a shop where the only machine that could handle such a large piece was a planer. The roller was mounted on centers and was free to turn about them, subject to the control of a spiraling arm, which was setscrewed into the roller shaft and carried on its end a small roller that traveled up and down on a stationary bar as the whole rig, except the bar, was reciprocated by the motion of the planer bed. A spring set in the far side of the swivel arm kept the roller tight against the bar all the time. After each cut was made, the setscrew was loosened and the roller turned an amount equal to the spacing between the spiral teeth, and then the arm was tightened for another cut. The cutting was done by a tool ground to shape and fed directly downward into the roll. Spirals made in this way answer nicely on such pieces as feed rollers on woodworking machines, leather feed rolls and for grinding. — D. Hampson, Middletown, N. Y.

Cutting a Spirally Grooved Roller in a Planer without the Use of Expensive Machinery

KINKS FOR THE BUILDER

Simple Framing for a Cove Ceiling

Shingles Nailed to Planks Prevent End-Splitting

Useful Roller for Handling Long Timbers

Wood Protector for Projecting Pipe

Glass Supported on Blocks Is Less Likely to Crack

Old Nail Kegs Make Pier Forms

Stovepipes Set in Forms and Filled with Sand Provide Openings in Concrete Floor

Preventing Cable from Cutting Tree

Foundry Flasks from Truck Wheels

A foundry in the middle west received an order for some 24-in. wheels and gears but had no flasks suited to the job. As the order was likely to be repeated, it was

Old Automobile Rims Used as Flasks in Foundry

decided to make flasks specially adapted to that work alone. The ordinary round flask made of cast iron was rejected as it was too heavy. In the yard there were some old truck tires with the inside steel rim left on, and someone conceived the idea of stripping the rubber off and using these steel rings, as they were as near the diameter and width as could be desired. The old rubber was cut through with a metal band saw and was peeled from the rim. For ease in handling, particularly in turning over to dress the mold, a pair of iron trunnions were attached to each ring. The plan was so successful that later more of the flasks were made in another size for other work. Naturally the cost of the flasks was extremely low.—Donald A. Hampson, Middletown, N. Y.

Bending Ford Bendix Setscrew Washer

It is rather difficult to bend up the lip on the lock washer under the bendix-head setscrew on Ford-starter motors when replacing them. If a punch and hammer are used, the shaft turns at each blow and greatly lessens the effect, and an ordinary pair of pliers will not compress with enough force to bend the washers. A simple method is to grasp the partly bent lip on the washer and the screw head in a pair of pliers and turn the bendix until the pliers rest against the frame of the car. Now hammer on the opposite jaw of the pliers until the washer is bent, keeping a strong grip on the plier handles.

Shellac and Graphite Replace Gaskets

Powdered graphite and ordinary orange shellac, when mixed to the consistency of putty, form a solid sealing gasket, which resists heat and holds pressure. This mixture is also of use for small cracks in the water system around radiators, or various places where slight leakage occurs. If used to seal slight crevices, it should be made quite thin and worked into the crack with a putty knife.

Keeping Tractor Oil Warm in Cold Weather

Lubrication of tractors during cold weather presents the problem of keeping the oil thin. A good method of doing this is to arrange a tight-fitting box over the exhaust pipe, so that quite a bit of heat will be retained in the box. The oilcans are kept in it, and freely running oil will then be had in the coldest weather. For drying wet mittens and gloves this box is also a great convenience.—G. G. McVicker, North bend, Nebr.

Keeping Lubricating Oil Thin during Cold Winter Weather in a Box Built over the Exhaust Pipe

Hints on Driving Nails and Screws

NEARLY everyone knows that a nail or screw has greater holding power when driven into the side or edge of a board than when sunk in the end grain. It is commonly supposed that a nail driven with light blows requires a greater force to draw it than one driven with heavy blows; but opinions seem to conflict as to whether or not the usefulness of a screw is impaired by tapping it in for a distance with a hammer before sinking it home with the screwdriver.

Again, the amateur is told by the professional woodworker that a hammer held by the end of the handle is less likely to bend a nail being driven than if held near the head, only to find upon trial that, in his own case, the reverse is true. It appears to him that he can turn in a stubborn screw more easily with a long screwdriver than with a short; yet this seems as absurd as to suppose that, by merely lengthening the rear axle of an automobile, it could be operated with less power.

What are the facts in this case? All have a basis in the two elementary mechanical powers involved, that is, the lever and the inclined plane—in other words, the pry, as exemplified by a crowbar thrust under a rock to raise it, and a sloping runway to an elevated platform up which a barrel too heavy to be lifted can be rolled.

When a nail is driven, the little pointed iron cylinder, being forced between the fibers of the wood, cuts them and wedges them apart. Those at the sides are crushed into a compact mass, their cell

Fig. 1, Left, Nail Driven with Heavy Blows, and Right, with Light Ones; Fig. 2, Left, Screw Turned All the Way In; Right, Driven Halfway with Hammer

13

walls broken, their elasticity destroyed; while those forming the end grain are bent downward, some breaking off, but many remaining firm.

It is evident that the crushed side fibers contribute little friction, and are almost useless in holding the nail. The end fibers, therefore, must do most of the work in retaining it. When a force tending to draw the nail is applied, the downward bent fibers, already forced tightly against it, follow the nail upward. But the instant this occurs, they also tend to occupy the space containing the nail, and the leverage so gained forces them still more tightly against it. If the force applied is sufficient, the pressure becomes so great that the tip-end fibers are crushed and broken, as a lever is broken when forced beyond its strength, and the nail can then, with little effort, be pulled out entirely.

In short, these downward-bent fibers form what is known as a toggle joint, as illustrated in Fig. 5. The lever ends, A, bear against the nail and move upward with it. They also tend to move horizontally, until the levers themselves lie in a horizontal position; but since the horizontal distance, CB, through which they move, is much smaller than the vertical distance, the thrust against the nail is much greater than that applied to lift the nail, according to the law of levers. Moreover, as the levers approach a horizontal position, the horizontal motion approaches zero, while the vertical remains almost constant, so that the crushing effect exerted on the nail increases toward infinity, to the limit of strength of the material. It is no wonder, then, that a properly driven nail holds strongly.

Now, it is reasonable to assume that if the nail is driven with many light blows the fibers will be bent down slowly, and will have time to accommodate themselves to the strain, reducing breakage to a minimum; while if heavy hammer blows are given, some fibers will break back at a considerable distance from the nail, and thereafter be valueless. That this is indeed the case is proved by Fig. 1, a photograph magnifying two split-out 16-penny box nails. That at the left was driven with heavy blows, that at the right, with light. However, an actual test proves that the difference in

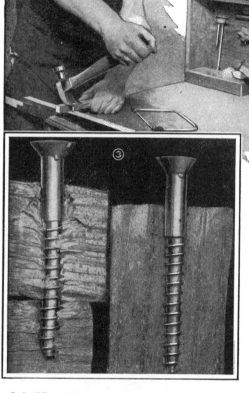

Left, Effect of Screw Binding in One Member; Right, Screw Driven in End Wood

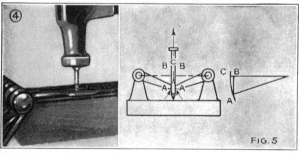

FIG. 5

Left, Tapping Screw to Start It; Right, Toggle Effect of Downward-Bent Fibers holding power is only around 12 per cent; which is not enough, in most construction work, to warrant the extra time required for light driving, since it is common experience that materials, and the mechanic's judgment, will vary more than this.

A screw has wound about it a thread, which is in effect an inclined plane. Here leverage is obtained through the greater rotary than lengthwise motion. This mechanical advantage acts in drawing the screw into the wood, and especially in clamping together the two pieces joined. It does not act to hold the screw in, although the threads naturally must strip out the fibers when the screw is drawn like a nail. Apparently, if the screw is driven for a distance before being turned in, the fibers are bent down, and in addition to the "baffle" effect of the threads, the toggle action is brought into play.

This additional force is not to be discredited. As a matter of fact, tests prove that a screw hammered halfway in holds about 25 per cent more in fir than one screwed all the way in. Probably driving one-quarter of the thread length is best. Fig. 2 shows split-out screws, the one at the left screwed in full distance, that at the right driven halfway with the hammer before being turned. Evidently the carpenter who taps the screws to start them when dapping in hinges, as in Fig. 4, acts on sound principle.

Fig. 3, at the right, illustrates a screw sunk in the end wood. Plainly, to draw it out, it is only necessary to strip the fibers parallel with the grain—in the case of this 1½-in. No. 10 screw, about 1 sq. in. of cross section. As the shearing resistance of fir or pine parallel with the grain is only about one-tenth of that perpendicular to the grain, small reliance can be placed on a screw entered in the end of a board.

Fig. 3, left, also illustrates a problem met in joining two members with screws, in which the upper member has not been bored sufficiently large to permit free movement of the screw. It is easily seen that the screw advances as fast in the upper as in the lower piece, keeping them the same distance apart until the head bears against the upper piece, when the threads that are cut in it must strip out before it will come down against the lower member. The force required may be sufficient to break the head.

Fig. 6 illustrates the drawing of a nail. The hammer,

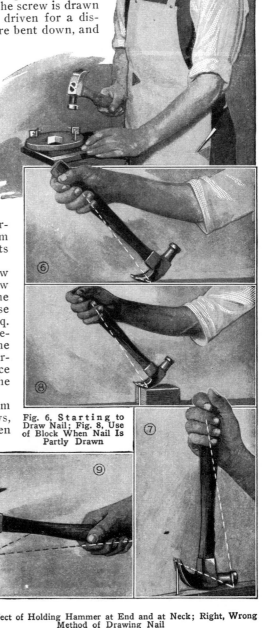

Fig. 6, Starting to Draw Nail; Fig. 8, Use of Block When Nail Is Partly Drawn

Left, Effect of Holding Hammer at End and at Neck; Right, Wrong Method of Drawing Nail

as the dotted lines indicate, forms a bell lever, with the handle arm nearly 16 times the length of the claw arm, so that 1 lb. pull on the handle applies an upward force of 16 lb. on the nail. When, as in Fig. 7, the nail is partly drawn, the hammer rocks backward, the weight arm is greatly increased in length, and the pull on the handle must be increased. Nearly all hammer-handle breaks are caused by trying to pull nails with the face edge as a fulcrum. The proper way is to place a block under the head, as in Fig. 8, thus restoring the short weight arm.

Hammers are so designed that a line drawn touching the width of the face intersects with

greater velocity to the head, and can consequently strike a harder blow.

The face of the hammer is slightly rounded, so that if it strikes a little out of true the face may still be at right angles to the nail. This convexity also makes it possible to drive home a nail without bruising the surrounding wood.

If a screwdriver were held truly in a line with the screw, the short driver would be just as effective as the long one, since only the direct torque, or twisting force, would act in each case. In practice, however, the driver is invariably held to one side or the other; and granting that the

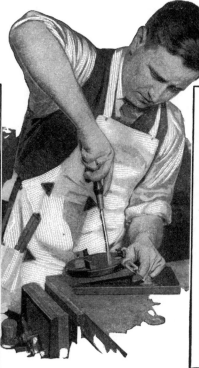
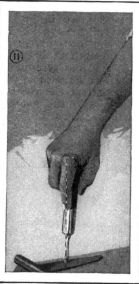

Fig. 10, Effect of Using Long Screwdriver; Note Lever Arm Indicated by Dotted Lines; Fig. 11, Short Lever Arm Formed by Short Screwdriver

the center of the handle end. When a blow is struck on a nail, the face meets the nail head squarely and forces it in along its length, whereas, if the handle is grasped near the head, the front of the face is thrown upward, and the inclined plane transmits a portion of the blow as a sidewise force against the nail, bending it. See Fig. 9.

A novice finds it difficult to drive nails by holding the hammer handle near the end because he handles it so inexpertly that the head wobbles from side to side, striking at angles in spite of him. Yet, if he practices a short time, he will find that the correct method is much the easier. Not only so, but he is able to give

angle of inclination is the same for the large or short tool, the power arm developed is longer in the longer driver, and a greater leverage is produced. Figures 10 and 11 illustrate this.

Fitting Piston Rings

The auto mechanic who has piston rings to fit will appreciate any new idea that will serve to cut down the time required for the job. Usually such a small amount of metal is to be taken off that the clamping and loosening of the vise take most of the time. Instead of setting each ring in the vise twice for filing, take one of the old rings that are to be discarded and break off a piece equal to about one-fourth of its circumference. Choose a ring that has not been worn too much in width. Clamp this piece vertically in the vise, concave side outward, about ⅛ in. from the left side, and extending about ⅛ in. above the jaw of the vise. This leaves the vise open the width of the ring and a recess of ⅛ in. into which the ring to be filed is placed. Just a slight pressure of the thumb and finger of the left hand will suffice to hold the ring while it is filed and a little practice will enable any mechanic to file the end squarely with a small flat file. The piece of old ring is not removed from the vise, but each succeeding ring is merely set into the vise and held as explained, while one side is filed, then slid out of the vise, inverted and replaced for the other side. This applies to step-cut rings. If diagonal-cut, file only on one side.

Bumper for Lumber-Yard Posts

Discarded truck tires of the solid type have been used effectively as bumpers for posts supporting the sheds in a southern lumber yard. The tires were mounted on stakes, notched as shown and pointed at the lower end to facilitate driving them into the ground. These tires are mounted on iron rims, which gives them enough strength to sustain a considerable impact. A bumper of this kind provided around each post prevents the latter from being broken off, which might cause the shed to collapse.—F. E. Walker, Atlanta, Ga.

DISCARDED TIRE AND RIM
STAKE
NOTCH

Solid Truck Tires on Rims Used as Bumpers around Posts in Lumber Yard

Gate for the Stock Corral

The photo shows a novel turnstile gate for a stock corral. One can enter or leave with both arms full, yet no cow or horse can go

Novel Wooden Turnstile Gate Found Convenient in Western Stock Corral

through, no matter in what position the gate is left. Two pairs of crossarms are mounted upon a heavy post, which is hewn round and notched for the arms. The arms lie across each other at right angles. Planks are bolted to the crossarms vertically. By keeping the bearings lubricated with hard oil, the gate turns easily. The arms are made of 2 by 8-in. planks, about 6 ft. long. The gateway is 7½ ft. across.—Dale R. Van Horn, Walton, Nebr.

Handling Celluloid Triangles

Most draftsmen appreciate the difficulty experienced in picking up celluloid triangles. This difficulty can be overcome by the addition of an ordinary glass push pin. Drill a small hole, slightly smaller in diameter than the pin, through the triangle. Countersink this hole slightly on one side and then insert the push pin. Clip off the pin so that only a small end projects. Rivet this portion over until it holds the push pin securely and then file away all the surplus metal so that the triangle will lie flat on the board.—Richard H. Robinson, Detroit, Mich.

Concrete Steps on High Curb

In towns built on hilly or rolling ground the curbing is often too high to mount easily. This makes steps of some

Concrete Steps on High Curbs Make It Easier for Automobilists to Reach the Sidewalk

sort necessary. The drawing shows how steps of concrete are built integral with the curb. They are braced as indicated, and are neat in appearance. The braces are not run clear to the pavement as this would check the flow of gutter water and stop refuse.

Wet Air in Compressed-Air Hammer

In a small shop I noticed that the air hammer in one of the worker's hands was spraying water out of the exhaust hole. He said that it always did this when it was started. One look at the compressor installation showed me the trouble. The air receiver was a small one, and the air from the compressor entered the tank at the top, while the outlet from the tank into the air hammer was about 4 in. from the bottom of the tank. This was what was wrong with the installation. Moisture is heavier than air and, of course, it settles in the bottom of the receiver and, as the receiver was small, it merely acted as a pipe for the air to flow through from the compressor, carrying the water along with it. In explaining the proper pipe layout to the boss afterward, I strongly urged him to supply a larger receiver so that the air

would have an opportunity to remain stationary long enough to cool and deposit part of the moisture. The larger tank would likewise provide ample storage against fluctuations in pressure, and give a steady volume of air to operate the air hammer.—August Jeffers, Bedford, Ind.

Removing Soldering Flux

Anyone who has worked with solder containing the flux, has no doubt experienced the difficulty of removing the hard crust which is formed around the solder. If this crust is left on, it not only shows poor workmanship, but the crust will later dissolve and run off in the form of acid, which is very injurious to other metal parts. The flux can be removed by dipping the soldered parts in cold water. If it is impossible to dip the parts in water, good results can be had by placing a wet cloth over the soldered parts for a few moments and then wiping them off. Either method will leave the metal bright and clean. It is best to apply the water to the soldered parts while they are still hot.—Ed Sundholm, Albert City, Iowa.

Holder for Signal Lantern

The warning lantern used to indicate the presence of excavations or obstructions in the road or for similar purposes

can be displayed conspicuously on the holder shown in the illustration. Two pieces of flat iron, one a few inches longer than the other, are notched in the end to fit the lantern frame as shown, the longer one being bent at right angles. A spacer, riveted to the uprights and holding them rigid, also serves as a shelf for the lantern. If desired, a suitable sign can be attached to the frame as indicated. A wooden block or a concrete slab can be used as a base, the latter being preferred, as its greater weight lessens the possibility of the holder being overturned by the wind or otherwise.—A. C. Cole, Chicago, Ill.

Bleachers for Small Athletic Field

By ROY M. SINGER

HERE is a grandstand for a small athletic field that can easily be built, and that will prove a splendid project for the manual-training class of a boy's school. The woodwork is not at all difficult, but it will afford the boys a valuable study in practical problems, as well as form a monument for a particular class. The necessary concreting and painting can also be done by the class, thus making the project still more comprehensive.

All details of the stand are given in the drawings, so that little description is necessary. It consists of trusses supported by concrete piers; at the rear, lateral bracing is used to furnish stiffness. The piers are constructed as shown in the sketch, and should go down into the ground at least 3 ft. below grade, and always below the frost line.

The lower member of the truss consists of two 2 by 8's, the end post of three 2 by 10's, the intermediate post of two 2 by 20's, the diagonals of 2 by 10's, and the top chord of two 2 by 12's. A 2 by 4-in. rail is provided, as shown in the sketch.

The seats are built of two 2 by 8's and a total seating width of 20 in. is provided. The difference in elevation of the tiers is 16 in. The whole arrangement is designed for comfort and safety.

It may be well to add here a word of warning to anyone who contemplates building a seating arrangement of this kind. Remember that each member in the assembly must take a different load and that if one member does not take its full load, some other member must carry more than its load. Be careful, then, to see that all joints are tightly nailed and that all materials used are of good, sound

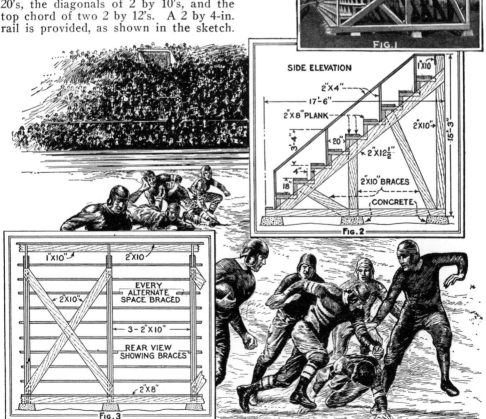

Fig. 1, Left End of Stand; Fig. 2 Detail Drawing of Left-End Assembly; Fig. 3, Details of Stand Showing the Bracing

19

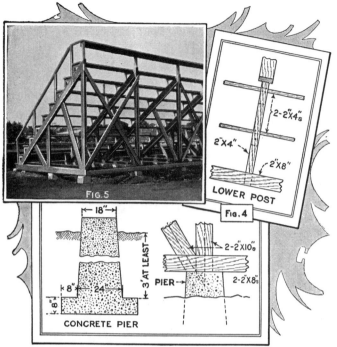

Fig. 5, Photo of Part of Rear of Stand; Fig. 4, Lower Post and, Below, Concrete-Pier Details

kept clear and the pool saved from filling up with sediment. This is usually accomplished by building a small dam above the pool, the storm water being carried around through a spillway. A dam that operates automatically can be arranged by making the opening to the spillway wide enough so that the normal low-water flow will go over it in a thin sheet. The water at this point is made to run over a 2 by 8-in. plank, bolted edgewise to the concrete dam wall. In front of this, and at an angle to it, is placed another plank, the edge of which is beveled to provide an opening of uniform width, say ¼ to ½ in. between it and the vertical plank, through which the low-water overflow runs into a separate pool as shown. A slight rise in the stream will cause the water to run with greater speed and in greater volume, so that it will skip the gap between the two boards and flow into the spillway around the pool. A baffle can be set up just behind the dam to hold back trash. This device is in use at the Georgia state college of agriculture, and a very small rise in the stream causes the water to switch to the spillway.

lumber. For an arrangement of this sort, the trusses should not be spaced farther apart than 10 feet.

Spillway for Bathing Pools

Bathing pools, fish ponds and lakes, fed from springs or small streams, must have some provision to prevent storm water from entering them, if the water is to be

Automatic Dam Allows Water at Normal Level to Flow into a Pool, While a Small Rise in the Level Causes It to Run into the Spillway That Diverts It around the Pool

Battery Economy

To those who use dry cells in telephone or telegraph circuits, the following method of using them on closed circuits will prove valuable. This method permits the use of dry or any other open-circuit batteries on telegraph or telephone lines where the circuit is closed. The ordinary methods of doing this require sufficient battery power at each end of the line to operate the system. This doubles the necessary cost of batteries. The better method is to get just enough batteries to operate the system. Place half of them at one end of the line and the other half at the other, and connect the zincs at both ends of the same line, and the carbons to the other, or to the ground. The voltages of both sets will then be equal and, therefore, no current will flow on the line. When either party wishes to call the other, he simply reverses the connections of his set of batteries and uses the instruments. By this reversal the current of both batteries flows through the line. When through talking, he restores the connections to their original condition. The direction of the current through the line depends upon which party has called the other. The apparatus may be grouped in any way, and distributed anywhere on the line. The only condition to be observed is that the open-circuit voltages of the two sets of batteries should be equal, so that no current will flow until one set is reversed. Any batteries may be used together.

Safety Handle for Chisel or Punch

For holding chisels or punches while working in places where minor injuries may occur, pieces of air hose may be used to advantage. A slit is made in the hose about 1½ in. from one end, through which the tool is inserted, and a piece of wood is driven into the hose from either end to hold it securely. In this way the tool can easily be shifted to work from any angle. The idea originated with G. L. Knotts, service supervisor at Du Pont, Washington.

Pieces of Discarded Air Hose Make Safe and Convenient Handles for Chisels

Spring Holder for Metal Plates

When marking, lettering or cutting designs on brass plates it is important to have the work held so that it will not move, or else the worker may spoil the

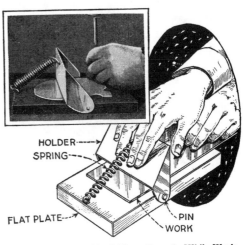

Device for Holding Metal Plates Securely While Working on Them

piece by marking it crooked. Such work is done best on a flat plate, and we have fitted a holding device to the plate that will grip a piece of the full width of the plate if necessary. The holder is made out of a piece of flat metal, formed as shown and attached to the plate by a pin on each side. When in use, one end of a coil spring is passed through a hole in the holder, and the other end is attached to a hook screwed into the plate. The operator lifts the holder by pulling it toward him, shoves the work underneath, and then releases it. This holds the work securely, and the continued tapping with a hammer when marking the work will not, with ordinary care, change its position. —Harry Moore, Montreal, Canada.

¶A good paint for wire screen consists of dropblack, ground in oil, and about a third as much of asphaltum varnish, thinned with turpentine. Add some drier and strain the paint before using.

Steps Hinged to Truck Prove Great Help in Loading

Permanent Steps on Truck Aid Loading

The idea illustrated shows a set of steps for loading platform, which is used by a firm of private scavengers for conveniently dumping the contents of garbage cans into the truck and will find application in numerous other places where loads of material must be placed in the truck by hand. Both the loading platform and the steps attached to it are hinged, the former to the bed of the truck and the latter to the outer edge of the platform. When lowered, the platform is held securely by two lengths of chain and when raised, the steps hang down behind.

Stopping Leaky Steam Lines

Leaky joints on steam lines can often be permanently stopped by the use of a calking tool and a little lead wool. Occasions frequently arise when a small leak in either a water or steam line is causing inconvenience as well as loss of power. Repairs cannot be made while the line is in service, but a little lead wool worked tightly into the joint while the pressure on the line is reduced often eliminates the necessity of making an expensive repair.

Quadruple Tile Joint

In constructing a farm-drainage system it sometimes becomes necessary to join three or more tiles at one point; such joints are not regularly manufactured and it is rather difficult to build one that will not wash out, break down or resist burrowing animals.

A practically indestructible concrete joint, simple to make, is shown in the illustration. It accommodates a 14-in. outlet pipe and three branches of respectively 10, 6 and 4-in. diameter. The form is made of old 1-in. boards, is 20 in. long and at least 20 in. deep without top or bottom. These dimensions are required because there should be space below the pipes for a floor of 2 or 3-in. thickness, and above and on the sides for 4-in. walls around the largest tile. If a larger outlet pipe is used, the form should be dimensioned according to this rule. Openings are cut in the sides with a keyhole saw to fit the tiles. The lowest point of these holes should be the same distance from the bottom edge of the box as the thickness of the floor, that is, 2 to 3 in. The form is then nailed together and reinforced at the edges with lath.

Place the form on a level spot on the ground and build up some sand around the outside to keep it in place. Insert the tiles, pushing the 14-in. pipe far enough to project 4 in. inside of the box; the smaller ones are pushed in farther, or so that the distance between opposite open-

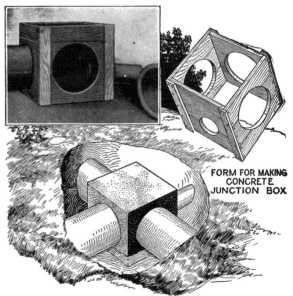

FORM FOR MAKING CONCRETE JUNCTION BOX

Practically Indestructible Four-Way Junction Box for Drain Tile Made of Cement

ings in no case is less than 14 in. Now pour in the cement—1 part cement to 3 of sand—until it reaches the lower edge of the tiles. After the floor has set, put in more cement around the tile in the lower corners of the box, troweling it down around the tile so as to bond with the cement of the bottom. Then, using wet sand, fill the openings in the ends of the tiles and build up a core in the central space until it is level with the top edge of the largest pipe. The remaining space in the upper part of the form is then filled with cement up to the top of the box. When the cement is set and nearly dry, the core can easily be removed by punching it loose with a piece of wood or iron. In regard to the relative sizes of outlet and branch tile, the rule is that the square of the diameter of the former should be at least equal to and preferably exceed the sum of the squared diameters of the branches.—J. R. Koontz, Bremen, Ind.

Copying Drawings and Photos

When copies of drawings, diagrams and photos in books or magazines are desired, it is too tedious and time-consuming a task to copy them by hand, if at all possible, and the accuracy of such work is also questionable. A good method of making photographic copies is shown in the illustration. Any good quality of photographic printing paper may be used, but those having a "hard" contrast are preferable. The photo paper and the print are put face to face and a piece of glass is put over the photo paper. Exposure is then made with an electric lamp from above, the duration of exposure depending on the thickness

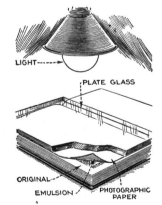

and quality of the photo paper, the intensity of illumination, the distance from the light to the print, and the reflective quality of the paper from which the print is to be made. The first photo is reversed and is used as a negative for making any number of prints. As the photo paper is kept so close to the original, the prints will be free from blurs.

Using U-Bolts in a Blacksmith Shop for Bending Jigs; Upper Detail Shows How an Eye Is Formed

U-Bolt Makes Good Bending Jig

A set of U-bolts or forms of round steel stock, bent so that the parallel legs are separated a little more than the diameter, is used by a western blacksmith for bending round or flat stock. In use, the form is clamped in a vise, as illustrated, and the rod to be bent is slipped between the legs. The drawing shows the steps in bending an eye in hot stock, but simple bends are easily made in cold stock by using a pipe over the end to give leverage.

Preventing Rust on Dials

In wet, damp or steamy places, the rusting of gauges and dials can be prevented by first cleaning and polishing the surface thoroughly and then giving it two coats of collodion. The first coat must be thoroughly dry before the second is applied. The collodion prevents the air and moisture from getting in contact with the polished surface. Engine gauges will last from six months to a year without repolishing if properly treated in this way. Exposed copper and brass piping and other metals can also be protected by this method. When necessary, the collodion can be removed with alcohol.

¶A T-handle tap wrench with part of the handle cut off can be chucked in a breast drill and used for holding small drills.

Easily Made Derrick

Farmers and others often need some means of raising heavy weights, such as logs, timbers, stones, pipe and machinery onto a wagon or truck. This can very easily be done by constructing a derrick

BASE
SUPPORT

Simple Improvised Derrick for Farm Use Which Makes It Possible to Lift Objects of Considerable Weight

of the kind shown, which is both inexpensive and portable. One end of a sound log or 6 by 6-in. timber, about 15 ft. long, is sharpened and base supports nailed on as shown. At the other end a short crossarm is attached with bolts or nails. To raise a heavy object, the sharpened end of the log is placed in the ground, and a hitch is taken around the crossarm with a rope, which is fastened to the weight, and should be long enough to reach to the ground when the pole is raised. Lifting power is supplied by a truck, horse or a group of men. When the weight is raised to the proper height, it can easily be pulled onto a wagon.—A. Bereskin, Winnipeg, Can.

Releasing Tight Collets

Spring collets that stick are a common trouble on handscrew machines. This may be the result of several causes; the rod being used may be old and rough, or it may be bent or a shade too large for the collet. When a rod fails to come forward as the clutch is released, the best thing to do is to tap it lightly on the end projecting through the collet; this loosens the latter and allows the rod to feed forward to the stop in the turret. Sometimes this is a frequent occurrence, and many operators keep a hammer handy for tapping the rod back when it sticks. The drawing illustrates a better way. The stop itself has a $\frac{5}{8}$-in. cold-rolled stock tapped at each end for $\frac{1}{4}$-in. studs, which

carry another piece of $\frac{5}{8}$-in. stock on their outer ends. A hole is drilled and tapped in the center of the outer piece for a $\frac{1}{4}$-in. screw. When a rod refuses to feed forward to the stop, the position of the latter being controlled by a stop on the machine, the device is dropped to a horizontal position where a pin driven through the stop holds it. The end of the rod is then tapped by bringing the turret forward, and as the collet releases it, the device is lifted back to the position indicated by the dotted lines, leaving the end of the stop free to locate the rod as usual. A device of this type enables the operator to keep up the regular swing of

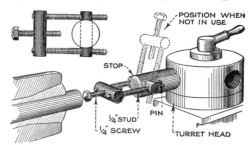

POSITION WHEN NOT IN USE

STOP

$\frac{1}{4}$" STUD
$\frac{1}{4}$" SCREW
PIN
TURRET HEAD

Attachment for Handscrew Machine for Releasing Stock That Sticks in the Collet

the turret, which is impossible when he must stop and pick up a hammer.

¶Oil paint has a tendency to wrinkle upon exposure to extreme cold but this may be prevented by adding a little turpentine to the paint,

Unloading Drain Tile

Unloading tile is a hard and tedious job, and it is nearly impossible to distribute them equally. A convenient method of laying them is shown in the drawing. The tiles are loaded on the grain wagon and a wooden trough, smoothed inside, is hooked to the rear end of the wagon and drags on the ground

Convenient Method of Unloading and Distributing Tile from a Moving Wagon Saves Considerable Time and Labor; Two Boys or Men Keep the Trough Filled

while the wagon is pulled ahead. Two or three boys or men on the wagon, lay the tiles in the trough end to end and the tiles slide down on the ground as the wagon moves along. Of course, the slant of the trough must be such that the tiles will slide down readily. In this way it is possible to unload the tiles in a few minutes and have them equally distributed.
—Simon M. Schwartz, Berne, Ind.

Repairing Cylinder Break

There are many methods of repairing cylinder breaks, the most common of which is welding. This is good practice, provided the parts are preheated, under which condition the weld can be relied on for service. Seaming the break with overlapping brass studs, tapped into holes drilled along the break, is also a good method if the break is in the center of the casting. Re-

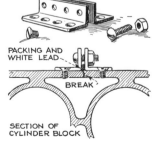

PACKING AND WHITE LEAD

BREAK

SECTION OF CYLINDER BLOCK

pair by means of a patch held with screws is also generally known, and is satisfactory if the patch is not near an edge or subjected to tension. An unusually effective patch, which not only closes the gap but also draws the sides of the casting together, is shown in the illustration. Two angle plates are drilled as indicated and holes of corresponding size are drilled and tapped in the casting so that the plates can be screwed down with a little space between the adjacent sides. Packing, saturated in white lead, is tamped down between these sides directly over the crack, and small bolts and nuts are used to draw the sides together, which forces the packing down still more tightly. The plates, also, are bedded in white lead.—G. A. Luers, Washington, D. C.

Rethreading Tire Valves

When rethreading the inside of a tire valve, it should be held with the outer end downward and the small tap used should be dry and clean. This will cause the cuttings to fall out of the stem, preventing later trouble with a valve inside. If a battered outer end of a valve stem is to be refaced, the valve should be held with the outer end down or the work done with air in the tire. The center pin of the valve inside will strike the refacing tool and release some of the air, which will blow away the cuttings as fast as they are formed.—E. T. Gunderson, Jr., Humboldt, Iowa.

Operating Snips by Foot

Much more power can be applied to an ordinary pair of tin snips by means of the simple foot attachment shown in the illustra-

Cutting Heavy Work with Ordinary Tinners' Snips by Foot Power

tion. This enables the worker to use the shears on much heavier work than can be cut by hand. A length of heavy wire is attached to one handle of the snips and reaches almost to the floor. At its lower end the wire is bent to form a loop for the worker's foot. The free handle of the snips is then held securely in a vise.— L. J. Trost, Kelly Field, Tex.

Planting Fence Posts Securely

Usually a post that is planted or driven into wet, swampy ground is hard to keep tight. It either becomes very loose or is lifted out of the ground entirely by hard freezing. Loose posts are certain to cause a loose, worthless fence. If this is your trouble, you can remedy it by digging the hole deep and wide. About 8 in. from the lower end of the post, saw a notch across it, a few inches deep. Get a piece of locust wood, about 18 in. long, mortise it into the notch in the post and nail it securely. When the post is planted and the hole is back-filled, the weight of the dirt will be on the crossbar and hold it down. The post will then stand solidly until it decays.— J. Marshall Porter, Cumberland, Md.

Chain-Block Sling for Tanks

Tanks can be handled easily with a chain block if there is a convenient hole in the tank. A shop doing this kind of work uses the special slinging device shown in the photo. It consists of a length of flat steel, 1 in. wide by $\frac{1}{4}$ in. thick and bent double, a crosspiece at right angles, $\frac{1}{2}$ in. thick, turning on a pin, and a sleeve fitting over the flat piece. This sleeve has a slot sawed out halfway around it to clear a screw turned into the doubled piece, and a slot on one side to clear the crosspiece. Before assembling, a chain ring is slipped into place in the bent piece for greater convenience in handling. One side of the crosspiece is heavier than the other; in other words it is off center. When inserting the device in the hole in the tank the heavy end is turned up inside the sleeve. When it has passed through the hole, the heavy end drops down to the horizontal position shown and is ready for lifting. To remove the sling from the tank, the sleeve is turned around till the other end of the horizontal slot stops against the screw. When the sling is pushed farther down into the tank the heavy end of the crosspiece falls down in line with the sleeve, enabling the sling to be pulled out. This device will be found useful also for lifting other pieces with holes in them when it is impossible to get inside of them with

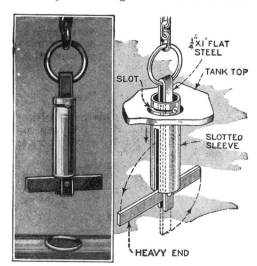

Convenient Chain-Block Sling Used for Hoisting Tanks Has Large Capacity and Is Simply Made

the hands. The lifter described, although of comparatively light material, has been used on tanks weighing up to 500 lb.— Harry Moore, Montreal, Can.

Shop Notes

Making a Convertible Toolpost Grinder

By RAY F. KUNS

THE machine shown in the illustrations was designed to serve in a machine shop where a great variety of automobile and general machine-shop repair and construction work is conducted. Two years of daily service, in which time a number of grinder wheels have been worn out, would seem to prove that the design is good. The only expense or repairs needed in this time, outside of the wheels, has been the replacing of the belt.

In automobile work as well as in many other instances in our modern shops, heat-treated steel is used to such an extent that grinding is becoming almost indispensable, if the materials are to be machined. It is necessary to grind after heat-treating, if the work is to be true and free from the inequalities occasioned by the hardening and tempering process.

Accurate grinding work requires an accurate grinding head and a machine free from disturbing vibration. Of necessity the wheel must turn at high speed, and bearings must be accurate and entirely free from play. For this reason ball bearings were given preference over plain bearings. Service h a s

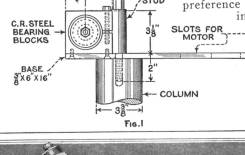

FIG.1

Upper Left, the Grinder Mounted on the Column for General Grinding; Right, Used to Grind Lathe Centers

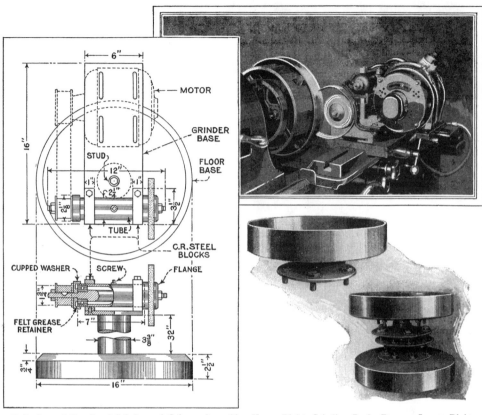

Left, General Details of Grinder and Column Assembly; Upper Right, Grinding Brake Drums; Lower Right, Some Reground Drums

proved the wisdom of the choice, since the bearings needed attention only once in a twelve-month period, and are still free of all play.

An essential to the use of ball or roller bearings in a grinder of this type is the exclusion of all grit which is floating in the air about the machine, and which, if it gains entrance, is certain to destroy the bearing quickly. With this in mind, it was decided to use a pipe or tube for the support of the ball-bearing races, and thus insure alinement of the bearings as well as exclusion of all dust from the inner sides. To prevent the dust from working into the bearings from the outer sides of the bearings they are protected by the cupped washers which come over the ends of the tube. Space is left, as shown, for a felt grease retainer which also acts as a dust excluder.

The size of the bearings is not indicated exactly, since it may be possible to adapt salvaged bearings to this service, as was done in the original machine. With the bearings at hand, the tube is selected to conform to them and machined to size on

the outer surface, the ends being bored out to receive the bearing races, which must be just a neat sliding fit. The shaft also must be designed to fit the bearings and the journal for the bearing cone must be just a snug sliding fit. A piece of a vanadium-steel axle was used for the original shaft. This is more difficult to machine, but is a most dependable material and one usually available without cost.

The bearing cones take the thrust of the cupped washers as they are forced on ahead of the grinder wheel on the one side and the pulley on the other. A flange of conventional pattern is made to hold the grinder wheel. The threads on the wheel end of the shaft are right-hand, while those on the pulley end are left-hand. It is a good plan to place a key in the pulley and shaft as an additional safeguard against turning.

As suggested by the title of this article, this machine is designed to serve double duty. When not in use on the lathe carriage, it is mounted on a column at one end of the lathe, where it is readily available as a tool-bit grinder and for other light work. To facilitate this change a stud is made of such length that the upper end extends above the body of the grinder head. This stud is used to clamp the base of the grinder to the top of the column or to the lathe carriage. The base is made from ⅜ by 6-in. machine steel. The grinder head is supported in blocks of steel on the front end, and the other end is slotted to receive the motor.

The cold-rolled steel blocks that carry the tube are bored out to the size of the tube and slotted at the rear side. A screw is used to lock the tube into the blocks, after they have been assembled onto the base by means of two taper-head machine screws.

The motor is ½ hp., and is fitted with a pulley to drive the head at 3,000 r.p.m. The slots in the base of the grinder are made to conform to the base of the motor. This arrangement allows ready adjustment of the belt used to drive the machine. A Ford fan belt was selected for this task, since it is readily obtained. The rubber-composition type is preferred to the leather belt because it is lighter and more flexible, and consequently less likely to set up vibration.

The column was made from a 3½-in. round machine-steel bar. The column base was machined from an old engine flywheel. The weight of these items helps to give rigidity when the grinder is used on the column. The base might have been made from 3-in. gas pipe mounted on a large brake drum and the entire column then turned over and filled with concrete to give it weight. When mounting the head on the lathe carriage, a nut to receive the stud is used.

The accompanying illustrations show some of the uses to which this little grinder has been put. Center grinding is always needed. Some brake drums may be turned in the lathe and again they must be ground as indicated in this case. By mounting the rotating knives or cutter heads of lawn mowers in the lathe and supplying a rest for the blade, extremely accurate grinding may be done on them with this machine. It is likely, too, that the cutting bar can be ground with it.

Magnet Holds Trouble Lamp

When making repairs or adjustments on an auto engine at night, it is rather difficult to hold the lamp over the work properly. A handy lamp holder can be made

Trouble Lamp Held to Auto Engine by Magnet and Detail Showing Construction

from an old magneto magnet, which can be picked up at almost any junk shop. The magnet will adhere to any iron or steel surface, and by having the lamp adjustable, it can be swung around to any desired position.—Edwin E. Burgess, Jr., Baltimore, Md.

Homemade Dump Truck Distributes Load Evenly

Where long stretches of highway are to be graveled at one time, a truck with a dump body having three divisions, each holding one third of a yard as shown, has been found a time and money saver. Common one-ton truck chassis are used. The body is bound with flat iron and has three compartments, each of which has a hinged door at the rear. The doors are of simple construction, each being provided with a knife lock, which permits dumping a load in three different places. This insures even distribution of gravel.

Truck Body Divided into Three Parts Permits Even Distribution of Loads

Time-Saving Forms for Concrete Steps

When making forms for concrete steps, it takes much time to notch the stringers and nail on the tread strips. This work

Convenient and Timesaving Forms for Concrete Steps Are Easily Made

can be eliminated by using the type of form shown in the illustration. As is evident, no diagonal cutting of lumber is necessary. The sides consist of 1 by 12-in. stringers, and 1 by 9-in. material is used for the risers. These pieces are cut to equal lengths so that they require only spacing and nailing. Lengths of 1 by 4-in. stock are used to brace the risers. After the concrete has been poured and troweled, a piece of roofing or sheathing paper is tacked over the whole incline. This will carry off rain and prevent the steps from being used until the concrete is sufficiently hard.—G. A. Luers, Washington, D. C.

To Save Honey Bees

According to the claims of experienced bee keepers, grass or weeds, growing in front of hive entrances, causes a heavy loss of bees during the honey season. The bees returning to the hive overloaded with honey or pollen frequently fall before the entrance and, alighting in the thick grass, become chilled before they can crawl or fly into the hive. To prevent this one bee keeper has placed pieces of tar paper or discarded linoleum upon the ground in front of the hives. These keep down and prevent the growth of grass or weeds and the bees settling upon them are exposed to the warmth of the sun where no obstruction is offered to hinder their flight into the hive after they have rested.— G. E. Hendrickson, Argyle, Wis.

Small Bottle Useful to Motorist

A bottle small enough to be let down into the gasoline tank with a piece of string tied around the neck is very handy to carry in the auto tool chest when out driving. Should a tube have to be patched, gasoline is recommended as a cleaner for the part of the tube to be repaired. Also, if a spark plug needs cleaning, gasoline is used to do a good job. Greasy hands can also be cleaned very easily with gasoline, and the small bottle provides an easy method of getting it out of the tank.— S. N. Swenson, Harris, Minn.

Screwdriver for the Arbor Press

In removing large screws, especially those of the flat-head type, the main difficulty is keeping the bit of the screwdriver in the slot, and the workman resorts to the use of a hammer and punch. This, of course, produces a very unworkmanlike job. However, the illustration shows a screwdriver that will take any size of screw on account of the detachable bit, and the fact that it is secured to the ram by a bail arrangement allows very fast use, the screwdriver following the up and down movement of the ram.

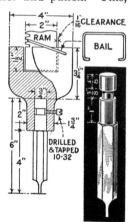

A wrench is put on the hexagonal section of the driver which turns in the fitting, the 10-32 screw simply holding the bit from dropping out. For use in removing the pole-shoe screws on motors and generator frames, a short piece of pipe can be put through the frame to keep it from turning, and the frame itself can be placed on a V-block made by sawing two triangular pieces out of a 12-in. section of channel iron. The body should be turned out of steel, allowing a clearance of $\frac{1}{16}$ in. between it and the ram. The bits, which were of different sizes to fit various screw slots, were made from old chisels that had their temper drawn, and were chucked in a lathe and a 2-in. section turned down and also slotted. The end of the bit was ground to fit the screw slot, leaving a part of the hexagonal for putting on a wrench. When removing or replacing screws the press-operating arm is used to keep the bit in a screw slot. The bail, made of No. 18 gauge steel wire, fits through the rack of the ram and into two holes in the side of the body of the fitting.

Collapsible Sides for Shop Truck

Fitted to a shop truck the folding sides shown in the illustration serve a double purpose: First, they prevent the load from scattering and second, they provide a gauge to limit the width of the load. When extended, the width should be such that the loaded truck will pass through any doorway in the building. Obviously, if the loading is restricted to this width there will be no danger of the load jamming or need of removing and rearranging it before it will go through. On the other hand, a truck nearly as wide as the doorways is not always convenient for other purposes, so the auxiliary sides are attached to the truck with hinges so that they can be folded down. In the center a strip of metal is pivoted, one on each side. These strips are bent at right angles at one end. When the sides are in use the strip is turned so that the bent portion rests against the truck; when letting them down it is reversed.

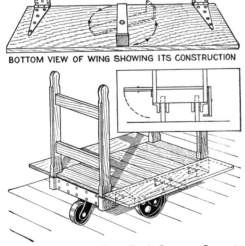

BOTTOM VIEW OF WING SHOWING ITS CONSTRUCTION

Collapsible Sides on Shop Truck Serve as Gauge to Measure Width of Doors

Skate-Sharpening Jig

While large machine shops usually have a regular supply of jigs for holding all the various models of ice skates for sharpen-

Above, Photo of Jig with Skate Fastened

Using Jig on Bench to Sharpen Skate

ing, the small shop has to work along with a makeshift or a quickly assembled jig. The jig shown herewith was designed by the owner of a small shop and will take skates of all sizes and types, enabling him to do a first-class sharpening job. The base consists of a heavy steel plate, 30 in. long, with a bolt at each end to act either as supports or to permit fastening permanently to the bench. The jig itself is a piece of angle steel somewhat longer than the largest-size skate. The vertical side rises 4 in. above the base and is drilled and tapped with holes, all along the edge, at about 1-in. intervals. One vertical end is drilled and tapped in the same way and a few holes are tapped in the vertical side. A skate is arranged as shown and clamped in position, with bolts and washers over the blade at the most convenient points. The jig is placed on the base, which has previously been adjusted in front of an emery wheel. By pushing the blade against the wheel and moving the jig to right and left the entire blade is ground evenly. The size of the wheel determines whether the blade will be flat or hollow-ground.—L. B. Robbins, Harwich, Mass.

Simple Safety Attachment
for Hoisting Barrels

Barrels are hoisted without risk of dropping them with the simple attachment

Simple Safety Sling for Hoisting Barrels Prevents Accidental Dropping of Burden

shown in the photos. It consists of a flat-iron ring large enough to fit over the head of the barrel, and heavy chains, which are slipped over the side and hooked securely around it near the lower head, so that the barrel cannot get loose.—R. G. Thackwell, Chicago, Ill.

Small Dams Prevent Creek-Bank Erosion

The erosion of creek banks and the resulting lowering of the water level which occur during flood periods, are especially undesirable in municipalities because the sewer outlets are uncovered with undesirable results. It can be prevented by building small concrete dams along the streams

as shown in the photo. The dams are placed from ⅛ to ¼ mile apart, depending on the slope of the stream, and are built just high enough to keep the bottom of the channel covered with water from bank to bank, during periods of extremely low flow. Concrete aprons, several feet wide, are built on the downstream sides to prevent damage from undermining.— Ivan E. Houk, Denver, Colo.

Proper Use of Pine Siding

Be sure all siding is thoroughly dry before installation. Do not put siding on walls immediately after a rainstorm, but let the sheathing and framework dry thoroughly first. To fail in this may mean loose nails, open joints or buckling of portions of the siding. The proper lap for bevel siding is as follows: ¾ in. on 4 in.; 1 in. on 5 and 6 in.; 1½ in. on wider stuff.

Siding should be cut with a miter saw at all corners. Wherever two pieces of siding join, it is best to use a splice joint. This is accomplished with a miter saw. Joints should be broken with as wide a space as convenient between the joints of overlapping tiers. Where siding butts up against window casings, a square, tight joint should be made. A metal flashing underneath the siding will prevent any possibility of water seeping in. For the finest finish and best work, nails in bevel siding should be countersunk and the depression filled with putty.

Before painting drop or bevel siding containing knots, a coat of thin white shellac should be applied. Siding should be given a priming coat as soon as it is laid, and for widths of bevel siding over

Small Concrete Dams High Enough to Keep Creek Bed Covered with Water Are Placed at Intervals of One Eighth to One-Fourth of a Mile to Prevent Erosion of Banks

8 in., it is advisable to paint the back side before it is put on. After the priming coat, it is well to let the building stand a few days, or as long as convenient, before putting on the finishing coats. This will insure that shrinking will have taken place, and that all surfaces will be properly covered.

There are always areas on the wall of a house where lengths of siding down to 18 in. must be used. Do not demand all long siding from your dealer. Considerable amounts of short siding develop in the process of manufacture and must be disposed of. If the mill man could not get rid of these short pieces, it would be necessary to charge more for the longer ones. Short lengths can also be used to advantage on the porch, on the garage and various outbuildings. At times, an excess of these shorts will accumulate and is sold at reduced prices. If you are in a position to use all short pieces, your dealer may be able to quote a very attractive price on such material.

Durable Nests for Poultry Made of Concrete

A simple and inexpensive method of forming the inside of a concrete hens' nest is shown in the illustration. The form is made of burlap, which is sewed in such a manner that it will have the juglike shape indicated. After the burlap form has been sewed, stuff it with rags, excelsior or similar material. Ordinary wooden boxes are used for the outside form. After the bottom of the box has been covered with concrete about 3 in. in thickness, the burlap mold is put in place and concrete is poured all around it. As soon as the concrete has set sufficiently to hold its own weight, remove the packing little by little. It is almost impossible to use wooden molds for this

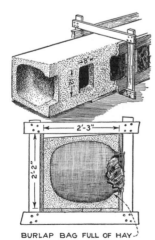

BURLAP BAG FULL OF HAY

purpose as they cannot be readily removed and will swell after the concrete is poured. —H. H. Siegele, Emporia, Kans.

Easily Made Tile Hook Facilitates Laying Drain Tile in Deep Ditches

Tile Hook for Deep Trenches

A tool known as a tile hook is valuable for laying tile in deep ditches. The hook consists of a strip of iron, 1 in. wide and 12 in. long, bent so that a 4-in. portion may be attached at right angles to a handle. With this tool the operator stands above the trench and puts the tiles in the correct position.—C. M. Baker, Wooster, Ohio.

Never-Slip Gauge Aids Glazier in Cutting Glass

In cutting glass for doors and windows, many glaziers employ a yardstick, or ruler, as a gauge along which to move the cutter. Unless firmly held, such a gauge is likely to move, causing more or less damage and expense. To prevent this, one need only obtain a discarded inner tube and from it cut a strip of rubber of the same length and width as the ruler. With this strip cemented firmly onto one side of the gauge, it will not slip and the worker consequently will be relieved of much strain on the hands or fingers.

Labor-Saving Snow Shovel

To clear the sidewalk after a sudden heavy snowfall, a janitor lashed a double thickness of corrugated paper board to the

Baggage Truck and Piece of Corrugated Cardboard Make Handy Snow Shovel

front of a small, two-wheeled baggage truck. The sharp steel nose of the truck slid under the snow as easily as under a trunk or box and scraped the sidewalk clean, while the corrugated board widened the sweep and carried big heaps of snow to the curb. In a very short time the broad sidewalk was ready for traffic, and the inventor found time to chuckle at his neighbors, who were still sweating over their shovels. — E. L. Bowman, Evansville, Ind.

Suggestions on Sash Installation

Sash should be well painted before, or immediately after installation. Dipping in linseed oil before the glass is applied gives a coating that will protect all points against the absorption of moisture. A good priming coat of thin paint should be applied as soon as the sash is in place. The tops and bottoms of the sash should be most carefully painted.

Good service demands that sash be back-puttied, that is, a small amount of putty be placed in the sash before the glass is laid in it, thereby forming an air-tight and water-tight cushion for the glass. On the outside of the sash, a mixture of pure linseed oil, white lead and

whiting will give best puttying results. Proper balance and fitting are essential. Weights that are too light or too heavy are often the cause of broken glass. Windows that are fitted too tightly or too loosely are sure to develop annoyances that cause repair expense or replacement.

In cold climates storm sash are generally approved and their use in winter assures comfort and coal saving. Window sash last longer by thus protecting them against melting snow and driving rains.

Sagebrush Mats Protect Canal Banks

In the arid western states erosion of irrigation-canal banks, due to high velocities of flow, can be prevented by lining the banks with sagebrush mats. Bundles of the brush are laid along the banks, covered with woven wire mesh and fastened securely at short intervals, either by piling large rocks on top of the wire, or by fastening the wire to posts set in the canal bed. The repairs are made during the winter and spring months when no water is carried in the canals.

Wooden Balls Plug Conduits

Wooden balls can be used to stop the flow in sewers, blow-off pipes through dams, or other conduits where valves have not been installed. The balls are made slightly larger than the conduits and are lowered in front of the openings where the suction of the moving water catches them and pulls them into place, after which they are held securely by the water pressure, which tends to push them into the holes.

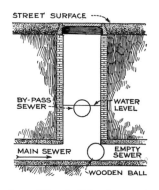

The ball is dropped through the manhole and will take the position indicated in the drawing. In plugging a pipe through a dam, where the water is often several feet above the opening, the ball is built around a concrete core so that it will sink. Canvas wrapped around the ball helps to seal the small irregularities in the edges of the opening. Such a method was recently used at an irrigation dam where the water was approximately 200 feet above the pipe.

Steam Cleaning a Stone Building

To meet the changing demand of present-day commercial conditions many old buildings are being altered or remodeled. In order to eliminate the undesirable contrast always present in such cases between the old dirty surfaces and the new stone put in the walls, some kind of cleaning of the old portions is generally carried out. Because of the detrimental effects of acid cleaning or sandblasting, scrubbing with soap powders and hand brushes is customarily employed. This method is effective, but slow and laborious, and in an effort to devise a faster and more efficient means of cleaning limestone, experiments with the use of live steam have been conducted at the bureau of standards.

An interesting demonstration of this experimental work was the steam cleaning of the remodeled building of the Baltimore Commercial Bank, Baltimore, Md., where the scheme was given a practical trial under commercial conditions. The use of live steam at 80-lb. pressure, blown directly against the stone through simple nozzles made of galvanized pipe fitted to the end of ½-in. steam-hose lines, was found to be very effective in removing the 20-year accumulation of dirt on this Indiana-limestone building. The cost of the job was somewhat higher than a bid received for acid cleaning. This increased cost is to be explained in part by the experimental character of the work, this being the first complete building ever cleaned with steam. The final color of the stone was not so bright as that of new stone work, but was considered entirely satisfactory, since it combined cleanliness with the appearance of age, which is usually thought desirable in stone buildings. The success of this practical test leads to the conclusion that steam cleaning would, in most cases, be an economical and effective method.

Cement Banking Saves Coal

An eastern coal dealer, having a location below the sidetrack, laid a cement floor over the ground and a section of the

Inclined Bank Faced with Concrete Brings Coal from Cars into the Yard by Gravity

banking up to the track, on which the coal is thrown from the cars. The smooth surface of the concrete brings the coal down to ground level without rehandling, which greatly assists shoveling and prevents considerable waste.

Drilling Holes in Edge of Disk

In a small shop having no milling machine and index head, the writer had a precision job of drilling three holes in the periphery of a brass disk, which was done with accuracy by the method shown in the drawing. Three toolmakers' buttons were placed around the shoulder of the disk as indicated and after being set the proper distance apart the mandrel was gripped in a machine vise, blocks with V-grooves being used to hold the mandrel securely. To get the distance between the buttons on a circle 5 in. in diameter, is a simple calculation, and the buttons are set in the usual way. One button was brought into contact with an accurate block and the hole was then drilled. The other holes were drilled in the same way. The job was entirely satisfactory.—Hugo Ljungqvist, Philadelphia, Pa.

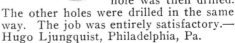

Drilling Holes in the Periphery of a Brass Disk

Reading the Incubator Thermometer

As incubators are usually installed in the cellar or basement of the home artificial light is necessary when reading the

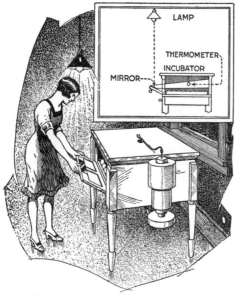

Lamp Directly Above and Mirror Inside of Incubator Door Facilitate Reading of Thermometer

thermometer. An overhead light is practical for this purpose in most cases, and if a mirror is placed on the inside of the outer door of the incubator the reading can be done instantly. By opening the door of the machine, as shown in the illustration, the light from above is reflected on the instrument and the temperature noted without difficulty.—G. E. Hendrickson, Argyle, Wis.

Care of Oilstones

Oilstones should be properly cared for in order to retain the life and sharpness of the grit, to keep the surface flat and even, and to prevent glazing. With few exceptions, like the India and Crystalon, new stones should be soaked in oil for several days before using. An oilstone should be kept clean and moist. Allowing it to remain dry a long time or exposing it to the air tends to harden it. If the stone is kept in a dry place, it should be put in a box having a closed cover, and a few drops of fresh, clean oil poured on it. To restore an even flat surface on an oilstone, grind it on the side of a grindstone, or rub it down with sandstone or an emery brick. An oilstone can be prevented from glazing by the proper use of

oil or water; either will prevent the particles of metal that are cut away from the tool being sharpened from filling the surface of the stone. Plenty of water should be used on all coarse-grained natural stones. On medium or fine-grained natural stones, such as Arkansas or Washita, as well as on all artificial stones, oil should be used invariably, as water is not thick enough to keep the steel particles out of the pores. To further prevent glazing, dirty oil should be wiped off the stone as soon as possible after using. This is very important, for if the oil is left on the stone, it dries in, carrying steel dust with it. Cotton waste is one of the best things for cleaning a stone. If a stone does become glazed or gummed up, cleaning with gasoline or ammonia will usually restore the cutting qualities; but if this treatment is not effective, scour the stone with loose emery or a piece of sandpaper fastened to a flat board.—J. S. Hagans, Chicago, Ill.

Marker for Sheet Metal

Workers in sheet metal, whether tin, brass or copper, will appreciate the usefulness of the line-marking tool shown in the illustration. Owing to the flexible nature of this kind of material it is difficult to hold a marking tool in contact with the work, and this is especially the case on brass sheets thin enough to be shipped in rolls. With the tool shown, however, it is impossible to slip off the work, as the metal is guided between two parts as it is slid along. The ½-in. washers, held together and riveted by a short piece of

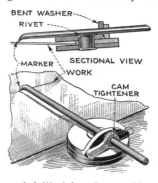

steel, make a good body for this tool. The bottom washer is used as it is; the middle one is cut away on one side to within about 1/16 in. of the hole, and the top one is bent up at the opposite side and drilled for the marking tool or scriber. This is held in place by a cam tightener made from a piece of metal, as shown, or from a length of wire, one turn of which is taken round the scriber, a short piece being left for a handle. By filing the outside of the loop it is made to tighten when brought over to one side and loosen when turned to the opposite. To mark off a strip of metal before cutting, the scriber is set the required distance with a scale from the middle washer and is tightened in place with the cam. Then, with the thumb pressing on the scriber near the point and the four fingers keeping the tool in contact with the edge of the sheet, it is slid along to mark any width of strip desired within the limit of the tool. It is, of course, not practicable to make the scriber too long, as the sheet of metal would then be likely to buckle.—Harry Moore, Montreal, Can.

Shorthand Mechanical Drawings

Complicated mechanical drawings may be simplified considerably by the use of symbols as shown in the illustration. The same steam piping is drawn in three different ways; the first showing the fittings drawn up in the usual way, the second showing the same somewhat simplified, and the lower one showing the drawing reduced entirely to symbols. Much work and time are, of course, saved by this method and the drawing is easier to read. A key of symbols is given in one corner of each drawing or separate key sheets, covering all the symbols used in each drafting department, may be issued.—Dr. Ing. Carl Commentz, Hamburg, Germany.

Method of Preventing Excessive Loss of Heat in Shipping or Receiving Rooms

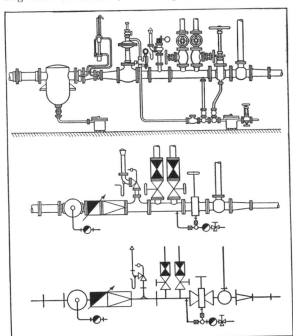

Mechanical Drawings Can Be Simplified Considerably by Using Symbols to Designate Parts

Winter Door for Receiving Room

Factory or store receiving rooms often cannot be kept warm and comfortable in cold weather because of the necessity of frequently opening a large outside door to receive small boxes and parcels from delivery trucks, and where lumber or metal bars are being unloaded from cars on tracks outside the building, the door may have to be kept open for hours at a time. The discomfort from cold and loss of money in wasted heat may be partly prevented, if the bottom part of the door is cut and hinged so that it can be opened independently. A glass panel should be put into the upper section so that the clerk can see what is being unloaded.

Brass Locknuts

In practically every power plant, and in every plumbing and steam-fitting shop, numerous old brass globe and other valves collect, which are usually sold as scrap brass. Before doing this, cut off the hexagonal ends from the old valves with a hacksaw. They can be cut off in a few moments and make locknuts, which are thicker and therefore better than the ordinary ones.

Support Helps Turn Thin Walls

In turning up large cylindrical pieces, such as belt pulleys, etc., having thin walls, it is very difficult to prevent chat-

Support on Outside
Prevents Chattering
on Cylindrical Work

tering. However, this can easily be overcome by using a device of the kind shown in the drawing. A 3-ft. arm is made of heavy strap iron, about ⅜ by 1½ in., and bent to the shape shown. A roller, about 1½ in. in diameter and 1 in. long, is held in a U-piece made from strap iron which is fastened to the arm so that when the end of the arm is hooked inside the carriage the center of the roller will come even with the cutting tool. A piece of wire and a spring hold the bar, and this, in turn, gives the right pressure on the material at the cutting point. Being hooked inside of the carriage, the bar is kept just opposite the tool at all times as the tool moves. For turning the outside, the roller can be fixed to press on the inside, and the same result will be obtained. This device will instantly stop the chattering and will help do a much better job of cutting.—Ed Sundholm, Albert City, Iowa.

Don't Overlook Your Battery Charger

The life of a battery-charger bulb can be greatly prolonged if it is properly handled. It may become inactive because of a sagging filament, for instance. But if the bulb is inverted as soon as any sagging is noticed, it will last much longer.

At a battery-charging station this has been the practice for some time, and the owner has reclaimed a number of rectifying bulbs by simply mounting the socket, in or outside of the charger, so that it will hang in an inverted position. Sometimes the bulb will light, but will not charge, and this trouble can usually be traced to a loose socket connection. A badly sulphated, or dead, battery may also cause this trouble. Chargers of the vibrating type occasionally cease to function before the battery has taken a full charge. If this happens, it is a safe bet that the adjusting screw has worked loose and the vibrating points are too widely separated. If the ammeter shows a discharge, the points are sticking together and should be separated at once.—Glen F. Stillwell, Collinsville, Ill.

Making Patterns for Small Sheaves

To the patternmaker with only limited molding practice, the making of a pattern for a small sheave pulley, such as shown in Fig. 1, for example, may be puzzling. He is not quite sure how the molder would prefer having it made, split on the line AB to be molded in green sand in a two or three-part flash or with a ring of green sand to make the groove, or perhaps a solid pattern with a core print turned on it as at B, Fig. 1, and a box to make the two half cores, these to be pasted together to form the groove. If the sides of the pattern are flat as in Fig. 2, he might be tempted to split the pattern through the middle on the line DE, doweling the two halves together in the usual way. When but one or two, or a half dozen castings are wanted, it makes little difference how the pattern is made, split or solid. The molder can produce the castings from a pattern made either way. However, I prefer a solid pattern with the groove made in dry-sand core; the pattern is stronger and will retain its shape much longer. If the bottom of the groove is sharp or has a small radius that does not call for machine finishing, the dry-sand core method is the better way,

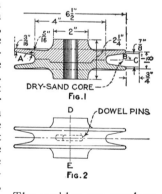

DRY-SAND CORE--
FIG.1

D
DOWEL PINS
E
FIG.2

as the sharp green sand would wash away with the pouring of the metal. The method indicated in Fig. 2 is not desirable.

If these sheave castings are to be made in large quantities, it is well to take the

Siding Saves Time in Stonework

Use of framework and siding in the process of building stonework walls, has enabled an eastern contractor to save

Wooden Frame Aids in Laying Stone Walls and Eliminates Need of Plastering

matter up with the foundry. When making a sheave pattern split through the middle, the apprentice patternmaker insists on making the joint faces of each half pattern recessed, as shown in Fig. 1. When but a few castings are wanted, this recessing is unnecessary; it calls for reverse chucking of the two halves of the pattern. By chucking with the joint face against the chuck, the half pattern can be turned and finished on both sides in one chucking and then doweled together with a single pin in the center. I have made them with only a piece of wire brad for a dowel. As an apprentice, the boy is taught to make his patterns up to a certain standard. A few visits to the foundry and a study of the jobs as they are made by the "old rounders" will convince him that it is not always necessary to line up to the so-called standard in the production of many patterns he is called upon to make.— M. E. Duggan, Kenosha, Wis.

much time in keeping the walls plumb, and the siding serves as a form to hold the inner facing of cement in place, eliminating the necessity of plastering after the wall is completed. The increased cost in erection appears to be more than offset by the saving in time.

Portable Desk for Shipping Clerks

Shipping clerks, inventory men, appraisers and others engaged in clerical work which necessitates moving about the store or warehouse with facilities for writing, figuring and checking, will find much convenience in the adoption of a portable desk of the type now in use in a Wisconsin factory. The desk was originally a small writing desk. The back legs were shortened about 6 in., and a pair of wheels and an axle from a discarded baby carriage were attached to them. Two handles were fastened at top.

Portable Desk Fitted with Wheels Is Convenient for Shipping Clerks and Appraisers

large oil company, utilizes the tailboard of his truck as a workbench, after having bolted his vise on it, as shown. The handy location and utility of the arrangement save much extra work and delay on rush jobs.—Richard C. Tarr, Gloucester, Mass.

Cleaning Auto Radiator

The tubes of Ford or similar radiators can be cleaned with a brass rifle-cleaning brush when the bottom tank has been taken out for repairs. This will remove the lime, oil and dirt inside of the tubes. Of course the brush must be used with care, or holes might be made in the tubes. The proper size of brush for the Ford radiator is a rod for a .22 rifle.—E. T. Gunderson, Humboldt, Iowa.

Vise Attached to Truck Tailboard Found Handy for Traveling Repairman

Tailboard Serves as Workbench

Obliged by the nature of his duties as truck inspector and traveling repairman to cut the working parts of his equipment to a minimum a mechanic, employed by a

Improved Sand Bucket for Wells

The ordinary sand bucket for use in removing sand deposits from large wells, is not entirely satisfactory. The city plant engineer of the pumping station at Lincoln, Nebr., has designed an improved bucket which works on the principle of dam dredges. It is built for an 8-in. pipe which is lowered with the jaws opened and locked. When the jaws strike the bottom, the impact releases the lock and the two halves automatically close and take a big bite. The action is rapid and positive, so that from a well 100 ft. deep it is possible to remove as high as five or six loads a minute. With the ordinary sand bucket, it sometimes takes fifteen or twenty minutes for the bucket to fill once. The accompanying photos show the two positions of the device.—D. R. Van Horn, Walton, Nebr.

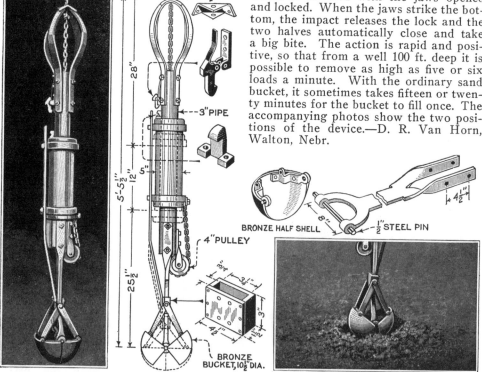

Improved Sand Bucket Works Like Clamshell, and with Its Use, Five or Six Loads Can Be Removed from a 100-Foot Well per Minute

Shop Notes

How to Treat Plastic Paint

By J. S. HAGANS

PLASTIC paint is a gypsum product marketed under the name of textone, which has some of the characteristics of the gesso that is now having a renaissance among home art workers. This material, which can be used for obtaining much broader effects just as well as it can for the finer gesso applications, is to be had at most paint stores and building-supply sources. While primarily produced as an architectural material, this fact does not necessarily limit its uses for building purposes, although it is here that its application will perhaps have the greatest appeal. This material comes in standard-size 10 and 25-lb. packages in the form of a white powder. It is not a plaster in any sense, but a true plastic paint. The addition of lukewarm water and coloring pigment, if desired, is all that is necessary to its application with an ordinary paint-brush. One pound of

Fig. 1, Mission Finish; Fig. 2, Paper-Stipple Finish

Fig. 3, French Finish; Fig. 4, Scroll Finish

the material will cover approximately 1½ sq. yd. of surface, or about as much as ordinary oil paint. It can be applied over any surface and a wide variety of charming and distinctive effects are within reach of any reasonably intelligent person capable of using a paintbrush.

Avoid Prussian blue, carmine and aniline colors. While chrome green and yellow can be used, the decorator must handle them carefully and limit the quantities. It is important that the pigment first be dissolved and then added to the previously mixed material.

Fig. 5, English Finish; Fig. 6, Stipple Finish, Using Brush; Fig. 7, Brush Finish

The richly attractive stone and rough - surfaced wall effects one sees in window backgrounds, wall finishes and surfaces on fixtures, polychrome or otherwise, if they haven't been obtained through the use of textone, can be. Therefore, the storekeeper, the home owner or the artistic person who wants to polish up something in an original way, will find in this material a very flexible medium that is susceptible of all sorts of manipulation.

Aside from the material itself, the only thing needed in the way of equipment is a paintbrush, large or small, as the surface to be worked upon may demand.

Use a 12-qt. water pail and add to the powder lukewarm water, from which the chill has just been removed, in the proportion of 1 pt. of water to 1 lb. of textone. Do not, under any consideration, attempt to mix it thin like calcimine. Allow the mixture to stand for about 30 minutes, after which it is ready to apply.

If a one-coat tinted effect is desired, this mixture can be colored to certain shades. The following pigment colors ground in oil, and slightly thinned with turpentine, or dry colors dissolved in water, can be safely used: For red, use Venetian, Indian or permanent reds; for browns and tans, use raw umber, burnt umber, raw sienna, burnt sienna; for yellow or creams, use yellow ocher; for blue, use cobalt or ultramarine blue; for green, cobalt green; for black, use lampblack or dropblack.

It is necessary that sufficient textone should always be prepared to complete the job, in order to insure the same color. Incidentally, it would be well to experiment with the color before applying to the surface to be worked, as it may be too dark or too light when dry. In either case, the proper effect can be obtained by adding either more textone or color, as required.

This plastic paint may be successfully applied over any surface, if the user is careful to remove from it all dirt, grease or efflorescence, so that it is clean and dry. Generally speaking, it will be found advisable to give the surface a coat of size, which is furnished with the material as it is bought, and this should be allowed to dry for six hours after application.

For finishing over sheet-rock plasterboard, or any of the other varieties of wallboard, be sure that all the joints and nail heads are completely concealed and that the surface is in a level plane at the joints. Textone cannot be successfully used over gloss oil or varnish sizes, and their use should be avoided for this work.

On new or old plastered surfaces, not decorated, the plaster must be at least two months old. If the plaster finish is found to be unusually soft or absorbent, proceed as follows: First, get a good grade of floor varnish and mix with an equal part of turpentine. Then mix this liquid with textone in the proportion of 1 lb. of the powder to 1 pt. of liquid, and apply as a sizing coat. When this is thoroughly dry, remove the sharp "nibs" with sandpaper and apply the previously prepared material. Where the plaster finish is normally hard and not too absorbent, sizing is not required.

A hard, smooth plaster surface is sometimes difficult to cover. In this case, apply a preliminary coat of textone, well brushed out; allow this to dry and then apply the regular preparation.

The plastic paint may be applied over a coat of brown plaster after it has been darbied to a true surface, troweled smooth and sized.

For application over painted surfaces, scrape off all loose and scaling paint and fill cracks and holes to a level surface. When dry, sandpaper smooth and color patches to match surrounding surface.

Great care must be taken to see that all grease, dirt or wax is thoroughly removed. If the surface, after being thoroughly cleaned, looks glossy or enameled, kill gloss with a 10-per-cent solution of sal soda or washing powder and hot water. Rinse with clear water and apply the plastic paint without sizing.

Calcimined surfaces must be washed clean, so that no color remains in the corners around the trim, after which directions for covering wallboard or plastered surfaces may be followed. If the under surface has a high gloss from previous sizing, treat as suggested for gloss-paint surfaces, and apply the textone without using any sizing.

Wherever possible, wallpaper should be removed and the under surface treated according to whether it is of plaster or wallboard. If the paper cannot be removed, it must be securely bonded to the surface. Remove any loose parts or paste them down. Wallpaper that has been applied with paste that will soften in 8 or 10 hours must be removed. Wallpaper that contains water-soluble dyes will discolor the material and must be removed. A damp cloth rubbed over the surface of the paper will be discolored by such dyes. Roughen a high-gloss wallpaper with

sandpaper. Wipe free from dust and dirt and apply the plastic material directly.

On glass, metal or wood, remove the grease and wax finishes and kill the varnish or glossy surface by an application of a 10-per-cent solution of sal soda or washing powder in hot water. Rinse with clear water. These surfaces should not be sized.

To apply the textone, use a clean wall brush, which is similar to a calcimine brush, and lay on a coat to a uniform thickness of $\frac{1}{16}$ or $\frac{1}{8}$ in. After it has set a little, until tacky or drawn up, stipple with a wall stippling brush, as in Fig. 6. Other effects can be obtained by the use of an ordinary paintbrush, Fig. 3, either slapping, pushing or dabbling it with a straight or side motion. A sponge or ball of crumpled paper, used as in Fig. 2, will vary the texture. Two persons work to the best advantage over large surfaces, one applying the material as the other does the stippling.

As hardened plastic paint of this kind is insoluble in water, do not allow it to spatter or harden on woodwork or trim. Wash them off at once with warm water and a sponge. Where the trim is in place, it is best to go over it with a rag moistened in boiled oil or kerosene, to make removal of spatters easy. Pails, tools and brushes should be kept clean. Do not let the material harden on them.

A moderate temperature should prevail in the room. While applying the paint, close the doors and windows to avoid drafts, opening them after application to permit a free circulation of air. Build a fire in cold weather.

When the coating has dried, place a piece of sandpaper flat on the surface and rub slightly. This enhances the texture by removing the rough or pointed edges and making it stand out more prominently. Plaster-molding effects are obtained by the simple process of covering ordinary wooden moldings with the textone.

The illustrations show a number of methods of finishing the material, and these are as follows: Fig. 1, Mission fin-

Spanish-Palm Finish, Made by Means of the Back of an Ordinary Kitchen Spoon

ish; the material is applied with a calcimine brush, and the texture obtained with a small brush worked over the textone with a circular motion. Use the palm of the hand to obtain smoothness where desired. Fig. 2, paper-stipple finish; the texture is obtained with a ball of wadded paper. The effect is a little coarser than if a stippling brush is used. Fig. 3, French finish; texture obtained by firm downward sweeps of a small whiskbroom; sandpapering the surface, when dry, will soften the effect somewhat. Fig. 4, scroll finish; the material is worked with the tips of the fingers in a circular motion. If the effect is too coarse, smoothing with the palm of the hand, or sanding when dry, will soften it. Fig. 5, English finish; the texture is obtained with a wide scraping knife or piece of tin, to imitate the effect of old tool mark-

ings. Fig. 6, stipple finish; material stippled with regular painters' stipple brush. This finish can advantageously be sanded when dry. Fig. 7, brush finish; the material is here applied with a wall brush, then stippled lightly with a wad of crumpled paper and finally brushed down with a large calcimine brush. Fig. 8, Spanish-palm finish; textone applied with a wall brush; texture obtained with the back of an ordinary kitchen spoon. The palm of the hand can be used to soften the effect, rubbing it over the marks made by the spoon, and this is suggested. Unless otherwise specified for these effects, the material is first applied with a large calcimine brush.

The effects obtainable are limited only by the ingenuity of the worker, and with the foregoing instructions he can easily work out new effects.

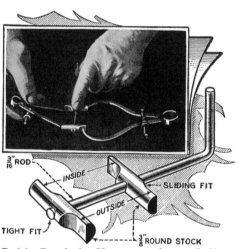

Tool for Transferring Measurements from an Inside to an Outside Caliper, and Vice Versa

Caliper-Setting Tool

It takes considerable skill to transfer sizes from an outside caliper to an inside caliper, and vice versa, owing to the small point of contact between the two tools. However, as it is a simple matter to set calipers against a flat face, the tool shown in the illustration is most useful for this work. Two pieces of ⅜-in. round stock are cut down to half their thickness on opposite sides, and carefully drilled and reamed in the center to fit a length of 3⁄16-in. rod bent to a right angle at one end. One of the pieces is a sliding fit and the other a tight fit on the end of the rod. Supposing a hole is to be drilled to fit a shaft; the outside caliper is first set to the shaft, then the setting tool is used to du-

plicate this measurement, as shown, and the inside caliper may be accurately set against the flats at the opposite ends of the cut-down pieces. This operation is, of course, reversed when setting outside calipers to an inside setting.

Lubricating Wagon Wheels

It is a rather disagreeable task to lubricate wagon wheels as the wagon must first be jacked up and the nuts on the axles must be removed. While performing this I have often wondered why wagons were not equipped with modern time and labor - saving lubricating devices, so I set about to adapt the wagon wheels to the grease gun. Adapters of the kind used on auto - spring bolts were obtained from a junk dealer. Four short lengths of pipe were tapped to take the adapters and a hole was drilled in each hub so that the lengths of pipe could be driven in snugly. The adapters were then screwed down into the tapped ends, as shown in the drawing, and it was then a simple matter to use a grease gun.— C. M. Wilcox, Torrington, Conn.

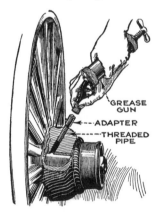

Rapid Stage-Erecting Device

A simple, effective and safe device for rapidly putting up stagings in the erection of buildings has been worked out by a Maine carpenter. It consists of two short lengths of scantling and four iron strap hinges. The larger stick is 3 by 4 in., and the second slightly smaller. The first is used as the beam upon which the stage

Simple Stage Brace, with Supporting Arm and Strap Hinges, Speeds Up Building-Stage Erection and Removal, and Is Entirely Safe

boards are resting. A large hinge is fastened to both ends of this stick. Half of each hinge hangs loose so that it can be attached to the side of a building and to the scaffolding. The smaller piece is fastened to the larger by a third hinge, and to the building in the same way as the big stick, by means of the fourth hinge at the building end of the stick. This forms a supporting brace for the scaffold. Three nails are driven into the wall, and a like number into the scaffolding, allowing the holes in the hinges to pass over the heads of the nails. Then, as the weight of the sill rests on the hinge, it is pushed down and the nail heads act as buttons, fastening the hinges securely to the building and scaffold. The side brace fastens in the same way. To release it, simply raise and let the nail head go through the large end of the hinge hole.—Sam E. Conner, Auburn, Me.

Connecting Pipes with a "Dutchman"

An excellent "dutchman" can be made, for straight work on large flanged-pipe lines that fail to meet and are too close to allow the use of a nipple. If flanges are not immediately available for making up the nipple, take a piece of the next size larger pipe. Face the ends off in a lathe, making the length of the dutchman the

same as the distance between the two flanges that will not meet. Cut two gaskets from $\frac{1}{16}$-in. sheet packing and force the lines apart so that the dutchman, with a piece of packing on each end, can be squeezed into the opening. Pull the two flanges tightly and evenly together all the

way around, using long bolts. This makes a very satisfactory job for medium steam and water pressures.

Removing Lead from Automatic Pencil

It is a rather laborious job to drill the lead out of a steel pencil when it becomes lodged in the point, as drills small enough are not always at hand and there is also danger of injuring the tiny lugs that hold the lead. The simplest way is to hold the point of the pencil in an alcohol flame for a few seconds while exerting pressure on the lead by turning the feed. The lugs will be expanded so that the lead can easily be forced out. Care should be taken not to hold the pencil in the flame too long, as heating it too much may injure the point.—L. A. Krider, Hatton, Wash.

¶Wallpaper can be washed with a soft cloth saturated with benzine; neither pattern nor color will be affected.

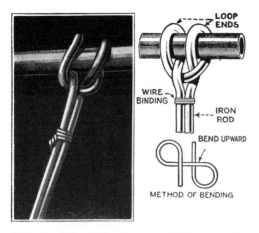

Handy Tool for Pulling Lengths of Pipe from the Stock Rack

Removing Pipe from Racks

The photo shows a handy tool used in a pipe warehouse for pulling out lengths of pipe from racks too high to reach easily with the hand. No machine work is necessary to make the tool, the work being a simple bending operation. A length of iron rod, about ⅜-in. in diameter, is bent round to form two loops in the center, with the ends of the rod pointing in opposite directions. An upward bend is given the loops to bring them in line as shown, after which the ends of the rod are bound in three places with wire, near the loops, in the middle and again near the end. The finished length of the tool is about 4 ft. To pull a piece of pipe from a rack, the loops are passed over it and the handle pulled. This binds the loops on the pipe and the latter is pulled out. If the pipe is short, it can be lowered bodily to the floor. Long pieces are pulled out of the rack until overbalanced and then let down easily to the floor.

¶ Rose reamers should never be used for any other metal than free-working steel, and then only under the best working conditions.

Starting a Stiff Engine

After tightening up the connecting rods of an engine, or possibly the crankshaft bearings, it often occurs that the engine cannot be turned with the starter. This condition may be discouraging, but if the owner of the car has an extra battery or can borrow one temporarily, it will be possible to turn over even a very stubborn engine. To use the extra battery, connect one side to the ground and the other side to the terminal of the starting motor, duplicating the connections as made with the regular battery in the car; in other words, connect the batteries in parallel so that the voltage will be the same but the amperage doubled. The extra battery can be placed on the running board of the car, and temporary connections made to the ground and to the starting-motor terminal. This method is used regularly by a mechanic of a small service and sales station. Also under other adverse conditions, as during extremely cold weather, with tight pistons, or a gummed motor, the method will prove helpful.

Ridding Deep Well of Foul Air

A resident found it necessary to clean out an old, deep well. Upon investigation the air at the bottom was found to be foul and unfit to breathe. Just how to get rid of this air was the problem until a neighbor suggested rigging up a blacksmiths' forge blower in the manner shown. The blower was set up alongside the well curb and secured with a guy rope and stake, as indicated. A piece of fire hose was clamped around the nozzle and dropped to within a few feet of the bottom of the well, so that it would hang just above the worker's head and yet give him enough room to work. The flaring end of a large tin funnel was used as a discharge nozzle to distribute the air in all directions. With an operator turning the blower crank slowly, the cleaner went to the bottom of the well and

Forge Blower Used for Supplying Air to Workers in Deep Well

there was no difficulty in supplying him with plenty of fresh air.—L. B. Robbins, Harwich, Mass.

Substitute for Draw-Filing

Draw-filing of cast-iron cylinders, which is a tedious job and produces uncertain results, can be done better by the use of knurling tools. The wheels, costing from 15 cents up, can be obtained for all sorts of fancy finishes. They give a uniform finish, and take only half the time required for draw-filing. This method can also be used on cylinders for finishing presses and similar classes of textile machinery.—H. M. Toombs, Chicago, Ill.

Mixing Concrete in the Wheelbarrow

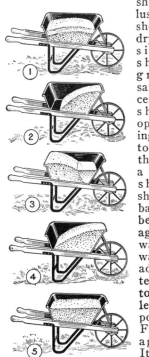

A simple and easy method of mixing concrete by hand in a wheelbarrow is shown in the illustration. Fig. 1 shows a batch of dry material consisting of four shovelfuls of gravel, two of sand and one of cement. Fig. 2 shows the first operation, working the material to the front of the barrow, with a round-pointed shovel. Fig. 3 shows the same batch after it has been worked back again in the same way and some water has been added. The material is worked to the front again, leaving it in the position shown in Fig. 4, and then again backward. It is now thoroughly mixed and will keep itself in the position shown in Fig. 5. The writer has used this method and found it entirely satisfactory.—H. H. Siegele, Emporia, Kans.

¶To prevent exposed black pipe from rusting, cover it with a grease made of 1 lb. lard, 1 oz. gum camphor and 1 oz. black lead.

Neat Wooden Boxes along the Roadside Hold Farmers' Cream Cans

Boxes for Cream Cans

Instead of following the usual custom of dropping the cans at the roadside to be jostled or stolen, one Texas creamery has had several hundred wooden boxes built and placed along the road. The boxes hold three 5-gal. cream cans, and when the truck drivers return the empty cans, they place them in the box and close the lid. The system has practically stopped complaints and theft, and is a method endorsed by the road commissioners. Each box is 18 in. wide, 40 in. long and high enough to take the cans. The cover is hinged and the outside bears this message, "Leave Cream Cans Here."

Keeping Moss from Choking Irrigation Canals

The aquatic moss which grows in the smaller lateral irrigation canals during the summer months, sometimes to such an extent as to interfere seriously with the delivery of irrigation water, can be kept down by dragging a heavy iron chain along the bottom of the canal. Two two-horse teams are used. One team is attached to each end of the chain and the two teams are driven along the banks, one on either side. The dragging is done about three times a week during the entire irrigation season. The work can be done whenever convenient, without shutting the water out of the canal.

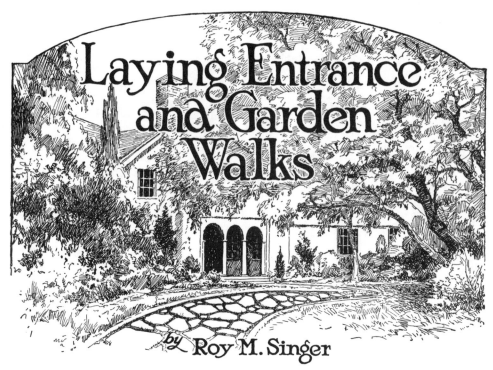

Laying Entrance and Garden Walks

by Roy M. Singer

ONE of the main features of a home is the walk leading to the entrance door. It is the first thing that meets the eye of the person entering. If the walk is neat and well kept, the impression is bound to be fair; if it is poorly laid and ill maintained, the impression is likely to be a bad one, notwithstanding the fact that the exterior of the house may be beautiful. Not alone the front but also the side walks and the garden walks, if laid in an attractive manner, will go far toward making the house good to look at.

It must be said at the beginning that the main purpose in writing this article is to show how to construct a well-built walk other than the ordinary concrete sidewalk, and to illustrate various patterns and different materials which may be used to good advantage.

The materials for the construction of a decorative walk depend a good deal upon the location of the town in which the walk is to be built. For example: in certain towns slate is available, in others it is not; in some brick may be purchased at a very reasonable figure, in others it will be found to be quite expensive. Thus, where cost is an important factor—and it generally is—the material should be selected from among those most readily available in the town.

There are four materials which lend themselves to decorative-walk construction, and they are stone, brick, tile and concrete. With stone, some very attractive walks of the flag-type may be built. Flag walks are of a rather informal appearance when laid with wide joints so that the grass grows between the stones, and are more suitable for gardens than for the front walks to homes, but where a rustic effect is desired, such as the walk for an English-cottage-type house, set in rather heavy foliage, nothing blends into the picture so well as a flag walk with the flags about an inch apart and grass growing between them.

Brick and tile present a more formal or citylike appearance than stone, although brick may be laid with wide grass-grown joints to give a garden-walk effect. It is more often, however, laid in a simple pattern and the joints filled with cement grout. Ordinarily the joints in brick walks are not greater than ³⁄₁₆ or ¼ in., although when a grass-grown brick walk is desired the joints should be at least ³⁄₈-in. wide but not more than ⅝ inch.

Tile used for walks is of the kind known to the trade as quarry tile. It is not quarried, however, as its name might indicate, but is made of burnt clay in the same manner as brick. It comes in sizes ranging ordinarily from 4 by 4 to 8 by 8 in. It may sometimes be had in larger sizes than 8-in. squares, but seldom smaller than 4 by 4-in. The thickness may vary from ¼ to 1 in. depending upon local kiln practice.

Concrete is a good material for ornamental walks in that it may be used to make concrete flags or tile, and thus this material may be used in localities where the genuine is not available. One advantage of concrete is the fact that it can be had everywhere. With concrete flags a very attractive effect may be obtained by coloring the pieces. All that is necessary is to add some mortar color to the mixture when it is made up. A varicolored walk may be built up by using units of several tints. This makes a very attractive walk provided the colors are subdued and blended harmoniously.

We will first take up the construction of a walk, of which there are two main types, that with a concrete base, and that without. Where climatic changes are considerable no walk should be built without a concrete base, lest it be destroyed by being uplifted due to the action of frost; but in warm climates, where heavy frosts are not encountered, the concrete base may be dispensed with.

Fig. 1 shows a section through a brick walk with a concrete base. Brick walks, by the way, should always be built with a concrete base. Some change in the surface due to settlement is bound to occur in time if they are not. The first step in the construction of a walk is to excavate the top soil to a depth of about 10 in. so that a firm base for the walk may be obtained. The surface should then be thoroughly tamped to make it solid. In the center of the walk a line of drain tile should be placed, if the ground is low and the drainage poor. In high ground, where the natural drainage is good and the soil fairly sandy, the drain need not be installed but it must be used where natural drainage is poor and the soil is clayey. It is better to fill the pocket in which the drain tile is set with gravel than with cinders, as is sometimes done, for the gravel will let the water seep through to the drain tile easier than will the cinders. Notice in the sketch that the bottom of the excavation is sloped toward the pit in which the drain is laid. This slope should be about ¾ or 1 in. per foot.

After the drain is installed, the excavation should be filled to a depth of 6 or 8 in. with cinders, well wetted down and

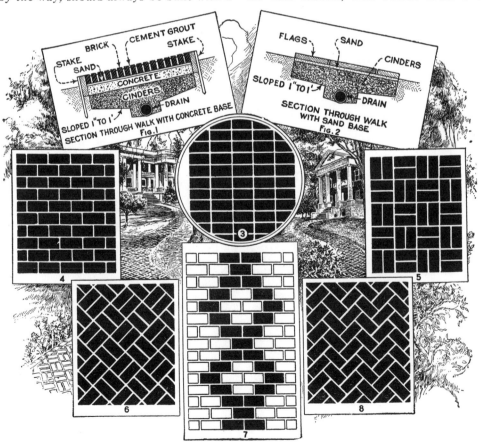

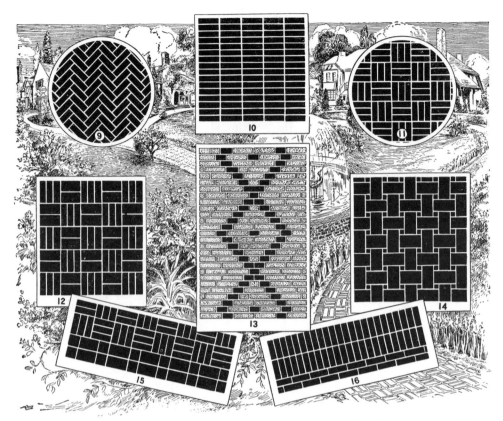

tamped firmly and solidly. Next the concrete base is applied between the forms, as shown in the sketch. The forms consist of 2 by 4-in. lengths held in place by stakes. The stakes are made high enough so that an additional 2 by 4-in. piece may be attached and used as a guide for laying the brick. The concrete used should be a 1:3:5 mix, and should be allowed to set for 24 hours before the brick are laid upon it.

Before beginning to lay the brick, a thin layer of fine bank sand, about ⅛ to ¼ in. thick, should be spread on the concrete. This sand cushion will take up all the little unevenesses in the surface of the concrete and make the laying of the brick easier, in addition to providing a cushion for the walk. The brick are laid to the desired pattern on the cushion of sand, and the joints are then filled with grout. This grout is made by mixing one part of Portland cement with one part of fine bank sand and adding enough water to make the mixture flow easily. In filling the joints take care that any grout lying on the edge of the brick is quickly removed with a wet rag, for after it sets, it will be difficult to scrape off and the walk

will not look well. At intervals of about 18 or 20 ft., the joints should be filled with tar or asphaltum in order to provide an expansion joint. Another way of grouting a walk would be to fill the joints with a dry mixture of cement and sand, and then sprinkle it with water. The first method is to be preferred, however, for, though it requires a bit more care to pour the grout than to pour the dry mixture in the joints, the effort is well repaid by the assurance that the entire joint is filled with concrete instead of the possibility of having the top half filled with concrete and the bottom half with a dry powder.

Where walks are laid without a concrete base, the construction is shown in Fig. 2. This is practically the same as for the construction with the concrete-base walk except that the concrete is omitted and the sand cushion laid directly upon the cinders. The sand cushion should be made ½ to 1 in. thick. Walks with only a cinder base are not grouted, but are intended for use where it is desired to allow grass to grow between the joints in the walk.

Many beautiful patterns may be laid in

brick walks. Brick lends itself especially to pattern work due to the proportions of the units, the ordinary building and paving brick being about 2 in. thick, 4 in. wide, and 8 in. long. Thus, allowing for a mortar joint of suitable width, two thicknesses of brick make one width and three thicknesses make one length. Thus, various arrangements of width, thickness and length may be made. There are two ways of laying brick walks; the first with the brick flat, and the second with the brick laid on edge. Laying the brick flat, fewer brick are required for a given area than setting the brick on edge, but the laying will be found slightly harder. Flat-laid brick adapts itself better to wide, grass-filled joints than does brick laid on edge. It may be taken as a commonly accepted rule that brick laid on edge should always be laid on a concrete base, and the joints filled with cement grout. Brick laid flat, however, need not be laid on a cement base and need not have the joints grouted. A good width for the ordinary front walk is about five bricks wide, or approximately 42 in. A four-brick-wide walk (about 33 in.) may also be used if the first width

is too great. Garden paths and winding lanes through shrubbery may be made three bricks wide.

In Fig. 3 is shown the southern style of walk. This consists of brick laid flat in a regular pattern. In Fig. 4 is shown a variation of the southern style, which calls for the breaking of the joints in each row. The brick could also be laid with the length of the brick parallel to the length of the walk, instead of perpendicular to it as illustrated.

Fig. 5 illustrates the hearth pattern. Here two bricks are laid parallel, with alternate pairs at right angles. A variation of the hearth pattern is shown in Fig. 6. This consists of laying the brick at an angle of 45° with the border of the walk instead of parallel to it. In this, the brick at the edge of the walk must be cut in order that the line at the edge of the walk be preserved. Fig. 7 is the same pattern as Fig. 4, except that a diamond design is worked into it by the use of different-colored brick. In laying a walk in this pattern it is not well to have too great a contrast between the brick colors. If the two colors are just differ-

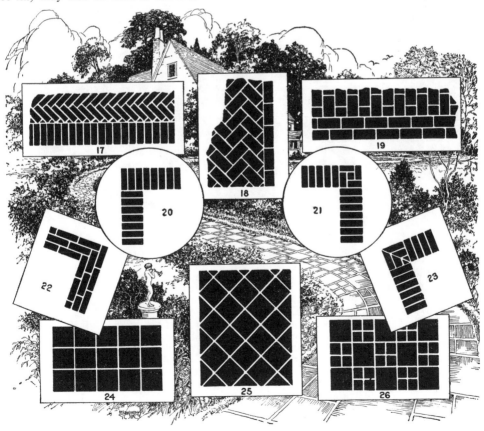

ent enough so that the diamond design is only slightly discernible, the best effect will be obtained.

The herringbone pattern shown in Fig. 8 is a neat one, and is quite popular. It is comparatively easy to lay and less cutting is required than for the design shown in Fig. 6. In Fig. 9 is shown the herringbone pattern with the brick laid on edge. Laid on a cement base, this pattern with the joints grouted, provides an especially strong and durable walk.

Edge-laid brick, illustrated in Fig. 10, makes an easily built and strong walk. The brick can also be laid with the joints broken, as shown for the flat-laid brick in Fig. 4. In Fig. 11 is illustrated the basket-weave pattern, somewhat similar to the hearth pattern shown in Fig. 5, except that the bricks are laid on edge, and that three bricks are used instead of only two. Fig. 12 is a combination of the basket-weave and the hearth pattern. Fig. 13 shows a diamond design worked into an edge-laid walk. A little study will show that this design differs considerably from the diamond design shown for a flat-laid walk in Fig. 7. A combination brick and tile walk is illustrated in Fig. 14.

In some cases, it is desirable to have

borders for the walks, not only for the added decorative effect, but because, with the pattern used, small pieces are left at the edge and a border is required to hold them in place and prevent their being chipped out. Thus, while the design shown in Fig. 14 would not require a border, that illustrated in Fig. 9, the herringbone walk with the brick laid on edge, would need a border in order to keep the small triangular filler pieces from being knocked off the edge. Figs. 15 to 19 illustrate borders of various designs which may be used. Figs. 21 to 23 show various ways of building up a corner in a brick walk.

Some patterns for quarry-tile walks are shown also. Fig. 24 illustrates a walk with the joints laid regular. A variation of Fig. 24 would be to break joints similar to the manner used in the flat-laid brick walk shown in Fig. 4. Fig. 25 shows a walk with the tile laid at an angle of 45° with the edge of the walk. This is a pleasing design but the cutting of the tile for the edges is quite a task, and a good many will be wasted due to their failing to cut properly. In Fig. 26, two different sizes of tile are used, as is also the case in the pattern shown in Fig. 27. As a great many sizes and colors are obtainable in this material, some very beautiful patterns and color schemes may be worked out. It should be borne in mind, however, that of the several types of walk described in this article, those built of quarry tile are the least durable, and are more suited to interiors and semi-protected places than to open spaces where they may be subjected to the continuous action of the elements.

Perhaps the most decorative walk of all is that made of flags. Flags are large stones about 10 by 24 in., or thereabout, although they may run in size from 6 by 8 to 12 by 36 in. They may be laid on a cinder-and-sand base without fear of great distortion, and they appear particularly attractive when they are laid about 1 in. apart with grass between the joints. In some localities stones of different colors are obtainable and they may be used to advantage in laying a walk in a desirable color scheme. A combination of reds and browns, or greens and blues, or any other colors which do not clash, is very pleasing.

Where stone is not readily obtainable, concrete flags may be made. A gang mold for making concrete flags is shown in Fig. 28. Here three flags can be made at a time, two large and one small, although the number, size and shape may be varied to suit the requirements of the job. The mold consists of two planks fastened together with cleats to form the bottom, and enough cleating nailed around the edges to give the desired shape and size. The flags are molded in the same manner as any other kind of concrete casting. They should be about 3 in. thick, and it is well to reinforce them with chicken wire, especially the larger sizes. When applying the wearing surface, color effects may be obtained if a little mortar color is added.

Fig. 29 shows a walk built of field stone; this is, as its name implies, a walk built of stones of random sizes and shapes, fitted together in a kind of crazyquilt pattern. The stones are laid with rough edges, just as they are picked up in the field. This is an ideal rustic walk for heavily wooded places. Fig. 30 is a similar walk with the edges cut to a line. The walk shown in Fig. 31 is what is known as random rectangular, that is, the stones are rectangular in shape but of random sizes, and are fitted together as shown in the pattern. A variation of the random-rectangular pattern is shown in Fig. 32. Here the stones are of one width in the respective rows, but of varying lengths. Figs. 33 and 34 show designs obtainable by the use of flags of two different sizes, and in Fig. 35 is illustrated a walk involving the use of three different sizes. Fig. 36 is a diamond pattern which may be worked into a flag walk somewhere along its length or at a crossing.

There are an infinite number of patterns for the different materials mentioned in this article. Anyone with just a little ingenuity can develop a host of patterns, using those illustrated as a basis upon which to work.

Auto Engine Runs Rock Drill

One might mistake the vehicle shown in the photo for a two-way automobile, but it happens to be an ordinary truck with an extra engine mounted on the rear. This is used for the purpose of running a rock drill, which is geared to it.

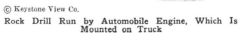

© Keystone View Co.

Rock Drill Run by Automobile Engine, Which Is Mounted on Truck

Handy Shop Scrap Box

To keep the floors and benches of the shop clean, a large concern is using scrap

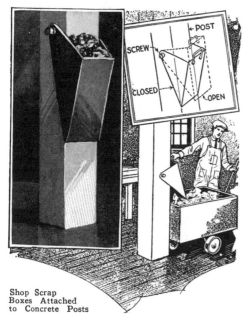

Shop Scrap
Boxes Attached
to Concrete Posts

boxes attached to the concrete pillars on each floor. Loose boxes were formerly placed at intervals around the shop, to be emptied at the end of each day, but very often they would be moved to suit some person's convenience, with the result that the man detailed to empty them would have difficulty in locating them. The shape of these boxes is clearly indicated; they are constructed of sheet metal and are held to the posts by means of a screw and washer on each side, the screws being turned into wood plugs driven into the concrete. The truck used to carry away the scrap is backed up to touch the post under the box, and the latter is then lifted by the handle in order to allow the contents to drop into the truck.

Testing Galvanized-Iron Wire

Many farmers send for samples of wire fencing before placing an order. Often two samples arrive that appear to be the same-gauge wire and, as far as looks go, galvanized alike. Usually the farmer rushes his order off to the manufacturer quoting the lower figure. This, however, might not happen if he realized that the life of the fencing depends on the thickness of the protective coating of zinc, and

tested the samples in this respect. Such a test may be made in the following way: Leave a sample of the wire in a saturated solution of sulphate of copper for one minute. After wiping it clean, replace it in the solution for another minute. Repeat this process four times, and if the wire keeps its black color, it is proof that the zinc has not been eaten away and that the galvanizing has been well done. However, should the wire appear copper-colored after the second or third immersion, the coating is too thin to make the wire economical for fencing purposes. Most farmers have sulphate of copper, or blue vitriol, about the farm, as it is used widely in spraying solutions. A saturated solution is made by dissolving as much of the crystals in water as the latter will take up.—C. M. Wilcox, Torrington, Conn.

Ball-Bearing Adapter

Bearings from old automobiles, tractors, etc., can be used to advantage for lineshafts and countershafts on various sorts of machinery. To mount the bearing on the shaft, a sleeve is made from steel tubing of the proper size, which requires the least labor to machine. The sleeve should be a close sliding fit on the shaft and a press fit in inner race; the bearing is made to project from the bearing race approximately 1½ in. on each side, is turned slightly tapering at each end, and threaded and slotted into three or four sections in the tapered parts. Two nuts are provided to fit the tapered ends and, when tightened, will clamp the bearing sleeve firmly to the shaft. The outside casing for the bearing is made from a piece of cast-iron bushing stock, which may be obtained from an iron foundry. The casing is machined as shown, being made a light press fit for the outside of the ball-bearing assembly. Recessed sections are provided at each end of the casing in which are fitted the steel covers, made of ⅛-in. mild steel, these covers being held in position by machine screws. To exclude dirt and retain grease,

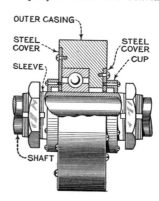

OUTER CASING

STEEL COVER

SLEEVE

STEEL COVER

CUP

SHAFT

two cup-shaped pieces, made of cast iron, are attached with machine screws. Care should be taken to select ball-bearing assemblies that are in first-class condition, to assure their satisfactory service. The outside casing is provided at two opposite points with small depressions to receive the points of the handscrews, and a compression grease cup should be fitted to supply the necessary lubricant.—Edwin Kilburn, Spring Valley, Minn.

Detachable Knob for Jigs and Fixtures

Many times the jig, fixture and tool designer is confronted with the need for a detachable knob or nut, not only for the purpose of removal so that the work or another piece can be taken from the stud, but also as a method of setting an adjustment that can be kept free from tampering. The drawing shows a nut of this type that has been used with satisfactory results. The fixture stud is machined with flats on opposite sides and the knob, which can either be cast or machined, has a slot in the side so that it will fit over the stud. Fig. 1 shows the construction of such a knob and its use in a fixture that holds a small pulley while drilling an oil hole. The stud is threaded and screwed into a hardened-steel nut at the back of the jig. By removing the slotted knob the work can be slid on the stud and the knob then replaced and the screw tightened. Fig. 2 shows its use on an adjustable V-block fixture. The object in having the knob removable in this case is to prevent altera-

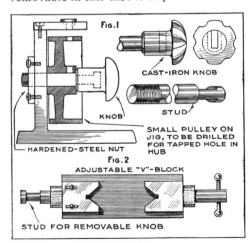

Detachable Knob Facilitates Handling of Tools, Jigs and Fixtures

tion of the adjustment as set in the tool room.—W. Burr Bennett, Honesdale, Pa.

Trailer for Gasoline and Oil Drums

In moving from place to place, contractors are often inconvenienced by the necessity of loading and unload-

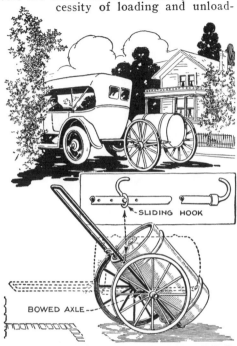

Trailer for Gasoline and Oil Drums That Will Be Found Useful to Contractors

ing gasoline or oil drums onto and off trucks. This difficulty can readily be overcome by providing a trailer like that in the drawing, which was made for the purpose. It consists of a bowed axle conforming to the curvature of the drums, and a frame made of pipe. In use, the frame is held in a vertical position against the drum, and the hooks on the frame are engaged with the end edges of the drum. The trailer is then leveled and attached to the truck.—G. E. Hendrickson, Argyle, Wisconsin.

Keeping Canal Banks Free of Grass

One irrigation district, where Johnson grass along the canal banks grows down to the edges of the water and causes sand and debris to accumulate and seriously retard the flow, has found that the grass can be kept down economically by pasturing herds of sheep and goats along the banks. The animals are confined by portable fences, which can be moved along the banks as fast as the grass is eaten off. Several other methods tried were either unsuccessful or too expensive.—Ivan E. Houk, Denver, Colo.

Using Broken Steel Fence Posts

Wherever steel fence posts have been in use you will find some have been broken off or bent out of shape and are considered useless. However, the drawing

Short Lengths of Old Steel Posts Keep Wire Fence Taut and Prevent Animals from Ruining It

shows a good use for them. Cut them into 18-in. lengths with a hacksaw or cold chisel. In this way you will get four or five pieces from each post, according to its length and condition. The pieces either have holes in them or a hook of some kind where wires have been fastened, except the part that has been in the ground. That part should have a small hole drilled through one end. With a sledge or maul drive one or two of these lengths between each of the line posts along the fence; fasten the bottom wire of the fence to one of the holes or hooks near the end of the post and drive it down until nearly all is in the ground. These posts will stay as long as the fence is there, and no hog can lift the fence and get under it, and it will also prevent cattle and horses from crowding the fence in trying to get what is on the other side.—J. R. Koontz, Bremen, Indiana.

Economy in Steam Heating

By running a steam-heating plant in the following way, much fuel can be saved at little expense. Repack all the steam valves with valve-stem packing. Get a ⅛-in. pipe plug for every radiator air valve. Repack the gauge glass, try all the cocks and see that everything is tight. Close all radiators, except one. Raise the steam, taking off the air valve on the radiator left open, and wait until the steam comes free-

ly. Then, with a glove on or a rag wrapped around the hand, to prevent scalding by the escaping steam, insert a ⅛-in. plug, with a little paint applied to the threads, and screw it tight. Do the same with the other radiators. Also, if there are any air valves on the lines, take them off and plug the holes. Be sure the air is all out of the system. Do not try the petcock underneath the gauge glass, unless the gauge shows steam. The whole house will be heated without an ounce of steam showing on the gauge. As there is no air in the system, the radiators act as condensers and pull the steam toward them. The radiators of the plant where this experiment was made were all warm in the morning, and the boiler was shut down all night. It will be necessary to carry out the above preparations every season.—Alexander Gray, Chief Engineer, Colored Orphan Asylum, Riverdale-on-Hudson, N. Y.

Locating Reversed Field Coils

Occasionally the motor trouble shooter is required to locate a reversed field coil in a direct-current motor. The usual method of going about this is to employ a compass, which, if the field cannot be energized, is the only instrument that can be used for this purpose. Under some circumstances even this method is uncertain, depending largely upon the quality of the compass as well as on surrounding magnetic influences.

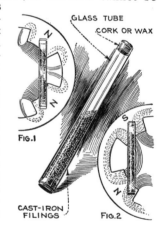

FIG.1 GLASS TUBE CORK OR WAX CAST-IRON FILINGS FIG.2

If the field circuit can be separately energized, a little device that will never fail to indicate a reversed field can be made cheaply and quickly. Cut a ½ or ⅝-in. water-gauge glass to a suitable length, according to the size of the motor to be tested. Plug one end with a cork and pour in cast-iron filings until the tube is half full. (Do not use steel filings as steel holds residual magnetism.) Then seal the other end. Tests can be made without removing the armature, but it is better if this can be done. Like poles repel each other and unlike poles attract each other. This will be clearly indicated by the filings, which follow the form of the lines of force within the tube, when it is placed across any two poles. Figs. 1 and 2 of the drawing indicate respectively the action of the filings when placed in dissimilar and in similar magnetic fields.

Glazing Brick Walls

On brickwork in boilers, a rich brown glaze for the side walls and arch is very desirable. The addition of 12 per cent of sodium silicate to the ordinary mixture of fire clay and ganister for the bonding of the brick, and a final wash of sodium silicate and fire clay for the surfaces, help to produce a uniform glaze of this kind. It gives a surface which is impervious, prevents air leakage and helps to eliminate clinkers from becoming attached to the walls.—H. M. Toombs, Chicago, Ill.

Fixture Facilitates Pin Stamping

An unusual device to aid in stamping the part number on pins has recently been adopted by a concern manufacturing a popular article on which a large number of pins are used. The fixture is held in a bench vise when in use. The two main parts are a sheet-metal hopper and an old gear. The hopper is bent to the shape shown in the drawing and two slots are cut in it where it is turned over to form a spring or indexing finger. The gear turns on a solid shaft slightly longer than the gear width and all parts are held together by a pin passing loosely through the shaft and hopper ends, and riveted over on both sides. The spring stop piece just fits between the gear teeth to prevent the gear from turning while the top pin is being stamped. The operation is simple: A couple of handfuls of pins are laid straight in the hopper. After each pin is stamped the gear is indexed one tooth. The pins feed themselves on the gear and drop into a box on the other side after being stamped. —Harry Moore, Montreal, Can.

Safety Attachment on Extension Ladder for Hanging Up Eaves Troughs

Ladder Attachment Aids in Hanging Eaves Troughs

The usual method of attaching eaves troughs to overhanging cornices is to place the ladder against the side of the building under the cornice. This obliges the worker to stand on the ladder with nothing to steady himself while putting up the trough. The attachment shown in the drawing eliminates the danger of over-balancing, and has proved a time and money saver. It consists of three boards assembled as indicated and pivoted on the top rung of the ordinary extension ladder. In use, it is held at a right angle by means of a stout hook, so that the ladder clears the eaves trough, enabling the worker to stand steadily in a natural and safe posture, and to see what he is doing.

¶In tempering small dies, heat until a piece of wire solder will just melt when touched to the dies, and then quench.

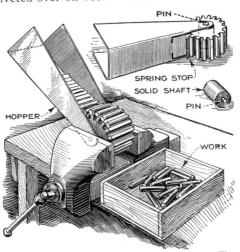

Sheet-Metal Hopper and a Gear Make Fixture That Facilitates Stamping Pins

Preventing Danger of Explosion of Hydrogen Gas in Storage Batteries

Examining Storage Batteries

Owing to the danger of igniting hydrogen fumes that arise from storage batteries, it is good policy to keep matches, candles and cigarets away. A flashlight is much handier to use for examining the inside of the cells and will eliminate the danger of blowing up the battery and injuring the eyes.

Repairing Lathe Tailstock

Machinists in small shops are often handicapped when the tailstock spindle of the lathe is worn so loose that it is impossible to clamp it tightly, which gives the lathe a tendency to chatter and makes the work inaccurate. This trouble was remedied by a mechanic in the following way: From a piece of shafting he made a new tailstock spindle just like the old one, except that the diameter was left large enough to fit into the rebored hole. He finished the taper and the seat for the threaded bushing before he started on the tailstock, and prepared long plugs for both ends of the new spindle, as shown in the illustration. He found a bor-

ing bar about 3 ft. long, fastened one end in the chuck and ran the other end on the old center, after which he adjusted the steady rest to the bar, close to the outside end. The tailstock was pulled out toward the end of the lathe, and the spindle and the cap in the end were removed. Then the steady rest was removed without disturbing the adjustment, the tailstock shoved up over the boring bar and the steady rest put back in its previous position. Now all that was necessary was some method of feeding the tailstock along while the boring bar revolved. A hook, closely fitted to the tailstock and the carriage, performed this duty. The tailstock clamp bolts were adjusted and the ways oiled so that the tailstock would slide with the carriage without binding. A smooth cut was made through the bore, and this part of the job was done.

He could not use the tailstock for turning now, but he had thought of that in advance when he prepared the plugs for the ends of the new spindle. One of these he held in the chuck, and the other was run in the steady rest having the carriage in between, and although he could not cut from one end to the other, he could turn the surface with two settings of the tool. The diameter was carefully turned to size and filed down smooth, to make a good fit, and the new spindle was lapped into the hole with valve-grinding compound. The lapping had smoothed out all roughness in the bored hole, and gave a slow-wearing surface on both parts.

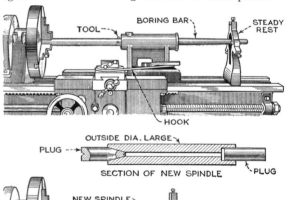
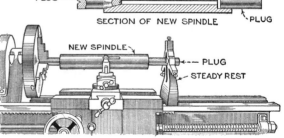

Worn Lathe Tailstock, Which Gives Lathe Tendency to Chatter and Makes the Work Inaccurate, Can Be Easily Repaired

Shop Notes

Getting Service from the Hacksaw

By JAMES TATE

BECAUSE the hacksaw is such a simple tool, there is a feeling that "anyone can use a hacksaw." While this is perfectly true, there is a great difference between merely using a tool and getting the utmost in service out of it, and even with such a simple tool as this, there is a right and a wrong way of handling it.

There are a few fundamental rules that are imperative, if the proper service is to be obtained from handsaw blades. First, having selected the proper blade, strain it well in the frame. This is important, to insure true cutting and to prevent breakage of blades. The saw is inserted in the frame with the teeth pointing away from the operator (this may seem foolish instruction, but I have seen them put in the other way), and the "hard edge" or flexible backsaw will be found to need greater tension in the frame than a blade of the "all-hard" type.

For light and medium work, stand at the vise and grasp the saw frame as shown in Fig. 1, with the forefinger of the right hand pointing along the handle of the frame in the direction of the cut, and holding the end of the frame between the thumb and first two fingers of the left hand (Fig. 2). Start the cut easily, using the same stroke as in filing, and be sure to put on enough pressure to make the teeth bite and not slide over the metal, as allowing the saw to rub over the metal on the start of the cut glazes the teeth and starts the saw on the road to the junk box. After the first few strokes retighten the saw in the frame. Lift the saw slightly on the return stroke so as to prevent the teeth from dragging or rubbing on the work, as any pressure on the return stroke also blunts the teeth. Keep the speed of the strokes to from 40 to 50 a minute, and the work will be cut more quickly and with less wear on the blade than if a faster stroke is used. Where a heavy pressure is required the end of the saw frame may be held as shown in Fig.

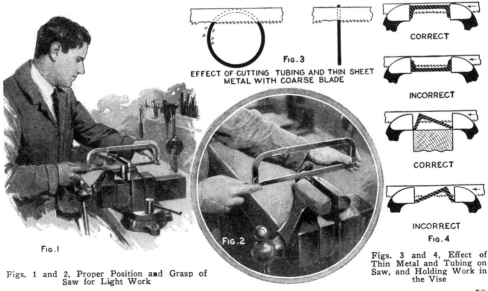

FIG. 3

EFFECT OF CUTTING TUBING AND THIN SHEET METAL WITH COARSE BLADE

CORRECT

INCORRECT

CORRECT

INCORRECT

FIG. 4

FIG. 1

Figs. 1 and 2, Proper Position and Grasp of Saw for Light Work

Figs. 3 and 4, Effect of Thin Metal and Tubing on Saw, and Holding Work in the Vise

FIG. 2

59

5, all the weight and pressure of the hand being transmitted to the blade through the fleshy part of the hand at the base of the thumb.

In most small shops each man owns his own frame, and there is comparatively little handsawing done; what there is, being on different materials from time to time as necessary in the course of assembly or erection of machinery. In this case, it is naturally impossible for the men to change blades to suit the material to be cut, and a blade is selected that will work fairly well on all material to be

held between two pieces of wood, as in Fig. 6, when sawing it in the vise, and the cut taken right through wood and metal; this helps greatly in reducing breakage. If this is not possible, then

Fig. 5, Grasp of Saw for Heavy Pressure; Fig. 6, Sawing Thin Metal between Blocks; Fig. 7, Cutting Thin Metal to Avoid Saw-Tooth Breakage

Fig. 6

CUTTING SHEET METAL
Fig. 7

handled; at least that is what should be done, although the men in the shop may be more or less at the mercy of the purchasing department. The blade selected is usually one with about 14 teeth to the inch, and this will work well on brass, cold-rolled steel, cast iron and tool steel. Even in the small shop, however, there is a decided advantage in supplying the men with a finer-tooth blade for work on thin sheet metal and tubing, one having 32 teeth to the inch being suitable for this purpose. It is an even greater advantage if the blades are kept in separate frames so that they can be picked up and used at once.

Most hacksaw troubles come from trying to cut thin sheet metal or tubing with a blade that is too coarse for the work. Fig. 3 shows what happens to the blade when a coarse-pitch saw is used for this work. For thin metal a blade should be selected having teeth so fine that two or more of them will engage the work at once. If the teeth "straddle" the metal, they will be stripped from the blade. Wherever possible sheet metal should be

care should be taken to saw through the metal at an angle, as shown at B, Fig. 7. If the metal is so thin that, with the blade at hand, even cutting at an angle will allow only one tooth to bear on the cut at a time, then the sheet should be sawed flat, as shown at A. The main thing to observe is to have as many teeth as possible cutting at once; never less than two and preferably three.

When cutting structural shapes there is a right and wrong way of holding them in the vise. Fig. 4 shows the correct and incorrect methods for two common shapes, and a little study will show how the correct method makes it easy for the blade. The same principle applies to other shapes.

Recommendations of leading saw manufacturers, who have made a study of the art of saw cutting, are: For cast iron, solid babbitt, brass, copper, bronze, aluminum, cold-rolled stock, soft steel, annealed tool steel and heavy structural steel, 14 teeth to the inch; practice differs to some extent, one maker recommending 14 teeth for solid cold-rolled machine steel, 18 teeth for tool steel, cast iron and brass; for light structural steel, tool steel and hard metals, one recommends 18 teeth and another 24. Both unite in recommending 24 teeth for steel pipe, iron pipe, brass and copper pipe, and conduit, and for thin sheet metals and tubing under 18-gauge, 32 teeth to the inch. Flexible-back saws are not recommended for use in tool steel, cast iron or brass by one maker, while another lists them for use in these metals. However, their recommendations are to be taken merely as a guide, or a basis on which to choose trial blades for any particular purpose, and they are very useful in this respect. In fact, it will pay any hacksaw user to get the literature of the saw manufacturers on this subject, as it contains much practical information on the subject of hand and power sawing as well as charts for saw selection.

Serviceable Metal Paint Paddle

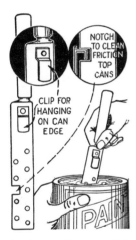

A cheap case-knife, with the end ground off and a clip riveted to the blade near the handle as shown in the illustration, makes an ideal paint paddle for the home workman. Holes drilled through the blade make stirring quicker, and if a notch is cut in one side with a file, any small trace of white lead or paint remaining under the rim of a friction-top can, can be easily scraped out. To facilitate cleaning, file down all the rough edges before using.

Cleaning Lantern Chimneys

In street work, where many oil lanterns are required for warning signals, the cleaning of smoky chimneys each day is a time-consuming task. A very convenient and efficient method of cleaning a chimney is to scoop in some dry sand until the chimney is half full; then, stopping both ends with the hands, shake it vigorously. The rock particles will scour off all the grime in a few moments.

Forms for Concrete Culverts

Forms for concrete end walls for small road culverts are easily made from a few sheets of corrugated-iron roofing. The

Forms on Ends of Concrete Culverts Made of Corrugated-Iron Roofing

ends of the sheets are nailed to a 2-in. plank wide enough to give the desired thickness to the wall. A hole is cut for the tile and the form is ready to be poured. The corrugations help strengthen the form so that less bracing is required; at the same time the sheet iron permits bending so as to make a semicircular wall if desired, a feature that would require considerable work if a wooden form were used. The form is light and easily handled, and the wavy surface adds to rather than detracts from the appearance of the finished wall.—M. W. Lowry, Athens, Ga.

Safety Pawl on Truck Brakes

While playing in a truck, which was parked on a hillside, two small children released the brake, allowing the truck to run down the hill with considerable speed and resulting in a smash-up against a tree at the bottom. To prevent a similar accident, the driver put a safety pawl on the brake as shown in the illustration. This makes it impossible for a

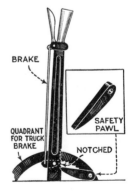

child to loosen the brake, as considerable force is necessary to pull it back to release the pawl. The front lower portion of the brake lever is notched as indicated, and the pawl is pivoted in front of it on the ratchet quadrant.—G. A. Luers, Washington, D. C.

Convenient Rope Cutter

One of the clerks in a San Francisco store has devised a very efficient cutter for rope. It consists of a sharp blade ar-

Metal Hook with Sharp Blade Cuts Rope Quickly

ranged on one side of a metal hook. By this means the heavy rope can be easily and quickly cut off by pulling it forward against the sharp blade, as shown in the accompanying photograph. — Charles W. Geiger, San Francisco, Calif.

Tool Setter for Lathe Work

When cutting threads or turning tapers in the lathe, accurate work demands that the exact tip of the edge of the cutting tool be in the same horizontal plane as the lathe centers supporting the work.

To get this setting quickly and with accuracy, the tool setter shown in the drawing was devised. It consists of a rectangular strip of hard brass, to one end of which is attached a short angle strip. To the angle strip is sweated a length of brass tubing of sufficient size to admit a commercial level glass, with about 1/16 in. clearance. An angle block is carefully plumbed and the tool setter is clamped to it, plumb in

both directions. A level glass is smeared with a little soft putty, put into the tube and adjusted until the bubble stands central. After the putty has set, the tube is closed up with more putty and the device is complete. In use, a preliminary cut is skimmed off the work to insure its being cylindrical and coaxial with the lathe centers. The tool setter is then placed between the work and the tool, and the latter adjusted. When the exact tip of the tool is dead on the center of the work, the tool setter will stand plumb, with the bubble in the center of the level. The device can be used on cylindrical grinders, thread millers, and like machines.— H. A. Freeman, Willimantic, Conn.

Stopping the Shaft Quickly

Shafting in long lines always carries many good-sized pulleys and the energy stored in these causes the shafts to run for considerable periods after the power has been cut off; longer, of course, when the shaft turns on anti-friction bearings and is well lined up. When a belt breaks or gets tangled up in another and goes thrashing around, there is urgent need of stopping the shaft before great damage is done, and when the accident involves a human being, there is all the more need for quickly stopping. One

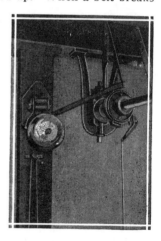

factory has installed the type of shaft brake shown in the photo. The couplings are of the type having smooth outer surfaces and a band brake has been installed on one near the motor driving the shaft. It is an automobile brake with the band altered to suit the coupling, securely mounted so that, normally, it is free from the coupling. But when one pulls on the handle of the rod, which is at a convenient height for applying the whole weight of the body, the brake takes a very effective hold. After shutting off the power, one shaft usually ran 40 seconds before it stopped, but with the brake, it was stopped in 10 seconds.

Stamping High-Speed Drills

Shanks of high-speed drills or end mills are often too hard to stamp after hardening, and if stamped before that process, the lettering may be ground off, as a high-speed mill or drill will bow toward the stamped side when hardened. We take the end mills, after they are hardened and ground on the shank, and give each shank a coat of etching varnish. When the varnish has dried right to be scratched, we place a piece of thin white paper on the shank and roll the stamp lightly over the paper just the same way as is done when stamping soft work, except that the paper is touched lightly over the hardened shank. The letters and figures on the stamp make the varnish on the shank stick to the paper, and strong muriatic acid is then applied to the bare surfaces where it etches the mark. If the paper sticks to the figures or letters on the shank, leave it alone, or apply a little wet acid, which will loosen it. Straight stamping will act the same way, but do not hit too hard. Place the pieces etched in hot soda water to neutralize the acid, and then wash off the varnish with benzine. The shanks can then be oiled.
—W. L. Miles, Warren, R. I.

An Eight-Row Garden Marker

With the aid of the marker shown in the photograph the rows in large truck gardens can be marked accurately and quickly. It consists of a long board with pointed wooden pegs extending from the underside and a handle by which the device can be

Simple Homemade Garden Marker Which Marks Eight Rows at the Same Time

pulled. Bricks are tied on the marker to weight it down so that the pegs will make a deeper impression. As eight rows can be marked at once, the task of marking a large garden is considerably shortened.

Carpet Bumper Protects Door Jambs

A western building-management firm recently offered a prize to any employe suggesting the most efficient means of protecting the highly polished mahogany door jambs while moving furniture in or out of the rooms. The prize-winning device was made of heavy carpet, 4 ft. long and wide enough to cover the jamb properly, as shown in the photo. Three strong spring-steel bands, heavily padded, served to attach the protector to the door jamb.

Filling Holes in Brass

Experimenters are often puzzled as to how they are going to get rid of holes in brass castings, etc., which are drilled in the wrong place or which become superfluous as the result of some change or improvement. The following method will do the trick: Fill the holes with solder to within $\frac{1}{32}$ in. of the surface, then file a piece of brass of the same shade as the casting with a medium fine file, catching the filings on a piece of paper. Put the filings in a cup, pour killed muriatic acid over them and leave standing for a few minutes. Then sift them over the solder in the holes so that they can be seen to be a little higher than the surface. Heat is then applied until the solder runs and adheres to the filings. When cool, the surface is sandpapered smooth and polished. This idea works well also on copper or iron castings but not on aluminum. The acid is killed by dropping in some zinc stripped from old dry cells. Both the acid and the filings must be clean and free from other kinds of filings and dust. The holes to be filled must be perfectly clean and tinned right to the top.

¶Plaster of paris casts can be toughened by boiling in paraffin and polishing.

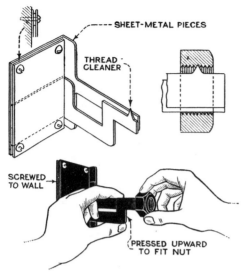

Scraping Out Threads of Secondhand Nuts Is a Quick and Easy Job with This Fixture

Cleaning Out Old Nuts

One of the hindrances to using second-hand nuts is the thick scale or hard paint, lead, etc., which often accumulates in the threads. Using a hand scraper to remove this takes too much time to make it profitable. However, anyone in charge of a small storeroom can make a handy fixture for this work that will do the job nicely in a minimum of time. The accompanying illustration shows the construction. Three pieces of sheet metal are used to make up the scraper. The piece nearest the wall is cut as indicated and bent at right angles; the second is cut somewhat differently, with a V-projection on the top. The third piece is a plain one which holds the completed device to the wall by means of four screws. The scraper here described was dimensioned to clean out any size of nut from ¾ in. up. To operate it, the projecting parts are pressed together until the "V" fits the threads and the nut is then turned to scrape out the dirt.—Harry Moore, Montreal, Can.

A Tool Makers' U-Iron

For taking the place of the ordinary angle plate, the U-iron illustrated will be found a valuable addition to the tool maker's equipment. A block of tool steel is used, which, after the machining operations are completed, is casehardened and ground to the finished dimensions. The block is milled out as shown, for the sake of lightness, with a round-nosed end mill. Turn the work to mill the various surfaces and do not upset the height of the table until you have gone all around the work. Allow 1/32 in. when taking the roughing cuts for finishing. V-slots for holding either square or circular work are machined at right angles to each other on the edge and top of the block, while a T-slot is milled into the opposite side for bolting the device to the bed of a machine. A third and smaller V-groove is cut at right angles to the one on the front face of the block, for holding work of small cross section. Bolt holes for the clamps are drilled and tapped in the stock at the sides of the several grooves and slots. Two strap clamps of the style illustrated will be needed and grooves are cut into one end and the middle, the better to conform to the work being held and minimize the possibility of its slipping.

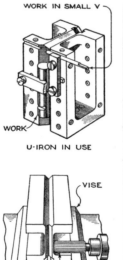

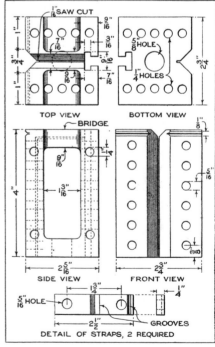

An All-Around Tool Which Takes the Place of the Usual Angle Plate

Crankcase Oil Keeps Mites Away

Poultrymen find it necessary to use some means of destroying red mites especially during the summer months. Formerly coal tar mixed with kerosene was used extensively, but the strong odor is rather objectionable in cities, although its use is permissible on the farm. Worn-out crankcase oil, applied liberally to all parts of the roosts and supports and also to the nest boxes, has been found to be an effective substitute. Only three applications have kept the mites down an entire season.—G. D. Willits, Adrian, Mich.

Saving Gasoline

Finding that our gasoline bill was rather high we started to investigate all possible causes of loss. A number of ways were found to make a gallon of gasoline last longer. Among other losses that were figured was the loss due to evaporation, which was surprisingly large. We had two 50-gal.

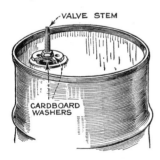

tanks, each of which had a small hole in the cover to let in air when the gasoline was drained out. On a warm day one could easily smell the gas as it escaped through the holes. The condition could not be bettered by making the holes smaller as this hindered the flow of gasoline. The caps were removed and the air holes drilled large enough to receive the valve stem of an old inner tube. Cardboard washers were placed on both sides of the cap and the nut screwed down tightly. No gas can now escape, as the valve remains closed until gasoline is being drained out, when it is opened to let in air.—Jonas J. Byberg, Silverton, Oreg.

Clipping Horses

By clipping the legs and under part of horses in the springtime, the animals will be much more comfortable while working. Mud, which would become incrusted in the long shedding hair of an unclipped horse, can easily be brushed from the clipped animal, while the top coat is sufficient protection from chilly winds and too rapid cooling after a working period. —C. M. Baker, Wooster, Ohio.

Small Platform Hung on Ladder Rungs Prevents Sore Feet or "Ladder Cramp"

Platform on Ladder Prevents Cramp

A small platform or board, about 10 by 15 in. in dimensions, attached to a ladder, as shown, by means of two ¼-in. iron rods, hooked to go over a rung, will give quick relief to any worker who is troubled with sore feet or "ladder cramp." To prevent splitting, strips should be nailed or screwed to the bottom, as shown. The rods should be about 26 in. long, threaded for at least 2 in., and each one should be provided with two nuts and two washers.

Removing Paint Residue

Paint residue often collects under the edge of friction-top cans having a rim. This can easily be removed with the scraper shown in the illustration. It is cut from a piece of sheet iron to the shape shown and a hole is punched through it to permit hanging it up. It should be

made of fairly stiff stock and then it can be used also to remove the covers.

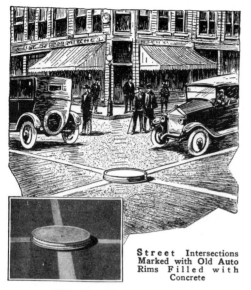

Street Intersections Marked with Old Auto Rims Filled with Concrete

Old Auto Rims Serve as Crossing Markers

In one small Texas town, every street intersection is marked with an old auto rim filled with concrete. Obviously their cost is small compared to that of specially made markers, and autoists will take care not to ride over them for fear of damaging their tires.

Marking Location of Studding for Base Nailing

The illustration shows methods of locating the studding for base nailing, all of which are good, though some are better than the others. Fig. 1 illustrates how the studs are located by sounding, that is, by tapping the wall lightly with a hammer in order to ascertain the exact location by sound. This is the method quite commonly used. However, sounding for every stud is not necessary. When one stud has been located, the others can be found by

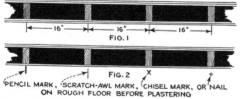

Several Methods of Marking Location of Studs to Permit Easy Attachment of Baseboards

measurement in the manner illustrated. Fig. 2 shows another commonly used method. Here the location of each stud

is marked before the plastering is done. The mark is placed directly in front of the center of the stud, on the rough floor, with a dark crayon or a heavy lead pencil. A scratch awl, too, will give good results or the marking can be done with a wood chisel. If the chisel is somewhat dull, the marks will show up better. A lath nail, or other small nail, can also be used for the purpose, driving it about 2 in. from each stud and leaving the head slightly projecting above the floor, so that it can be seen and pulled easily.—H. H. Siegele, Emporia, Kans.

Homemade Pipe Vise Easily Made and Carried

The pipe vise shown in the drawing can easily be carried from one job to another, and can readily be made by anyone with little labor and at small expense. The clamping bars are made from 1¼ by ¾-in. flat steel, 6¼ in. long. The jaw is filed to the shape shown, after laying out to take the smallest and largest pipe to be handled. With the stock size given above, the largest pipe that can be handled is the 1½-in. size. The two clamping bars are held together by 1 by ⅜-in. bars and ½-in. pins, the latter being secured by ⅛-in. cotter pins. A piece of 1 by ½-in. flat steel is bent to fit over the clamping bars and is fastened to the bottom bar with a ½-in. pin, which is also held in position with cotters. The top of the U-strap is tapped for a standard ½-in. bolt of the proper length to take in the range of pipe sizes. Two holes, ¼ or ⅜ in. in diameter, are drilled in the bottom bar to enable one to fasten it to a post or table, or it can be used in a common vise. —Frank N. Coakley, Buffalo, N. Y.

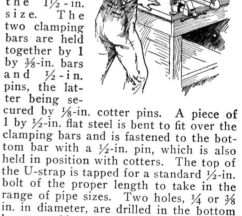

¶A good cutting compound for drilling hardened steel is made by mixing sulphate of copper, 1 oz.; alum, ¼ oz.; salt, ½ teaspoonful; vinegar, 1 gill, and nitric acid, 20 drops.

Quieting Turbulent Water

Wave disturbances, or other turbulent water-surface conditions, which accompany the high velocities existing in stream channels below overflow dams, spillways, d r o p s, etc., can be broken up and entirely eliminated, by the use of brush baffles. Large branches of trees, or even whole trees in the case of the larger streams, are cut and placed in the channels, where they are held in place by steel cables run to suitable anchorages. The smaller pulsations in flow, which cannot be damped by symmetrical baffles, because of their regularity, are e n t i r e l y eliminated by the irregular brush obstructions.

A Telephone That "Honks"

A telephone that honks can be used to advantage i n s h o p s where noise prevents the ordinary ringing apparatus from being heard. To make this change on an ordinary telephone the following materials are required: A Ford cutout, a 6-volt battery, a Ford horn of the battery type and pieces of wire. Disconnect the wires leading to the ringer magnets of the telephone and connect them to the cutout, as shown in the diagram. The spring tension of the cutout points should be lessened. When the circuit is closed at the telephone exchange, the cutout is closed, which in turn closes the battery circuit to the horn and causes it to sound. —Mabel Ellis, Richland, Mo.

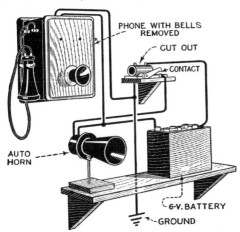

Substituting an Auto Horn for the Telephone Bell When Loud Signals Are Desired

Cutting Seed Potatoes

To cut seed potatoes rapidly, a box designed to allow the tubers to roll closely onto the operator's hands is used as

Cutting Seed Potatoes Rapidly with the Aid of an Inclined Box Which Facilitates Handling Them

shown in the accompanying photograph. The potatoes are cut so that each piece contains one or more eyes. Thus each tuber must be handled and cut several times. The sloping box allows the spuds to be examined and selected easily for rapid cutting.

Tumble Weeds Burned in Wire Cages

One irrigation district has found that the tumble weeds and miscellaneous debris which collect in the canals at checks, turnouts, bridges, and other irrigation structures, and which must be removed almost daily in order to keep the canals open, can best be disposed of by drying and burning them in huge woven-wire cages. This prevents the weeds from causing further annoyance by b e i n g blown back into the ditches or on adjacent farm lands. The cages are placed along the canals at points where the debris collects, and the wet weeds deposited in the cages one day are allowed to dry until the next cleaning, then burned just before the new accumulations of wet material are removed from the canals.

¶When using a reamer or tap that is too small, cut a narrow strip of tin and bend it over one or more of the teeth to make them take a larger bite. The same idea will work on a pipe or bolt die.

Combined Micrometer and Work Holder

Micrometer holders are handy for many kinds of measuring work, and the one shown in the illustration has an added

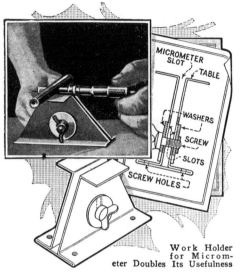

Work Holder for Micrometer Doubles Its Usefulness

feature that makes it doubly useful. It consists of a small table whereon the work can be laid. The body of the holder is made from a piece of 1/16-in. sheet metal, bent and cut to the shape indicated. Two large washers, a screw and wingnut, working in a slot in the body, complete the device. The holder is made for use when batches of parts are to be tested. The micrometer is located in the holder in a position that will bring the measuring faces in the center of the work, and the clamping fixture is moved up or down as required to fasten it. Thus, it is only necessary to lay the work on the table on which it is at once located centrally and squarely, making a true measurement certain.—Harry Moore, Montreal, Can.

Homemade Elevator Wings

Wings of a grain elevator loosen quite readily and many of them are lost entirely during a season's run after the third year unless they are overhauled every year. We did not realize this fact until we removed the chain and wings and were surprised to find sixteen of the wings gone. We had but six new ones, so we took a piece of No. 16 gauge sheet metal— the heaviest on hand—and with a compass marked the circles, which were cut out with a 1/2-in. cold chisel, using a piece of casting with a flat surface to cut on. On cutting through the sheet, the chisel

turns down the edge so that, when the wing is completed, it is strengthened considerably by this upturned edge. A washer was placed on the head of the rivet, and we found that these wings, although thinner than the old ones, were just as good.—G. McVicker, North Bend, Nebr.

Marking Triangles for Identification

Many draftsmen lose triangles simply because they have no identification mark on them. A simple but effective method of marking them is as follows: Obtain a heavy writing pen with a new point, and after dipping it in a solution of anhydrous acetic acid, you will be able to write your signature on the surface of the triangle neatly. A little black ink can be added to the solution if you wish the mark to show very plainly. The use of acid alone gives the same effect as if the surface had been sand-blasted.—L. H. Georger, Buffalo, New York.

Cutting Circular Holes in Plate

In boiler making and allied trades circular holes of large diameters must often be cut in heavy plate. This is usually done by first scribing a circle of proper diameter and then chiseling by hand or cutting with an acetylene torch. Where the latter method is not available the work of chiseling can be made much easier by using the tool shown in the illustration. It is a combination of a compass and a holder for the chisel so that the latter can

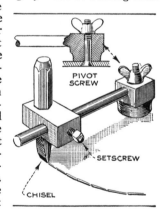

be guided in a circular path with practically no danger of striking the hand with the hammer. The parts are a center block, a length of 1/2-in. iron rod welded to the side of this block and a movable tool holder slipped on the arm and held at any point by means of a small setscrew. In use, a small hole is drilled in the exact center of the hole to be cut, and the screw in the center block is slipped through from the underside and tightened, but not too much, since the center block should turn freely.

Tapping Collets

We had 50 large-sized collets with a ¾-in. threaded hole in the shank end. The hole was hardened and ground and it was then discovered that the thread gauge would not enter. They could not be annealed for fear of spoiling them, so I gave them a coat of oil on the ground surface and cleaned all the dirt out of the threaded hole. The collets had a small part of a drift-key hole break into the threaded hole and I plugged this opening with wax. I then placed the collets on the bench, with the threaded hole up, and poured strong muriatic acid into each hole and let it eat for about five minutes. I cleaned out each threaded hole with hot soda water, to neutralize the acid, and then found that the thread gauge fitted nicely. Acid will not eat the wax. The tap used for finish-sizing on these collets was just a couple of thousandths, or so, small. We have applied the same method on the railroad to eat through a hard scale in order to be able to drill a hole that could not at first be started.—W. L. Miles, Warren, Rhode Island.

Making Potato Hills Pay

Forty-two bushels of good potatoes were successfully harvested from a crate bin, 8 ft. long, 6 ft. wide and 6 ft. high built of 4-in. boards, ½ in. thick, leaving 2½ in. space between the boards. To keep the dirt from sifting out, the bin was lined inside with coarse straw and then filled with alternate layers of manure and soil. The potatoes were planted 1 ft. apart each way, two eyes to a hill, the top layer sloping to the center to prevent water from running off. To make it possible to test the moisture in the soil, a piece of timber, about the size of a man's arm, is put into the center of the bin, halfway down, leaving 1 ft. protruding above the dirt. The moisture condition can be determined by removing the timber and inserting the hand. This should be done each week.—A. I. Hunt, Pasadena, Calif.

An 8-Ft. Bin from Which 42 Bu. of Good Potatoes Were Harvested in One Season

Improvised Carpenters' Plumb

For an ordinary level as a plumb on walls, one carpenter got a 5-ft. length of

Plumb Made from a Length of Two-by-Four with Level Set in Slot

2 by 4-in. stock, smoothed it on four sides and cut a slot out of the center to accommodate the level. Small metal links, pivoted to the wood at both ends of the slot, hold the level in place securely.—R. M. Singer, Chicago.

Repairing an Air Compressor

While repairing an air compressor, rated at about 75 lb., it was found that the pressure hose was unserviceable. As no other pressure hose was available, a piece of ordinary rubber tubing was taken and rolled, for its entire length, in a piece of 2½-in. adhesive plaster, such as is sold at all drug stores; then it was bound again with a narrow strip of the same plaster, but laid on a bias to prevent the lengthwise strip from loosening. As both ends of this improvised hose were clamped to connections, there was no possibility of its unraveling, and when completed, the hose withstood 100 lb. of pressure.—F. St. Boulanger, Alexandria, La.

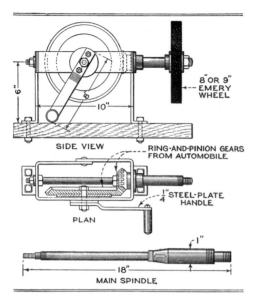

SIDE VIEW

8" OR 9" EMERY WHEEL

10"

RING-AND-PINION GEARS FROM AUTOMOBILE

PLAN

¼" STEEL-PLATE HANDLE

1"

18"

MAIN SPINDLE

Side View and Plan of Mechanics' Bench Grinder Made from Old Automobile Parts

Grinder Made from Auto Parts

Discarded automobile parts can often be used to advantage in making useful tools and devices for the workshop, as, for instance, the hand-operated bench grinder shown in the drawings. It consists of a wooden base upon which the frame is mounted, and mechanism comprising a main spindle, the ring-and-pinion gears taken from an old automobile, and an 8-in. emery wheel.

The frame is made from a piece of ¼-in. steel plate, cut to the shape and dimensions shown. It is cut out flat according to the pattern, drilled at the points indicated and bent at right angles along the dotted lines. The legs are securely bolted to the base with ordinary machine bolts. The spindle is turned down and threaded for nuts at the points shown and fitted with main bearing and thrust rings, made of brass. The shaft for the ring gear and crank is turned down and threaded on both ends, so that nuts

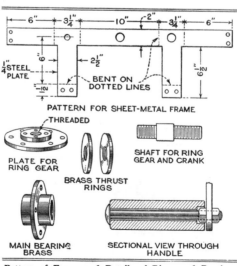

PATTERN FOR SHEET-METAL FRAME

THREADED

PLATE FOR RING GEAR

SHAFT FOR RING GEAR AND CRANK

BRASS THRUST RINGS

MAIN BEARING BRASS

SECTIONAL VIEW THROUGH HANDLE

Pattern of Frame and Details of Rings and Bearings

can be screwed on to hold the two parts in place. The crank is made of ¼-in. flat steel, cut and bent to the shape shown, and a handle, consisting of a carriage bolt slipped through a wooden sleeve, is provided on the end.

A grinder made in this way is larger and heavier than the usual type of bench grinders, and with it work can be accomplished that is beyond the range of the ordinary type.

Making Soldering Fluxes

The extensive use of solder for general work in the shop calls for a variety of fluxes suited to the metals that are to be united. As the mechanic works with such metals as copper, steel, cast iron and aluminum, each one requires a different kind of flux in order that firm joints may be made.

The necessity for using fluxes in soldering lies in the fact that the oxide, which always forms to a greater or less extent upon all brightened metal surfaces, prevents the proper joining of the pieces. The fluxes, by removing the oxide, allow the solder to stick directly to the metal.

For soldering electric wires, commutator risers and other copper-soldering jobs, a flux should be used that will not corrode the metal as a result of electrolytic action. An excellent and easily used flux for this, as well as all other copper soldering, is made by carefully melting equal weights of vaseline and rosin together. The mixture is well stirred when melted, and poured into convenient containers. This flux, when cold, has the consistency of butter, so that a small particle of it will stick on the joint. As rosin varies in density, it may be found advisable to increase the amount used. Increasing the rosin will also result in a harder flux.

A liquid flux for copper electric wires is made by mixing 5 parts of a saturated solution of zinc chloride with 4 parts alcohol and 2 parts glycerin. The saturated zinc-chloride solution is obtained by filling a bottle half full of hydrochloric acid and then adding small strips and cuttings of sheet zinc, a few at a time, until the acid will dissolve no more. Mix the alcohol and glycerin together and add to the zinc solution. The operation of dissolving the zinc in the acid should be done in the open air on account of the fumes that arise.

For uniting wrought iron and steel, a good flux is made by dissolving zinc in muriatic acid to saturation as described above; then diluting the mixture with twice its amount of water and adding a small lump of sal-ammoniac. The latter assists the solder to adhere, and in addition helps to prevent the soldering copper from corroding. The chemical action of this flux depends upon the fact that muriatic acid unites with iron and steel and in so doing deposits a film of zinc on the materials to which the solder will most readily adhere. In using any acid flux, all joints should be well washed and dried to prevent corrosion.

An excellent flux for steel parts, that will not blacken or rust the work, is made from 6 oz. of alcohol, 2 oz. of glycerin and 1 oz. of zinc oxide. Cast iron is a difficult metal to solder so as to make the parts hold, but this can be done easily by brightening both surfaces and coating them with copper. The coppering solution is made by dissolving a few crystals of copper sulphate in a small bottle of water, and is applied with a brush. Copper sulphate, like practically all other metallic salts, is poisonous when taken internally. Aluminum is a metal that offers the greatest difficulty in uniting it either to aluminum or to other metals. However, a solder prepared by melting together 84 parts tin, 16 parts aluminum and 3 parts of copper in the following manner, will be found quite satisfactory. Melt the copper first, add the aluminum a little at a time, stirring constantly with an iron rod; then add the tin and a small piece of tallow. Stand a dry, grooved board upright, stopping the ends of the grooves with wooden plugs and pour the hot metal into the grooves to mold the solder into sticks the thickness of lead pencils. Use an aluminum soldering iron. The flux is composed of equal parts of tallow and rosin; after melting, add half the quantity of zinc chloride.

Fastening Plaster Board to Ceilings

A Wisconsin contractor, who builds many homes wherein plaster board is used, found great difficulty in supporting

DETAIL OF HINGE

Handy Supports for Holding Sheets of Plaster Board against the Ceiling While Nailing Them

without a helper the ceiling sheets for easy nailing until he devised the hinged T-supports shown in the illustration. Each support consists of a 4-ft. crosspiece and a 10-ft. standard. The latter is cut in two pieces joined with a stout spring, as shown. With these supports, one workman can raise a sheet of plaster board to the ceiling and wedge the board in place.

Protecting the Outdoor Motor

On a large country estate several electric motors are used to run pumps for filling and emptying a swimming pool. New water is pumped into the pool directly from a well. The old water is pumped through underground tile to irrigate a citrus orchard. The motors are mounted on concrete foundations the tops of which are recessed to form a ledge, and galvanized sheet-iron covers are made to fit on this ledge as indicated in the photo. It is claimed that the motors are as well protected from the weather as if they were inside, although they are uncovered when used.

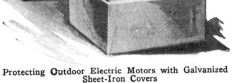

Protecting Outdoor Electric Motors with Galvanized Sheet-Iron Covers

Brush for Garage Washroom

A handy and efficient device for garages, machine shops and other shops where it is necessary to wash one's hands frequently,

Handy Brush Holder in Garage Facilitates Cleaning Hands and Keeps Brush Clean

is a handbrush supported on a bracket. A pair of ordinary handbrushes are mounted on a strip of flat iron, which is bent to clamp loosely around the water pipe at the back of the sink, as shown. The bracket should be long enough to bring the brushes under the faucet, and a band of heavy wire, drawn tight around the pipe below the iron, will support it at the desired height. In use, the brush is swung under the faucet so that the water flows directly on it. In this position, the workman can scour his hands more quickly and easily than is possible when the brush must be held in one hand, and the brush is always clean.—G. E. Hendrickson, Argyle, Wis.

Using Stained Lumber

At times during the seasoning process small patches of stain may unavoidably develop in lumber. This discoloration is usually caused by a mold and is not an indication of decay. Numerous tests have shown that stained lumber is entirely satisfactory for painted or enameled woodwork. Lumber containing stains is always less expensive than bright stock, whether it is purchased in the grades admitting it, or in special "stained" grades. Money may be saved by using it in all painted work without lowering the quality of the finished product. Its use is recommended in many houses.

Drilling Rubber

We use rubber in the shop for strippers on punch-press tools, but have always had trouble in drilling smooth or accurate holes in it, until I hit on the following method: If the rubber is to be a tight or friction fit, use a "drill" the same diameter as the piece the rubber is to fit over; otherwise allow for clearance. The drill is a piece of thin tubing, beveled to a sharp edge, all the bevel being inside. Run the drill chuck at high speed with water as a lubricant. The hole will be smooth, and slightly smaller at the bottom than at the top. This method is only applicable to through holes and cannot be used for blind holes.—John A. Blaker, West Auburn, Mass.

Compressor for Split Sleeves

In shops where considerable repair work is done, a tool for compressing split sleeves, which are often used on roller bearings in axles, transmission and drive shafts, is almost a necessity. Such a tool can easily be made in a short time. It consists of a piece of flat iron or steel, bent to fit around the sleeves uncompressed. The ends are formed as indicated in the illustration, one being drilled and tapped

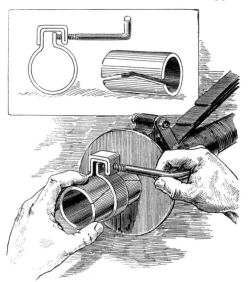

Compressor for Split Sleeves Made from a Piece of Flat Iron and a Screwhook

for a screw, which is used to tighten the device down on the sleeve to compress it.

¶It is dangerous to wear jewelry on your hands in a machine shop.

Shop Notes

Attachment Fits Breast Drill to Vise

By G. A. LUERS

THERE are many occasions, in the small shop or garage that has no drill press, when the mechanic wishes for some easier method of drilling a small hole than that of pushing it through with a breast drill. Even if a drill press is available, occasionally a part is encountered of such a shape that it is more convenient to drill a hole with the breast drill than to spend the time in blocking and clamping the work to the drill-press table. In such

A Simple Attachment That Converts the Breast Drill into a Drill Press with a Positive Feed

cases the attachment shown in the illustrations will appeal to the mechanic. With this, the part to be drilled is held against a rest, while the drill, held in a bracket fastened to the movable jaw of the vise, is fed against the work by means of the screw. The advantage of this is apparent. The breast drill, being held rigidly, makes a truer hole with much less labor than when held in the usual way.

The rear plate, against which the work is held, is simply a piece of ⅜-in. plate

steel, cut to the shape shown in the detail drawing and bent to fit against the back of the rear jaw, to which it is held by means of two hook bolts. These permit the plate to be attached and detached quickly. The bracket for the drill is also of ⅜-in. plate, the lower end being cut and formed to fit the front jaw, in a similar manner to the rear plate, and fitted with two hook bolts also. The upper end is cut to form two clamps that will grasp the drill, one clamp just behind the chuck and the other on the handle rod just behind the top of the cast-iron frame. The bracket is then twisted as shown, and holes are drilled for the clamping bolts. This construction allows the drill to be removed for use in the regular manner when desired. It is desirable to face the rear plate with a block of hardwood, fastening this to the plate by means of wood screws driven in from the back, at the corners, so

73

that they will not be near the drill point; the block can thus be renewed when too many spots are drilled in it. A loose

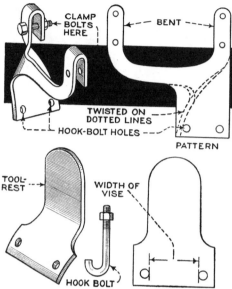

Details of the Brackets and the Hook Bolts for Attaching Them to the Vise

block may, of course, be used if desired, but fastening the block to the plate makes the operation of the attachment more convenient. Work can be held against the rear plate by means of large C-clamps, thus leaving the hands free for turning and feeding the drill.

Simple Outfit Filters Used Oil

Anybody can make the simple oil filter shown in the drawing. It consists of two large bottles, a funnel and some waste. Put the dirty oil in one of the bottles, place the waste in the funnel and insert the latter into one bottle as indicated. Invert the bottle containing the oil, placing it on a shelf or platform to hold it securely. As soon as the oil has filtered through into the lower bottle, the bottles may be reversed if it is desired to refilter the oil. It is a simple matter to renew the waste,

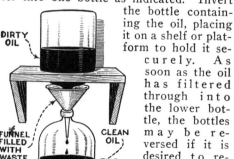

and as the bottles are made of glass, the condition of the oil can readily be seen at all times.—W. F. Schaphorst, Newark, New Jersey.

Cleaning Enamel

To clean enamel, wipe it off with a moist cloth dipped in precipitated chalk and rub gently. Soft flannel is best, and Paris white, which is a very fine grade of whiting, will do. First dip the flannel in hot water and wring it out as dry as possible; then dip it in the whiting. Wash off with clear lukewarm water, and rub dry with a soft chamois skin or flannel cloth.—A. A. Kelly, Malvern, Pa.

Hip Holster for Auto Service-Station Attendant

Here is a holster that is of real service to one who attends cars at filling stations or garages all day long. Made from light, pliable leather, it holds a tire-pressure gauge, a small screwdriver and a pair of pliers. The leather costs about 60 cents and the stitching can be done on a sewing machine. The best way to make the holster is to mark out the size and location of the tools on a piece of paper. Then trim down to the smallest practicable space, and cut out the leather, allowing ¼ in. for the seams on all sides. One of the leather pieces has two strips extending from it at the upper corner. This piece goes next to the body and the ends of the strips are riveted down to form loops for a belt. —Dale R. Van Horn, Walton, Nebr.

Testing Soundness of Posts

A coal trestle was being replaced, which was very old and had a large number of posts badly decayed close to the ground. An external examination of the caps seemed to indicate that it would be necessary to replace all of them. To make an internal inspection meant that a ⅜-in. hole had to be drilled through them in several places. However, the following kink was used and proved to be as reliable as the physical inspection. An ordinary watch was held tightly against one end of a cap. The inspector placed his ear at the opposite end against the butt of the cap. If the tick of the watch could be heard through the wood, the cap was sound. If not, there was a rotten heart, or the inside was decayed sufficiently to necessitate replacement. The operation was reversed as a check. In every case examination of the timber when removed proved the accuracy of the method.—H. M. Toombs, Chicago, Ill.

Use for Old Hypo

When hypo solution can no longer be used for fixing, it will do for cleaning developing trays of the dark precipitation that forms after long usage. Fill the trays with the hypo solution and leave them stand overnight. In the morning wash the trays with hot water and soap to remove all the hypo before using them again for developing.—Edward H. Flaharty, Denver, Colo.

Motor-Driven Stirring Device

Stirring sauce such as catsup, which requires considerable cooking before it is canned, is tiresome to do by hand, and the motor-driven stirring device shown in the drawing will be found convenient. It consists of a 1 by 4 by 30-in. board to which an electric-fan motor, a couple of pulleys, and a stirring arm are attached. The fan is unscrewed from the motor and a small V-grooved pulley is substituted. This in turn is connected with rubber bands to the two pulleys to reduce the speed of the arm to about 60 r.p.m. The pulleys may be turned on a small lathe. The stirring arm has five holes drilled in it, as indicated. Five heavy washers are tied to lengths of strong cord, which are slipped through the holes in the arm, as shown, and knotted. The strings should be just long enough to let the washers drag on the bottom of the pan.—William L. Hunter, Iowa City, Iowa.

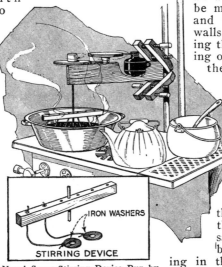

Novel Sauce-Stirring Device Run by Means of Small Electric Motor

Construction of Window Frames

Satisfactory service from frames and windows depends first of all on proper

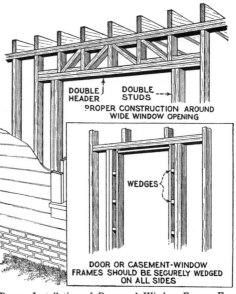

PROPER CONSTRUCTION AROUND WIDE WINDOW OPENING

DOOR OR CASEMENT-WINDOW FRAMES SHOULD BE SECURELY WEDGED ON ALL SIDES

Proper Installation of Door and Window Frames Excludes Drafts

construction around the window opening. A double header should always be used. If more than two studs are cut away the space over the windows should be "bridged." This simply means the provision of braces to distribute the weight from the center to the supporting studs at the sides. Door and window frames should be securely wedged on all sides and an air-tight junction should be made between the frame and the inside and outside walls. A good method of doing this is to set a false casing on the outside flush with the sheathing. Tack tarred building paper over the false casing and extend it over the sheathing. Then place the outside finished casing over the paper. Rabbet the lower surface of the window sill on the outside edge to admit the siding, and the inner edge to anchor the plaster. It is necessary to use a non-combustible material for filling in the opening underneath the sill.

Wire Netting Protects Magazines

The display rack shown in the photo, in which magazines are protected against being stolen and handled, is used by a

Wire Mesh over Magazine Rack Prevents Handling and Stealing

newsdealer in Cincinnati. A wire strung in the middle of each rack keeps the magazines in place and preserves the covers.—L. R. Tichenor, Cincinnati, Ohio.

Improving Auto Valves

Leaky auto valves can be improved by cutting a ⅛-in. groove in the head at the same angle as the valve face and about 1⁄16 in. from the edge. This leaves a thin shell, which is flexible and improves the

seating of the valve, especially when the engine is hot. The force of the explosion tends to make the seating a tighter fit, and after the valve has been fitted, the surface takes on a very high polish. The hammering effect so noticeable in solid valves is entirely absent in this improved valve. When newly made, the seating surface of the valve is faced off at the same time as the slot and all valves are carefully ground in. More clearance must be allowed at the lower end of the stem than

usual. The slotting is done on the lathe, working with centers, as the slot must be concentric with the seating, and the walls must be the same thickness all the way down. The bottom of the slot should be rounded, which is easily done by using a round-nose tool.—Arthur N. Capron, Athelstan, Can.

Keeping Perpetual Inventory

Where a large stock of material is usually kept on hand, such as capscrews, small brass and iron castings, machine bolts, belt hooks, drills, etc., it will be found advantageous to keep the material in tin trays, as shown in the illustration. This also makes it easy to take inventory of the stock. The main features of this arrangement are the neatness, compactness and the possibility of counting the contents without touching a single item. A number of trays of suitable sizes are made of No. 16 gauge galvanized iron, the sides being formed by turning up the four edges ½ or 1 in. No fastening or soldering at the corners is needed. A number of tin tabs are cut out and folded over as shown in the insert; these are slipped over the front edge of the trays and the number of items in the tray is marked on them. The tabs are put on by the stock boy when he loads up the trays from the original containers before putting them on the shelf in the racks. If there is a duplicate supply of items in another part of the stockroom or warehouse, a red tab is fastened to the bottom tray of the tier. This informs the stock keeper that there is a reserve stock to be inventoried also.—E. E. Moffat, Pasadena, Calif.

Cutting and Bending Small Tubing

If thin metal tubing is filled with melted tallow and the tallow then allowed to cool and harden, the tubing can be held fairly tight in a vise without much danger of flattening it, and can be cut into ¼-in. lengths, if desired, without spoiling the diameter. The tallow can be removed by allowing hot water to run over the tubing until the tallow melts and runs out, or by placing it in some location where the temperature is sufficiently high to melt the

Preventing Scour on River Bank

A western city protects its river banks from scour during flood periods by paving the slopes with old stone curbing, which

Flood Banks of Western River Protected Effectively against Scour by Paving with Curbstones That Were Too Worn to Be Used in Street-Improvement Work

tallow. Often very thin metal tubes can be cut by using the back instead of the teeth of the hacksaw.

Exhaust Fan Driven by Compressed Air

The illustration shows a ventilating fan operated by compressed air. This arrangement is used to exhaust air from a room or small building where it would be uneconomical to have a motor idle most of the time. Four ¼-in. blower pipes are screwed into a cast-iron hub, which has four holes connecting with the air supply. The base acts as a receiver for the air and allows it to flow through the holes into the pipes. The ends of the pipes are bent over at right angles, swedged down, and drilled with ⅟₃₂-in. holes through which the air is ejected. The pipes and fan blades are securely fastened to the hub which, of course, should turn freely. Details of the construction are clearly shown in the drawing.—Frank L. Coakley, Buffalo, New York.

had become too worn to be reset in street-improvement work. The old curbstones are generally about 4 ft. long, 16 in. wide, and about 5 in. thick. They are laid flat on the bank, with their longer dimension parallel to the river channel, and the cracks are filled with cement. The slope-protection work should be started several feet below the river bed, preferably on a rock, concrete, or sheet-piling foundation.

Installing Interior Trim

Interior trim should not be installed while the plaster is wet; in fact, it should not even be brought into the house until the plaster has become thoroughly dry. Wide pieces of trim, and especially wide panels, should be painted on the back before installation, to prevent bulging or buckling. If exposed end grain is saturated with thick paint, absorption of moisture into the wood cells will be prevented.

All woodwork should be cleaned before being painted and knots coated with white shellac or wiped off with a cloth moistened with benzole.

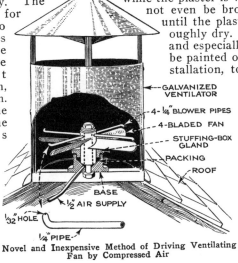

GALVANIZED VENTILATOR
4-¼" BLOWER PIPES
4-BLADED FAN
STUFFING-BOX GLAND
PACKING
ROOF
BASE
½ AIR SUPPLY
⅟₃₂" HOLE
¼" PIPE

Novel and Inexpensive Method of Driving Ventilating Fan by Compressed Air

Trailer Tow Rod

A telephone company in a western city has equipped its light roadsters with homemade tow rods by which trailers are

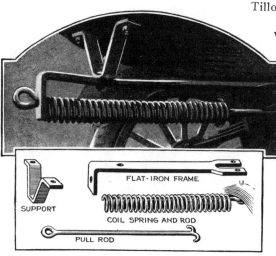

Coil-Spring Tow-Rod Attachment on Light Car Pulls One-Ton Trailer without Jerking or Straining

attached for hauling. A piece of heavy strap iron is split at the front end (relative to the roadster) and the other end is bent at right angles and drilled as shown. This forms a frame for carrying a heavy coil spring. The tow rod itself is made of ⅝-in. material, the front end being split to hook over the front end of the spring. A shorter rod is bolted to the middle of the rear spring of the roadster to hold the coil spring in place and prevent its front end from dropping. The rear end of the spring frame is held in line by a strap-iron support, which is bolted to the back end of the roadster body. Under ordinary circumstances, the spring will not contract more than 1 in. when a one-ton trailer is pulled on level dirt roads. Usually the load is much less than this, yet the spring prevents jerking and straining.—Dale R. Van Horn, Walton, Nebr.

Pump Aids Tumble Plating

A large tumble-plating mill, having only one tumble outfit of 45-gal. capacity, used it for plating four different metals as it was considered too expensive to purchase extra tumblers. A pump was installed, which could rapidly pump out whatever solution might happen to be in the tumbler, and store it in a large barrel. After the solution was transferred in this way, the tumbler was thoroughly rinsed out before the new solution was put in. To at-

tempt baling out these highly poisonous solutions with buckets would be quite impractical and a great waste of time. With the aid of the pump the solutions could be changed in about 10 minutes.—Ralph W. Tillotson, Erie, Pa.

Wax Supply in Hammer Handle Is Convenient When Driving Nails

The hammer that carpenters use for fine finish work can be made much handier by drilling a ½-in. hole about 1½ in. deep in the end of the handle. Melted wax or paraffin is poured into the hole. Small nails coated with wax by pushing them into this can be driven in much easier and are less liable to bend. It will also lessen the jar when hammering on solid material.

Reducing Oversize Bolt Thread

It was necessary in one case to reduce an oversize bolt thread. Neither threading dies nor a screw-cutting lathe was available, so I tried the following emergency method, which proved entirely successful. I picked up a nut about the size of the bolt, sawed it open on one side and spread it so that the bolt would screw in. I then put a filler piece in the sawed slot so that the nut would not close up when clamped in the lathe chuck. After making a center hole in the head of the bolt and screwing the bolt into the nut, the tailstock was brought up and clamped only slightly so that it would slip back

as the bolt was screwed out of the nut. While the bolt was being screwed out, a thread tool, which was set close to the nut, cut off a chip to within about one third of the thread of the end of the bolt. A couple of threads were cut off the end of the bolt, and the bolt could then be driven into place nicely. Care was taken to clamp the head spindle so that it would not turn.—R. B. Ware, Wadsworth, Ohio.

not have revealed themselves in a square box with a large cross-sectional area.— R. B. Hoffman, Pacific Grove, Calif.

Semi-Automatic Wrapper Paster

Pasting standard-size wrappers on packages can be greatly facilitated by using a semi-automatic wrapper paster

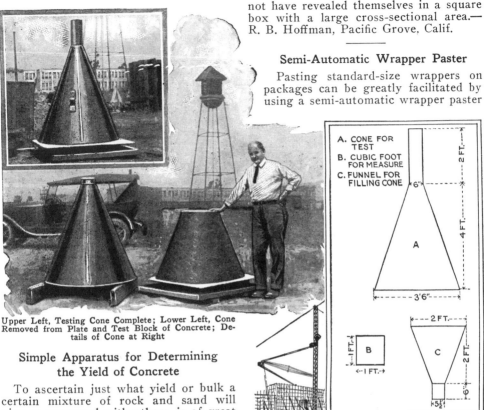

A. CONE FOR TEST
B. CUBIC FOOT FOR MEASURE
C. FUNNEL FOR FILLING CONE

Upper Left, Testing Cone Complete; Lower Left, Cone Removed from Plate and Test Block of Concrete; Details of Cone at Right

Simple Apparatus for Determining the Yield of Concrete

To ascertain just what yield or bulk a certain mixture of rock and sand will give as compared with others, is of great importance to the cement contractor. To make this test, I have used the outfit illustrated, consisting of a cone, a tube and a funnel of sheet iron of the dimensions given in the detail drawing. The lower end of the cone is flanged and a plate bolted to this flange. The concrete is mixed according to the specification selected, a cubic-foot box, just 12 in. on all sides, being used for measuring the dry material and a 1-gal. measure for the water.

After each mixture has been placed in the cone, the distance from the top of the concrete to either the top of the cone or the top of the tube is measured, and the increase or decrease in yield for different mixes is noted. Differences in yield amounting to 10 and 15 per cent have thus been found. The conical form of the test container was selected in order to bring out small differences which would

of the kind shown in the illustration. It consists of a narrow pan, about 1 by 1½ by 10 in. in dimensions, with a bottom perforated with narrow slits, ½ in. long and about ⅛ in. apart. A flange is soldered to each end of the pan, and two holes are drilled in each flange as indicated. Bolts, fastened to a baseboard and projecting up vertically, fit through the holes in these flanges. Small coil springs are slipped over the ends of the bolts and nuts are screwed on. This arrangement keeps the pan down tightly against the wrappers, which are laid face down on the baseboard with one end under the pan. In use the wrappers are pulled out one by one and will have just enough paste, which will spread out evenly when pressure is applied to the wrapper, making a neater bundle than when using a brush.

SPRING

SLITS IN BOTTOM OF PAN

Wrappers Are Easily Applied with This Semi-Automatic Paster

Boring-Bar Holder

The boring-bar holder shown in the accompanying drawing is for use on small

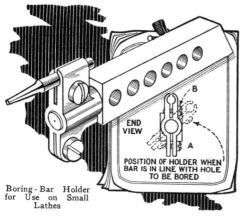

Boring - Bar Holder for Use on Small Lathes

lathes where light work is done, and will be found more convenient than one of the ordinary type. The bar is held in place entirely by the friction clamp, which is tightened by the two screws A and B. Holes as small as 1/16-in. may be drilled with this type of holder, owing to the rigidity of the body and the shortness of the bars. The main body of the holder is set in the toolpost so that it is in line with the shears of the lathe. Then the end of the holder is raised or lowered, in order to set the bar central with the hole to be bored, and the two screws are tightened. The bar holder should be made of good tool steel, hardened and tempered to spring blue. When changing bars, it is only necessary to loosen the top screw, which clamps each bar in exact alinement with the hole in the work.

Lubricating Rebored Cylinders

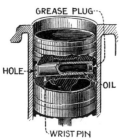

Many a rebored and reground cylinder job has failed to stand up because the new bearing surfaces fit snugly and were not sufficiently lubricated. If the new piston is too close-fitting, the heat of combustion and of excessive friction, prevents the oil from getting above the lower ring, leaving the upper portion without lubrication. The writer uses the method of oiling shown in the illustration

to prevent this trouble. One end of the wristpin is plugged with heavy cup grease, and the cup so formed is filled with motor oil. The opposite end is then plugged in the same way. Just before the piston is inserted into the cylinder, the grease plugs are punctured with a match stick, to allow the confined oil to flow out. The lower ring and the junk ring tend to hold the released oil in confinement and cause it to be carried up and down the cylinder wall.—C. M. Wilcox, Torrington, Conn.

Supports for Roadside Cables

Heavy steel-stranded cables are quite widely used as highway guards. It is common practice to drill the posts and thread the cables through these holes. Structurally this method is good, but in case of a collision or accident the cables restrain the automobile only until it reaches the first post, when the inside half of the post receives the impact, is uprooted or split, and the car seriously damaged. A post hit hard enough to be split must be replaced if the guard is to remain effective, and this means rethreading the cables from the nearest splice, which involves considerable labor. To

avoid this loss of time, and also to locate the cables so that they will tend to fend the car away from and thus protect the posts, one city adopted the type of clamp shown in the photo. Bolted to the post with two heavy lag-screws, the adjustable jaws of the clamp hold the cable firmly and permit quick replacement of either post or strand without affecting the line on either side in any way.

❡A good paint for wire screen consists of dropblack, ground in oil, and about a third as much of asphaltum varnish, thinned with turpentine.

Grinding Drills for Brass

When grinding drills for brass, it is common practice to grind a flat on each lip, in order to prevent the drill from digging into the work. A better way is to flatten the cutting edge with a small oilstone, until a face, about .010 in. wide, is attained. Thus a finer cutting edge is made and there is no unnecessary waste of the drill, such as occurs when grinding by hand.—C. Homewood, Ontario, Calif.

Soap Holder for the Workshop Washroom

A handy and convenient soap-saving device for the workshop washroom is shown in the illustration. A wide metal band is clamped around the upright supply pipe at the back of the sink, to extend to one side about 8 or 10 in., and the outer end of this band is bent to support a length of round steel rod. A piece of coil spring, with a short chain and a wire corkscrew attached, is slipped over the upright rod, and the device is complete. The soap is attached by driving the corkscrew into the center of the bar and thus is suspended out of the way when not in use. This arrangement keeps the soap in a more sanitary condition than if thrown about the sink, and a decided saving is also effected.—G. F. Hendrickson, Argyle, Wis.

Keeping Irrigation Canals Clean

In one irrigation district where the silting of the canals constitutes a serious maintenance problem, due to the settling of the fine sand carried by the flow and originally brought in with the river water, the conditions have been partly relieved by installing huge wooden water wheels at frequent intervals along the canals. The wheels are turned by the downstream movement of the irrigation water, while the turning of the blades keeps the sand stirred up so that it is carried along the canals to gate structures, where it can be sluiced back to the river channel.—Ivan E. Houk, Denver, Colo.

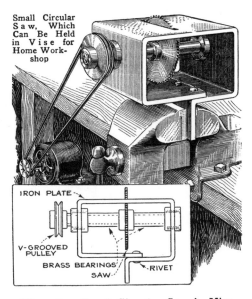

Small Circular Saw, Which Can Be Held in Vise for Home Workshop

IRON PLATE
V-GROOVED PULLEY
BRASS BEARINGS
SAW
RIVET

Mounting Small Circular Saw in Vise

A small power-driven circular saw is a handy tool for the home workshop. Often the expense of purchasing one is not justified, but a saw of the kind shown in the drawing will be found just as convenient and can readily be made by any amateur mechanic. It consists of a frame made of iron plate, which can be set up in a vise when needed. The saw is mounted on a shaft set in brass bearings and a V-grooved pulley is provided on one end of the shaft as indicated. The saw is belted to an electric motor located at some convenient point near by, the pulley of the motor, of course, being in line with the pulley on the shaft.

Holding Round Objects with Pliers

Round objects, such as nails, taper pins, valvespring pins, etc., are readily placed and easily held in a pair of pliers if a saw cut is made in the jaws as shown. Use two or three saw blades together to produce a broad slit. Accidental opening of the pliers and loss of the object may be avoided by placing an elastic band around the handles.—Richard C. Tarr, Gloucester, Massachusetts.

WORK END VIEW

Adjustable Roof on Hay Shed

Unless full, the ordinary hay shed does not give adequate protection against weather, as the sides are usually left open, and if the roof is 10 or 20 ft. above the top of the hay pile, it does little or no good. A Nebraska farmer built a shed with a roof, which can be raised and lowered at will. No matter how little or how much hay there is stored, the

roof can be dropped directly upon it. Four stout posts, 25 ft. long, are set up at the corners and the tops are connected with stringers, which serve to brace them. At each end a smooth-planed pole, with rods driven into the ends for bearings, fits between the posts. At the center, these poles are squared and fitted with iron collars. The roof is built in the usual way, with adequate bracing underneath, and each corner is provided with a square strap-iron collar, which fits freely over the corner posts. Wire cables run from the

Novel Hay Shed with Roof Which Can Be Adjusted for Height

corners of the roof, over pulleys at the top of the posts and then down to the horizontal poles at the ends. To raise the roof, two wrenches are used, as shown. One man makes a quarter turn while the other takes a new grip. When one end of the roof is raised about 3 ft., it is locked and the other end raised 2 ft., and so on.

Current Regulation for Electric Welding

Electric welding as practiced on a commercial scale, requires a current of from 75 to 200 amp. at a voltage of from 40 to 60. The work is connected to the positive terminal and the negative terminal is extended to electrodes, which are made of a suitable metal. For cast iron, for instance, thin rods of the same material are used, and for other iron, soft Swedish-iron rods are used. For light work in the

shop, however, an arc between carbon electrodes can be used to advantage, as it requires but a small amount of energy and can be fed from a lamp socket with somewhat heavier conductors, directly from a 30-amp. fuse. Any suitable device for holding the carbon electrodes may be used, similar to the one already described in the November, 1925, issue of Popular Mechanics Magazine. The carbons used are of the arc-lamp type. A spring mechanism should keep them separated and the proper distance should be maintained by moving the electrodes together.

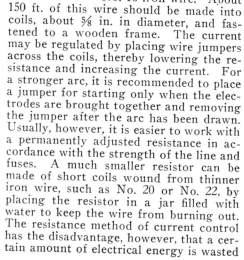

The main problem of successful work with this device lies in the proper regulation of the current through the arc, in order to have the device operative with a circuit from a 30-amp. fuse. The simplest method, which is applicable equally to direct and alternating current, is to introduce a resistor into one of the lines. This resistor can be made conveniently of No. 16 iron wire. About 150 ft. of this wire should be made into coils, about ⅝ in. in diameter, and fastened to a wooden frame. The current may be regulated by placing wire jumpers across the coils, thereby lowering the resistance and increasing the current. For a stronger arc, it is recommended to place a jumper for starting only when the electrodes are brought together and removing the jumper after the arc has been drawn. Usually, however, it is easier to work with a permanently adjusted resistance in accordance with the strength of the line and fuses. A much smaller resistor can be made of short coils wound from thinner iron wire, such as No. 20 or No. 22, by placing the resistor in a jar filled with water to keep the wire from burning out. The resistance method of current control has the disadvantage, however, that a certain amount of electrical energy is wasted in the heating of the wire. A more economical arrangement can be made with the alternating current by using a choke coil, though it is more difficult to make a satisfactory choke coil than a resistor. A choke coil designed for a frequency of 60 cycles will not work on a frequency of 25 cycles, and vice versa. The writer used a coil of the following dimensions for a frequency of 60 cycles: The iron core was 1¾ in. wide, 1 in. thick and was made of 75 laminations, each of which was about .0175 in. thick. Two coils were placed on the core, each containing 80 turns of No. 11 d.c.c. wire. The coils were connected in series. A very small air gap was formed between the ends of the laminations. The width of this gap controls the current, and with poorly assembled laminations and a larger gap, the current may become too strong for practical purposes for use with 30-amp. fuses. For first experiments with a choke coil, it is recommended to include in the circuit also an iron-wire resistor in series with the coil, in order to prevent the fuses from blowing out, in case the coil is not made right. The wire may be gradually cut out by short-circuiting its turns, until the desired strength of arc is reached. The arc will not be stable with current less than 10 amp., and the best results for light work are obtained with a current of from 15 to 20 amp. For 25 cycles the coil should have more turns and a larger core. Two coils of 120 turns each may be used with a core 2 by 1½ in. in dimensions. A bank of electric lamps may also be used as a resistor, although such a substitute is rather expensive. The work with the arc is easy, once the resistor or choke coils are properly adjusted. Light sheets or strips of soft iron, brass, copper and aluminum can be easily welded together. It is more difficult to weld carbon steel, and it is recommended to use soft iron wire for making joints. With a certain amount of practice the ends of a band saw can be brazed together by using a bronze alloy and borax for a flux. Care must be taken, however, not to burn away the edges of the saw. This usually happens if the arc is allowed to jump across the metal, instead of keeping it confined to the carbon electrodes.—J. P. Nikonow, New York City.

Putty Can for the Painter

Putty is a necessary item for the house painter but inconvenient to carry when working on a ladder. If a small, clean can is cut in the manner shown in the illustration and the projecting piece bent back to form a clip, it may be fastened either outside or inside of the paint pail and will provide a handy receptacle for the putty.— R. Tarr, Gloucester, Mass.

Turning Bar Stock on the Speed Lathe

Having a large quantity of ⁵⁄₁₆-in. rods to turn down on each end, I sought some method whereby the highest and fastest possible production could be obtained. The small turret lathes were all busy, and after some planning, it was decided to rig up a small speed lathe to do the work. A small box tool of the tangent-cut style, used on the turret lathe, was chucked in the regular lathe chuck. A drill chuck in the tailstock spindle held the work.

After the tangent-cutting tool was set to the right diameter, the lathe was not shut down when changing stock but was left running, the box tool rotating all the while. This is contrary to the usual practice, but works out well. The drill chuck is easily opened for the insertion or removal of a piece by a twist of the wrist. The work is fed into the tool by pressing on the feed handle. Because the lathe was not started and stopped repeatedly, much time was saved in this manner alone, and as a result four spindle ends were turned down per minute.—J. V. Romig, Allentown, Pa.

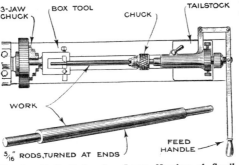

Turning Both Ends of a Large Number of Small Spindles at the Rate of Four a Minute

Spare-Tire Carrier for Truck

On many pneumatic-tired trucks the spare tire can best be carried under the frame behind the rear axle as shown. The

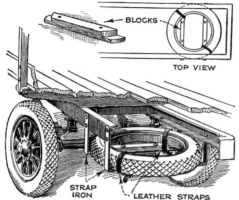

Wooden Blocks on Underslung Tire Carrier Prevent Tire from Chafing

objection to this mounting is the difficulty of keeping the tire from chafing against the parts of the carrier with which it comes in contact. A good method of preventing this trouble is to bolt two hardwood blocks, cut as indicated in the detail, to the carrier. Two heavy leather straps are wrapped around the tire and carrier at diagonal points to keep the tire on securely, and a heavy chain with a padlock is used to prevent theft.—G. C. Douglas, Raleigh, N. C.

Riveting Crankcase Supports

Ford repair men are well aware that the job of riveting the crankcase rear-supporting arms in place is awkward for one man, and will find the tool shown in the illustration convenient for this purpose. It is made of 1½-in. shafting, one end tapered to ½-in. diameter and a small cup-shaped depression made in it to accommodate the head of the rivet. The opposite end is tapered to ¾-in. diameter, and a 27/64-in. hole is drilled in this end, approximately 3 in. deep, and tapped about ½ in. for a 2½-in. capscrew. In use, a rivet is inserted in the proper position in the crankcase, the small end of the tool being placed against the rivet and the capscrew at the other end against a corresponding rivet on the op-

posite side of the case. The capscrew is tightened until the tool firmly supports the rivet to be driven in, and the work of riveting is done easily by one workman. The idea can, of course, be adapted to various situations other than the one just described.—Edwin Kilburn, Spring Valley, Minn.

An Adjustable Bench Stool

Many shops provide seats to be used when doing bench work that can be performed better while sitting. The illustration shows a bench stool which is adjustable for height, so that the workman can change it to the best possible position for the particular job in hand. The actual seat consists of a strong box, about 2 ft. high by 18 in. wide, the entire box being utilized with the exception of the lid. Along both sides, in the middle, a strip of wood is cut away to leave a slot about ½ in. wide. Two pieces of wood similar in width and thickness to the box sides, serve as legs and are drilled near the top to receive a ½-in. iron pipe. The pipe is threaded at each end, and passes through the holes in the legs and the slot in the seat sides, being held to the former by nuts and washers, so that the seat can slide up and down. To tighten it in any required position two pieces of larger pipe are fitted over the ½-in. pipe and connected by a tee. To obtain this effect in one movement, one of these pieces is screwed tightly into the tee and the other is left loose. A washer is placed between the ends of the pipes and the box, and when the tee is turned by means of the short piece of pipe on the branch, the distance between the ends of the piping is increased and the legs and box are bound firmly together. To keep the loose pipe from turning when the tee is turned, a hole is drilled in the ½-in. pipe and a larger one in the outside pipe and a pin then driven into the former.

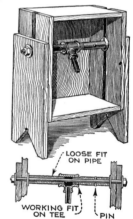

¶Draftsmen should never let a tracing lie in the sun between the time it is traced and finished.

Emergency Micrometer

I had occasion to pick out a piece of packing, which had to be of an exact thickness, and there was no micrometer available. After looking the tools over, I picked out a feeler gauge and a small C-clamp to serve as a substitute. The clamp was screwed down lightly on the feeler-gauge leaf of proper thickness, just as if it were a micrometer, and attention was paid to where the slot in the screw head stopped. The clamp was screwed down on various pieces of shim stock until a piece was found that stopped the screw on the same position. Later measurement with the "mike" showed the piece to be right. I have used this method several times since and found it to be highly satisfactory.—John A. Blaker, West Auburn, Massachusetts.

Caissons Substituted for Cofferdams

Caissons, somewhat similar to those used in sinking deep foundations for unusually large bridges, can also be used economically in building the comparatively shallow piers required for bridges of smaller size; only in the latter construction the caissons are left open at the top, instead of closed, and the men work under atmospheric pressure, instead of in compressed air, the water level being kept down by a centrifugal pump in one corner of the caisson. The caisson is built of concrete and is merely a shell of such size and shape that, when sunk to the proper depth, it can be filled with concrete to make the pier. It is built above the water level, either on an island or on a pile of gravel thrown up for the purpose, and is sunk by excavating the material inside by hand and lifting it out in a clamshell bucket operated by a dragline or derrick. Old railroad rails make ideal braces for the inside of the caisson while sinking, since they occupy but little space and can be left in, if desired, to strengthen the pier when concreting the interior. —Ivan E. Houk, Denver, Colo.

Concrete Caissons Used for Excavation in Bridge Building Serve as Piers When Filled

Bending Iron on Grooved Rail

Lengths of steel rail are well-known shop facilities and are commonly used for riveting and straightening. In one shop the employes have found another use for the rail block by grinding or planing a tapered groove in the face, as shown in the illustration. The ease with which square, round or flat stock can be bent in this groove is evident. It should have a gradual taper so that either sharp or round bends can be formed. Of course, the rail should be drilled and bolted solidly on the bench top at a convenient height.—G. A. Luers, Washington, D. C.

Kink for Jewelers

Jewelers, watchmakers, and other tradesmen who work at the bench with fine tools and small instruments, are often inconvenienced by the loss of some small but important piece that rolls off the bench. To overcome this trouble one jeweler placed two small hooks on the underside of his workbench, spacing them about 3 ft. apart, and set two brass eyelets into the extreme lower corners of his work apron. Now, when employed at the bench, he fastens the corners of the apron onto the hooks beneath the bench, and any small pieces accidentally dropped or brushed from the bench are certain to be caught in the apron and easily found.—G. E. Hendrickson, Argyle, Wisconsin.

Getting Rid of Cooking Odors

By EDWIN M. LOVE

A CEILING vent over the kitchen range is valuable not only to dispose of undesirable heat during the summer, but also to carry off cooking odors the year round. While most recently built houses have such ventilating hoods, many older homes have none, and would be greatly benefited by such an addition.

The neatest type is that illustrated in Fig. 2. This consists of a semicircular or elliptical depression in the ceiling with a rectangular hole in the center, through which the cooking odors escape. It requires about 2 ft. of clearance or rise of the roof above the ceiling joists for operation, and is therefore unsuitable for placing under the eaves. The ceiling opening is trimmed as nearly 2 by 4 ft. as possible. If the length of the opening lies across the ceiling joists, get above the joists, if possible, and nail a piece of 1 by 4-in. or 6-in. wood across several, about 3 ft. back from the wall plate against which the hood is to be nailed. This will support the joists to be cut. Select four joists embracing the space to be occupied by the hood, and drive through the plaster a small nail at each

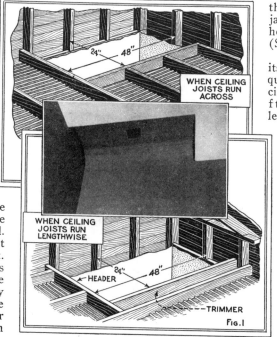

WHEN CEILING JOISTS RUN ACROSS

WHEN CEILING JOISTS RUN LENGTHWISE

HEADER

TRIMMER

Fig. 1

outer joist. Using these points, lay out on the ceiling the rectangle to be cut, 2 ft. wide, and remove the plaster by cutting around the mark with a cold chisel. Cut the laths with a compass saw. From above, cut off the ends of the two inside joists 2 ft., plus the thickness of the 2 by 4-in. header to be nailed on the ends from the wall, and fit the header tightly between the end joists. Spike thoroughly, driving the nails with light blows to avoid cracking the plaster. If the joists run lengthwise of the opening, only one joist section will need to be cut out besides the backing joist at the wall plate, but a trimmer will be necessary between the two headers, or between the header and adjacent wall if the hood is in a corner. (See Fig. 1.)

To build the hood itself, lay out eight quadrants (quarter circles) having a 1-ft. radius, on lengths of 1 by 10-in. stock. Miter the ends to form pairs, as shown in the detail, and saw out the curves with a compass saw, nailing cleats over the joints to assemble the sections. The notches shown at the bottoms of the curves are 3½ in. high and 1½ in. wide, and are

designed to fit over the sides of the ceiling opening. The four arches being completed, assemble them, in the manner shown, by nailing on the ends flush with the notched pieces of 1 by 4-in. stock. Secure rigidity by nailing, across one slope of the top, a third 1 by 4-in. piece. This done, build a rectangular jamb of surfaced 1 by 4-in. stock, rabbeting the ends into the sides, and making it 3 in. wide inside and just long enough to fit snugly between the two middle arches. Nail in place flush with the curved edges, and cover the top with screen wire to keep out flies.

Push the frame up through the openings and rest the notches on the trimmers or headers, as the case may be. Toenail through the 1 by 4-in. side braces into the trimmers. It will be seen that, thus far, provision is made only for lathing the curved surface. To catch the ends of the laths on the flat hood ends, nail onto the end arches projecting pieces of 1-in. stock.

If the hood is to be plastered, lath with ¼-in. spaces between; but if it is not desired to go to the expense of hiring a plasterer for so small a job, lath tight and paste on a muslin lining, over which wall paper or sanitas may be pasted.

Where lack of space above the ceiling prevents the use of a flush hood, one in the general style of Fig. 3 must be used. Build a front frame of 2 by 3-in. stock, making it 2 by 4 ft., with the four studs equally spaced. The upper plates of the ends are cut 2 ft., minus the width of front and back plates; the lower end plates, extending as they do to the wall, are 2 ft., less one width. Assemble with the front frame by toenailing to the front plates and to the rear upper plate (which is cut to run full length) and by spiking in two studs, as shown in the drawing.

Cut a piece of 1 by 6-in. stock about 3 ft. 10 in. long for a jamb front, and, centered on the length, cut two ¾-in. grooves or dadoes, ⅜ in. deep and 6 in. apart. Complete the vent jamb as shown, using 1 by 4-in. material, rabbeting the back into the sides. The inside measurements are 6 by 6 in. Cover with screen wire. Cut out the back upper plate and nail the jamb in the opening, the ends of the wide front jamb notching over the end plates. Using 1 by 4-in. stock, cut four rafters to butt against the front jamb and toenail to the sides of the front studs, as shown.

For this hood, an opening, 10 in. wide and 4 ft. long, must be cut in the ceiling.

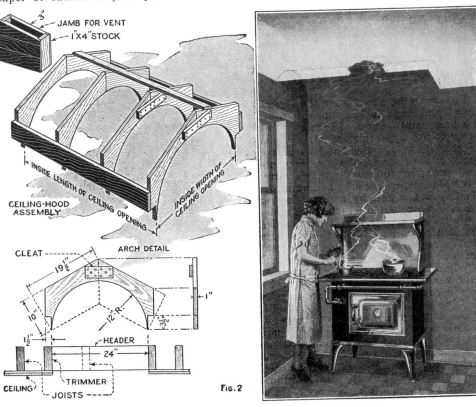

JAMB FOR VENT
1"X4" STOCK
3"

CEILING·HOOD ASSEMBLY
INSIDE LENGTH OF CEILING OPENING
INSIDE WIDTH OF CEILING OPENING

CLEAT
ARCH DETAIL
19½"
10"
12" R.
3½"
1"
1½"
HEADER
24"
CEILING
TRIMMER
JOISTS
FIG. 2

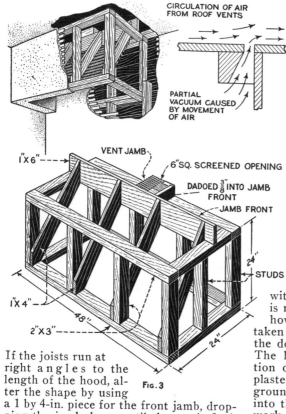

CIRCULATION OF AIR FROM ROOF VENTS

PARTIAL VACUUM CAUSED BY MOVEMENT OF AIR

VENT JAMB

6"SQ. SCREENED OPENING

DADOED $\frac{3}{8}$" INTO JAMB FRONT

JAMB FRONT

1"X6"

STUDS

24"

1"X4"

48"

2"X3"

24"

FIG.3

If the joists run at right angles to the length of the hood, alter the shape by using a 1 by 4-in. piece for the front jamb, dropping the jamb down until the top is flush with the top plates. It is then only necessary to cut a hole, 6 in. square, in the ceiling.

To put up the hood, brace the assembly with light strips tacked outside, prop in position and drive 16-penny spikes through the upper plates into the joists. If possible, locate the hood so that the backs of the ends may have nailing in the wall studs; but if this cannot be arranged, attempt to secure them by nailing into the plaster, and stiffen by nailing diagonals inside. Now lath up the slope, and on these laths nail 1-in. stock, sloping from the corners at the front to the vent jamb. Nail corresponding strips to the plaster at the back of the hood, and lath up the ends, forming the end slopes.

To avoid plastering expense, the whole may be covered with plaster board instead of being lathed.

The theory of the action of the hood is as follows: The circulation of air under the roof, blowing in one roof vent and out another, reduces the air pressure slightly over the hood vent, such a vacuum varying with the speed of motion of the air above. As a result, air from be-

low the hood is drawn up through it. Little material is required for either type of hood. The average home mechanic would have sufficient scraps for the building of the circle hood. For the hopper type, the following stock is required:

1 piece, 2 by 3 in. by 12 ft., pine or fir, S1E.
1 piece, 2 by 3 in. by 16 ft., pine or fir, S1E.
1 piece, 1 by 4 in. by 10 ft., pine or fir, S1E1S.
1 piece, 1 by 6 in. (or 4 in.), pine or fir, S1E1S.
1 sheet of wallboard, 4 by 8 ft.
Cost of materials, about $2.25.
Either hood requires about 8 hours' labor.

Blocking Out Plaster Grounds

Brick walls are supposed to be straight, but the mechanic who follows the bricklayer to put on plaster grounds, finds that they are usually not so straight. Wherever the brick wall is not straight the grounds must either be backed out with a scrub plane or blocked out. It is not necessary to use the scrub plane, however, as the high points can be taken for the wall line, which is shown by the dotted lines of the right-hand figure. The left-hand detail shows a cross section of a ground in place ready for the plasterer. It will be noticed that the ground is nailed to a wooden plug, driven into the perpendicular joints of the brick work. Ordinarily wooden wedges are used for blocking out grounds, but the operation is simplified and will give better results by using wooden blocks. As shown in the left-hand detail, two nails have been driven into the plug. The heads of these nails should project a little beyond the wall line, shown in the right-hand figure by the dotted line. When the ground is nailed over the two blocking-out nails, it can easily be brought to a perfect line by

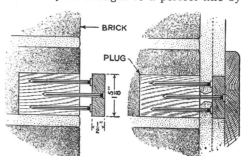

BRICK

PLUG

$\frac{5}{10}$"

$1\frac{1}{2}$"

Proper Method of Blocking Out Plaster Grounds Straight on Irregular Walls

using a block of wood and driving the three nails down at once, until the face of the ground comes to the plaster line. This method has been used repeatedly by the writer and has been found both substantial and labor saving in all cases.—H. H. Siegele, Emporia, Kans.

Greased Drill Holds Borings

When holes are to be drilled in parts, such as transmission covers, manifolds, etc., where it is undesirable that the cuttings should reach the inside, proceed as follows: Drill the hole only part way through, then grease the drill well. The cuttings will cling to the drill and can be lifted out of the hole. The same method is used with the tap for threading the hole. For best results, the drill or tap should be removed frequently, the grease and cuttings wiped off and new grease applied.

Combination Belt Shifter and Guard

Buffing and polishing machines are not, as a rule, provided with belt-shifters, and the operator generally uses a stick, or even his hands, to transfer the belt from the fixed to the loose pulley. Most belt-shifting devices are useless on these machines, because they are in the way and often obstruct the operator when working on long or awkwardly shaped jobs, but nevertheless the methods of moving a belt just mentioned are dangerous and have resulted in many accidents. However, it is an easy matter to rig up a belt shifter that will also form an effectual guard for protecting the worker's elbows, when standing sideways. Fasten a length of strap iron in the manner

SLIDE STRAP

GUARD

shown, to the oil cups on the machine. Then cut and bend the shifter guard as shown, drilling two holes to pass it over the slide strap, and afterward bend these lugs over to hold it square. The belt is moved by gripping the sides of the shifter and sliding it.—Harry Moore, Montreal, Canada.

Storing Ensilage

Silos on the farm sometimes are so packed with ensilage that it is almost impossible to use any other door than that at the top. One farmer recently devised a method of getting out ensilage with ease. A ladder was used to reach the top door of the silo; a bracket and pulley were attached over the door, and a box was used to bring the ensilage down by means of a rope, as shown. As the farmer was alone to do the work, the box was made self-emptying, as follows: A screweye was set into the bottom of the box and a small

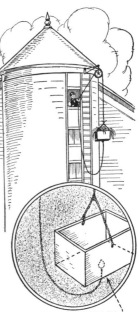

ROPE TO SCREWEYE IN BOTTOM OF BOX

rope run from it to the top of the silo. As soon as the box reached the ground, it was emptied by pulling this rope. It is possible, of course, to use the same rope for hoisting, lowering and emptying the box by making it twice as long as the silo is high. This is suggested in the drawing.—Charles Latour, Jr., Plattsburg, N. Y.

Oil Pads in Shock Absorbers

Certain shock absorbers on Fords have a recess in the casting or forging clamped to the spring of the car. This recess is occupied by the ends of the special bolts that compress the spring for removal. It has been found good practice to fill this recess, through the hole in the top, with waste well soaked with oil. The vibration of the car when running forces some of the oil out on the spring.—E. T. Gunderson, Jr., Humboldt, Iowa.

¶The rope-and-pulley method of drawing water from a well may be made much easier by using a bucket at each end of the rope; the empty bucket, on its way down, serves as a partial counterweight, to the full bucket.

Homemade Duster for Boll Weevil

For dusting cotton-boll weevils with poison, the homemade device shown in the drawing is resorted to in many parts

Improved Method of Dusting Cotton Fields with Poison for the Boll Weevil

of the south. Tied to the ends of a light but rigid frame, two cloth bags carry the poison powder. Each bag incloses an endpiece, which gently taps the bags as the duster is carried along by the worker. This tapping action makes possible a fine, even distribution of the powder by a slight wrist movement, instead of a more uneven dusting, which would result by shaking the bags up and down. It is claimed that an acre of young cotton can be dusted with this device in about thirty minutes. —Allen P. Child, Kansas City, Mo.

Drafting-Room Kinks

A double-pointed pencil, for drawing the guide lines used in regulating the height of lettering, can be made as follows: Take two pencils and make them flat, which can be done by filing or by holding them against a sander. Bind them together with a couple of rubber bands. As is evident, this method of binding readily allows the pencils to be taken apart for sharpening. To make a double ruling pen for drawing border lines, representations of railroad tracks, etc., obtain a piece of ¼-in. brass rod and thread it into a

crosspiece that has two tapped holes in it to take the pens. Most drawing pens are screwed into their holders and can be unscrewed and attached to the improvised handle. When the double pen is used, border lines always are sure to be of equal spacing.

A square can be held in close contact with the drawing board by screwing a small block of lead or brass to the underside of the top wing of the T-square. If you have trouble in keeping lines parallel, investigate the condition of the edge of the board against which the T-square is held. Quite likely you will find it uneven. To remedy this attach a strip of 1 by ⅛-in. cold-rolled steel to the board.

An Improvised Swallow-Tail Bevel

The swallow-tail bevel shown in the drawing is a good tool with which to set lathe rests to turn tapers. It consists of a cast-iron head, forked on one end and T-headed on the other, and slotted to take a pivoted blade as shown. The plane of the slot in which the blade works is an accurate bisector of the angle at the forked end, and the width of the forked end is the same as that of the T-headed end. The tool is used as illustrated, the forked end serving as a V-block. To transfer the angle to the lathe rest, a parallel is laid across the bed of the lathe and the bevel placed thereon, the head resting against the faceplate. The compound

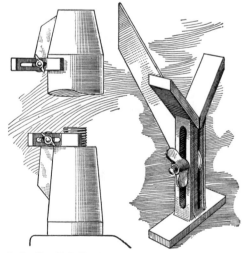

A Swallow-Tail Bevel Used to Set Lathe Rests for Turning Tapers

rest is then adjusted to the angle indicated by the blade.—Herbert A. Freeman, Willimantic, Conn.

Shop Notes

Sharpening Your Own Saws

By EDWIN M. LOVE

THE teeth of a saw are miniature chisels, designed either with square points to cut parallel to the grain of the wood, as in a ripsaw, or with beveled teeth to shear across the fibers, as in a crosscut saw. The large teeth of a coarse saw, receiving greater individual pressure, bite deeper than the smaller points of a fine saw, generally cutting faster and, incidentally, rougher. However, a coarse saw

cut it, and the more play given the blade. Fatigue and play both make for inaccuracy, to say nothing of lessening production. Do not blame the saw for pinching before knowing whether or not the binding is due to sagging of the board being cut, or closing of the kerf because of internal strains in the material. Rub the blade often with an oil pad, and in ripping, wedge open the kerf behind the saw.

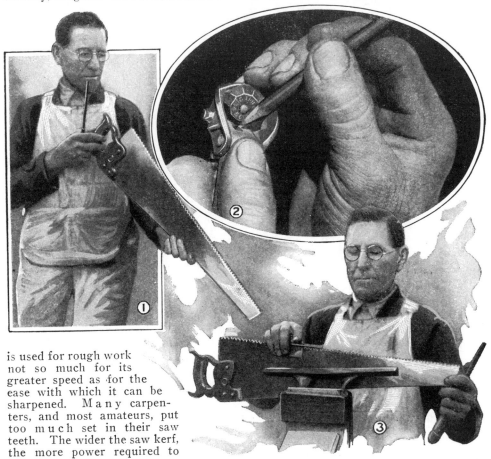

is used for rough work not so much for its greater speed as ·for the ease with which it can be sharpened. Many carpenters, and most amateurs, put too much set in their saw teeth. The wider the saw kerf, the more power required to

Some authorities advise the amateur to practice saw filing on an old saw, presumably one that has already been practiced on and cannot be made any worse. This is poor advice for the man who really

is offset. Do not make the mistake of bending out the beveled side, for then the saw will not cut at all. Hold the set always at the same angle, so as to give equal deflection to the teeth. This is important, since teeth which project more than their neighbors, do most of the cutting and

wants to get skill in filing a saw. It taxes the ability of an expert to straighten up a bungled saw. The best practice is on a saw fresh from the hardware store,

scratch the work, besides making the saw run out of true.

For general filing, the slim taper file is good, though for fine saws the extra-

since it has teeth of even length, pitch and spacing. A new saw is never quite pointed up, but requires a light going over. At any rate, start on a saw that has been well filed, and reasonable progress can be made.

Sight along the teeth (Fig. 1) to see if they are fairly regular in length. They should appear as a straight, or slightly crowned line of "V's." Clamp the saw in a vise, and, using either a regular saw jointer (Fig. 3), or a mill file held flat (Fig. 4), take one or two light cuts full length of the blade. Sight the points again, and if there are any kinks or local curves, joint down the high points. The rule is to file lightly and sight often. When the points are reduced to a smooth line, examine carefully to see that all teeth have been touched. Each should show a tiny triangle of bright metal at the tip.

A saw does not need setting every time it is filed. If it is taper-ground, it will run in dry woods with almost no set. Adjust the anvil of a saw set (Fig. 2), rest the stops on the teeth, and grip each tooth just enough to bend it without crushing (Fig. 5). Only the upper half of the tooth

slim taper is still better. A small file makes a smoother cut than a large one, and having sharper corners, gives a little more depth to the tooth and more sawdust clearance. Six-inch files are the shortest useful length, and they must be wide enough to project considerably above the points of the teeth. Drive the file tang solidly into a handle, to prevent turning, for a correct pitch cannot be maintained throughout the job if the file can twist.

To file a crosscut saw, clamp it solidly with the jaws about ½ in. below the teeth, at the tip of the blade. With the file pointing toward the toe at an angle of about 45° and upward about 20° (Fig. 6), make a light stroke with the pressure against the forward or cutting edge of the first far tooth, using the back of the near tooth as a guide, and cutting the latter as little as possible. A light stroke is essential with a new file, for a heavy cut may chip the corner, spoiling it for further use. Never use a dull file, since it not only cuts slowly, but irregularly as well. A dull corner means a shallow gullet and chattering of the file on the rounded bottom, with almost certain misshaping of the teeth. A good file may sharpen two or three saws; but these tools vary so much in hardness and toughness that it is not unusual to wear out one or more files on one saw.

The teeth and the spaces between them are 60° angles if filed straight across. Filing at an angle, however, makes them less acute. The natural result is that if the filing angle with the length is increased, some cutting on the back of the near tooth is inevitable, while if the angle is decreased, a certain play results that makes variation of pitch from tooth to tooth more likely. If regularity of this angle is kept, the pitch will therefore be more certain.

Up to a certain point, the more nearly the front of the tooth approaches the vertical, the faster the saw cuts, and generally, the rougher. The filer must make a choice between speed and quality. On fine saws the cutting edge of a tooth may be safely pitched at 25° or even 20° with the vertical, while with coarse saws the pitch may be still steeper.

If the saw is not very dull, one or two strokes to each tooth may be enough. File until the bright blunted triangle on the point all but disappears, and then go to the next tooth on that side. When for any purpose the file is removed from the work, keep the grip on the handle unrelaxed, and the correct pitch angle can be more easily duplicated on the next tooth. To repeat, this constancy of filing angle is most important.

Having filed one side, reverse the saw and do the teeth on the other side (Fig. 7). The file still points to the toe of the saw, but the position of the body and arms is quite different from the first. Take care to use the same angle as for the other side, or the teeth will be of different size. File on the cutting edge of the tooth until the bright tip disappears entirely, since there is no danger of cuts being taken from the back. Stop the instant a point is obtained.

Having finished the saw, examine it carefully for underfiled teeth. It is surprising how many dull teeth may be found after filing is supposedly completed. Carefully touch these up.

Most teeth now have clinging to the cutting edges burrs which should be removed by laying the saw flat on a fine oilstone (Fig. 8) and drawing it across, once for each side, or reversing the process by laying the saw on a flat surface and

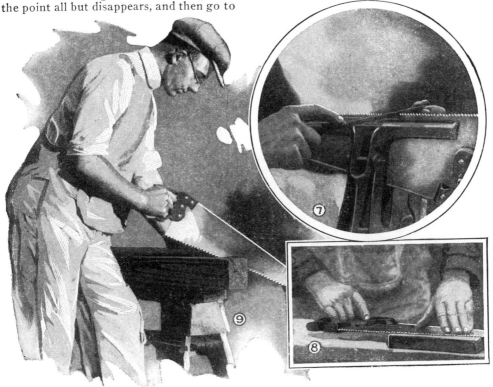

moving the stone over it. Sight down the teeth, and if the filing has been well done, the tips will show a smooth trough, in which a needle can slide full length without falling off. Give a further test by

three years, and himself for several years. A change to the above-described method, however, seemed to bring slightly better results, although it must be admitted the improvement may be imaginary. To the

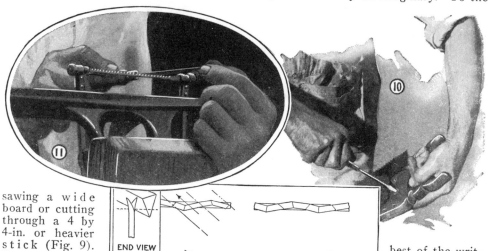

FILING ON FAR TOOTH; NOTE SHORT BACK BEVEL

⑫

FILING ON NEAR TOOTH; NOTE WIDE BACK BEVEL

END VIEW

sawing a wide board or cutting through a 4 by 4-in. or heavier stick (Fig. 9). Once started, the saw should follow the line almost automatically, cutting smoothly and quickly. If the

best of the writer's knowledge, all manufacturers recommend filing on the far tooth, and a reference to the diagram (Fig.

teeth on one side are long, the saw will be deflected toward that side because of the faster removal of waste there. For the same reason, if the teeth on one side are duller than on the other, the saw will "run" toward the sharp side. It is for this reason that it is so important to get absolute uniformity in the teeth.

A ripsaw is jointed and set in the same way as a crosscut, but all the filing is done from one side, taking all teeth in their turn. Use a large enough file, hold it level, and file nearly square across, making the fronts of the teeth vertical, or nearly so. Most authorities advise filing square across; but it will be found an advantage to give a slight bevel by pointing the file a little left or right, as the case may be. This does not injure the ripping qualities, and greatly facilitates cutting through knots.

Because the reader is sure to find a carpenter who files his saws against the cutting edge, rather than with it, a comment about this style of filing is in order. It has one very strong argument in its favor, namely, that no feather edge is turned up. This reason was sufficient to induce the writer's grandfather to use it during his lifetime, his father until within the last

12) illustrates certain differences in the shape of the tooth obtained, which may or may not prove the superiority of far-tooth filing to the other.

Whichever method is used, the filer generally has the point of the file higher than the tang. This establishes a fundamental difference in the resulting teeth. With the far tooth, the gullet slopes down away from the cutting edge, while, in the other case, it slopes up from the cutting edge. With any given number of points per inch, therefore, a longer cutting edge is obtained when filing against the tooth. It might seem that this is an advantage, giving greater sawdust space and a longer shearing cut per tooth, but it must be remembered that, because of setting, the point does nearly all of the cutting, so that the total length is not so important. It will be noticed, moreover, that with the accepted method of filing on the far tooth, the back of the tooth has considerably less bevel than in the other case, the point itself is less acute in the thickness, and the tooth is correspondingly stronger, less likely to break when struck against a nail, and more resistant to wear.

Avoid freak tooth forms. Once in a while a carpenter is found who pitches his cutoff-saw teeth like ripsaw teeth, but gives them the customary bevel. There is nothing to be gained by this. If a great deal of angular cutting is to be done, such as mitering sheathing, or cutting wall braces and floor-joist bridging, this style of tooth is excellent, and it is worth while to keep on hand for such work a saw filed so, but it is a poor tool for general work.

Whenever possible, avoid setting a backsaw, although a small amount of set is almost necessary for a miter-box saw. Do not pitch the tooth more than 25° with the vertical. Well sharpened, the saw should cut so smoothly that, to use a block plane afterward, would roughen the cut.

Compass saws and their variations may be filed as a compromise between rip and cut-off teeth, since they rip as much as crosscut.

Few people know that a coping saw can be filed. As a matter of fact, even a new blade is dull and can be improved by filing. Put it in a coping-saw frame and clamp it in a vise. Then file almost square across, with the file held level, taking each tooth in turn and giving a little bevel according to the set (Fig. 11).

By all means preserve the polish of a saw. Rusty spots mean binding, and the attendant evils of buckling and kinking. If the blade has been exposed to rain, rub it dry immediately, and oil it. Rain water, though considered s o f t, really contains some nitric and carbonic a c i d, discouragingly efficient as a rust producer. Beware of it. When tools are n e a r the seashore, take special precautions to prevent the salt air from corroding t h e m. K e e p saws out of the vicinity of dynamos and other electrical machinery, for once they are magnetized, the filings cling to the t e e t h, making sharpening difficult. Tighten the handle screws occasionally (Fig. 10), since true cutting c a n n o t be done w i t h a slack blade, and once in a while also give the handle a polish with linseed oil on a clean rag, finishing it with a dry one.

Lighting Manholes

Trouble-shooting trucks of a western gas and electric company are provided with a reel, holding a 30-ft. extension cord

Special Six-Volt Lamp on Extension Cord for Lighting Manholes

and a special lamp, which is operated on a 6-volt storage battery. This equipment is used for lighting the interior of manholes that are not fitted for plugging in with the city-lighting system.—Charles W. Geiger, San Francisco, Calif.

Easily Cleaned Feed Box

Feed boxes in horse mangers are usually permanently fastened to prevent their being overturned, and so become catchalls for chaff, dust, corncobs and similar refuse, that is apt to mold sooner or later and endanger the health of the horses. A Wisconsin farmer devised a self-locking hinged box which may be dropped down on the side of the manger, allowing all trash to be thrown out of the feed box. When the box is put back in place again, the latch drops down without any attention and locks the box. The latch is a 1 by 4-in. board, a b o u t 2 ft. long, bolted to the center of the d o o r and suspended like a pendulum a g a i n s t the back of the manger, as shown in the drawing. When necessary to turn it over for c l e a n i n g, the latch is raised to a horizontal position, and the box is swung over.

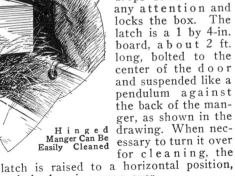

Hinged Manger Can Be Easily Cleaned

Improving the Combined Harvester and Thresher

In western Kansas there is a farmer who does not spend all of his hours in doing manual labor, but still farms broad fields and hires little help. The photo shows one of his methods of solving the hired-help problem. It formerly required two men to operate his combined harvester-thresher,

for the connecting link shown. The bar B is drilled and provided with a setscrew for holding the cutting tool, while the other bar is clamped in the right-hand head and wedged to hold it solidly. A machinists' jack is placed back of the bar B to prevent it from rising on the return stroke of the planer table. The swivel bolts in the head holding the cutting tool are eased up so

Combined Harvester-Thresher Changed So That All Adjusting Levers Are Located on the Rear of the Tractor, Which Permits One Man to Operate Both the Tractor and the Combination Machine

one to drive the tractor and the other to operate the adjusting levers. Removing the front trucks from the combination and mounting the adjusting levers on the rear of the tractor permitted one man to take care of both. Some of the levers had to be changed to make them set forward instead of backward. This gave a short-coupled outfit, much lighter than before the change. With it a worker can cut 160 acres of wheat yielding 6,500 bu., in 5½ days, and with one man to haul the threshed grain from the field, he placed the crop in the bin at about ¾ cent per bushel.

that the cutter can be pulled around in an arc when fed over by the feed box. The tool-holding head is clamped tightly to the cross rail. Set the tool bar to cut the required radius and start the cut, feeding the tool as desired.—R. W. Laing, Kirkhall, Canada.

Radial Cutting on Planer

Radial cuts on the planer are the exception rather than the rule for a machine primarily designed to form plane surfaces. However, by means of a simple arrangement curved work is easily produced. The bars A and B are the only extra parts required for the rig, and a hole is drilled in one end of each

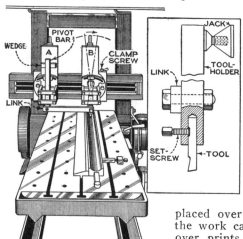

Radial Cuts on Planer Are Easily Made by This Set-Up

Hints for the Draftsman

Rub magnesia carbonate on vellum before beginning a drawing. This will permit complete erasure of all pencil lines and the drawing will remain much cleaner. It can be purchased in the form of a cake. Rub the cake over the vellum, then work it in thoroughly with a cloth. It seems to fill up the pores and harden and improve the surface in every way. The transparency of vellum is a great advantage for it can be placed over other drawings and the work can be traced. Moreover, prints can be made directly from a pencil drawing on it. The disadvantages are the great difficulty of erasing and the tendency to become soiled, and the kink mentioned above eliminates both. To prevent the T-square from soiling the drawing as it slides up and down, put a string over the drawing and fasten the two ends together under the board with a rubber band and a hook made from a paper clip. Two or more strings should be used, on which the T-square slides. The rubber bands keep the strings tight and can be shifted to avoid the triangles.

To prevent your pencils from rolling, cut a piece of eraser, about ½ in. square and ¼ in. thick; make a hole in the middle and slip it over the end of the pencil. The hole can be made by using the tin eraser holder on the end of an ordinary pencil as a drill.

Adjustable Jack for Repair Work

Screw jacks, ratchet jacks and hydraulic jacks are normally used in repair work on heavy machinery, to support parts when disconnected. A simple idea for a jack is shown in the drawing. The base is a pipe flange of large diameter. The body consists of a pipe screwed into the flange, with the upper end beveled. The jack bar is made of cold-rolled steel or any

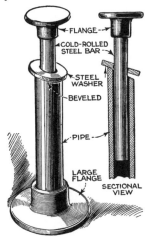

smooth iron bar. The upper end of the bar is fitted with a flange to provide a wide bearing area. The latch is simply a large heavy washer, fitting freely on the bar with several hundredths of an inch clearance. The washer in the canted position grips and locks the bar against downward movement.

Use of Gypsum Weakens Cement

Where gypsum and cement are mixed together and subjected to moisture the gypsum deteriorates or "rots," and the cement will be weakened considerably. Gypsum plaster on a cement wall, which becomes damp or wet, will also rot within a short time. Therefore, gypsum should never be used in cement.—L. E. Gulker, Rainier, Oreg.

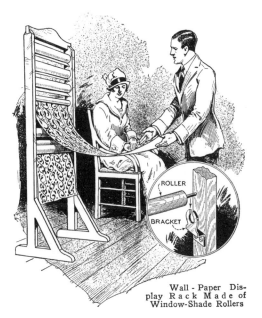

Wall - Paper Display Rack Made of Window-Shade Rollers

Display Rack for Wall Paper

A good display rack for wall paper can be made to hold a number of rolls by using common window-shade rollers, cut to the desired length and fixed in a frame with the regular brackets, as shown, so that the pattern will be uppermost when the paper is pulled out.—L. E. Brundage, Norwood, Colo.

Hanging Windows

Hanging windows so that they can be quickly opened and closed, can be done as shown in the drawing without the use of boxing. Light iron channels, placed along each side of the opening, provide grooves in which pins fitted into the ends of the lower sash slide. The upper sash is hinged to the top of the window casing and the bottom sash is hinged to the upper one in the manner indicated. Upward movement of the lower sash raises the upper one, and when com-

pletely opened, both sash will extend at nearly right angles to the opening. Counterbalancing should be provided or the window operated by rope and pulley.—A. C. Cole, Chicago, Ill.

Gang Slotting Fillister-Head Screws

We had a large number of fillister-head screws to slot and had been putting them one by one in a vise to do it, but found this method too slow. The work

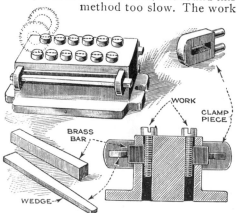

Fixture Which Makes It Possible to Slot Twelve Fillister-Head Screws at Once

was accomplished much more quickly in a milling machine, the table of which was operated by means of a hand lever. We made a cast-iron block, drilled 12 holes in it, and slotted a space for a brass bar on either side to hold the screws securely when tightened by means of a wedge, which was slipped into slotted endpieces as shown. With this fixture we were able to slot twelve screws just as quickly as one could be slotted in the vise. The holes for the screws were made slightly oversize to provide clearance.—J. H. Moore, Montreal, Canada.

Difficult Fitting Made Easy

One of the most difficult jobs in carpentry is scribing both ends of a board to fit it between two irregular surfaces. The upper detail of the illustration shows a

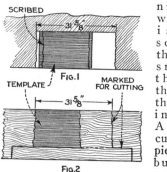

niche into which a stool is to be scribed so that it will fit snugly on three sides, the back in this case being straight. A template is cut out of a piece of stiff building paper and is placed at the right of the opening and scribed, which is indicated by the irregu-

lar line at the right. The template is then shifted to the left position and scribed, which is indicated by the irregular line shown to the left. The distance of the back of the niche must be transferred to the uncut stool, giving allowance at each end for the lugs. Place the template in such a position that the lines can be marked accurately. If the back is also irregular, a second template is made, on which the back line is scribed, and then transferred to the uncut stool. In such a case the back must be marked first.

Starting the Knurling Tool

From personal observation I have learned that many mechanics have great difficulty in getting a knurling tool properly started. The common straight knurled surface is, of course, very easily made, as the knurling tool has only one roller, but the trouble is when the novice attempts to use the double knurling tool, which has one roller milled with a right-hand spiral and the other with a left-hand spiral. The two rollers are generally set one above the other, and when properly applied to a job, make a knurled surface with a diamond pattern. The rollers must be in exact relation to each other when they revolve against the work, otherwise a surface is made that much resembles the teeth design of a crosscut file. In order to get the rollers properly timed with each other, I found it best not to apply the full width of the roller to the work in the beginning. After the knurling tool has been properly set at right angles with the job, it should be fed against the end so that only one half of the roller surface comes in contact with the work, as is shown in Fig. 1. By applying good pressure using the cross-feed screw, the rollers will time themselves properly and a true diamond-shape knurl will be formed by letting the tool feed along the work.— Chas. Homewood, Ontario, Calif.

¶Don't drive a key into place unless you have some means of getting it out again.

A Hammered-Copper Letter Box

The common purchased letter box is not a very attractive thing, yet, without paying a considerable sum, the home owner is usually unable to obtain anything

A Homemade Hammered-Copper Letter Box That Can Be Made into an Attractive and Profitable Side Line by the Neighborhood Mechanic

better-looking from the stores. The usual way out of the difficulty is to paint the box the same color as the trim of the house, and thus make it as inconspicuous as possible, but even this does not entirely satisfy the owner. The letter box shown in the accompanying illustration is not only pleasing in design but simple enough for the handy man to make himself. If a few of the boxes are made up as samples, a neighborhood mechanic should have little difficulty in disposing of them to the owners in his vicinity, and there is good opportunity to build up a side line that should prove remunerative.

The house number may be made a part of the box in the manner suggested in the drawing. If the number is one of four figures, these, of course, must be made smaller, and the number arranged on the box front diagonally. The rivets used in the assembly of the box may be omitted, if desired, and the entire box soldered, but the rivet heads add greatly to the "spirit" and attractiveness of the design, and it is recommended that the riveted construction be used. Sheet copper, 1/16 in. thick, is the material used.

This can often be obtained from an old tank, since the surface of the copper plates is to be hammered in any event, and small dents in the sheet from which it is made will not be any drawback. The amateur will have little difficulty in cutting the soft sheet to the outlines given with the shears. A sharp chisel should be used to cut out the interior parts of the design, supporting the copper sheets on a metal block. It is not necessary that the edges be exactly even, although they should not be left ragged. After the sheets are cut, place them on a piece of hardwood, and go all over the surface lightly with the ball-peen end of a machinists' hammer, in order to make the indentations on the surface that give the box its antique look. Do not try to have all the hammer marks exactly alike in depth, but do not vary them too much. The hinges and hasp should be of copper rather heavier than that of the body, and copper rod, 1/8 in. in diameter, used for the hinge pins. Fasten the box to the house with large copper ship nails, if these can readily be obtained. If not, use round-head brass screws, and slightly mar the heads, after driving the screws home, with the hammer.—G. A. Luers, Washington, District of Columbia.

¶Leave the oven of your gas stove slightly open for a few minutes after the burners are lighted, to prevent rust.

Wooden Flues Help Ventilation

To help the ventilation of a town hall in a small Oklahoma town, a number of wooden ventilators of the kind shown in the photo were made for the windows on the south side of the building. The hood extends down about 6 in. below the top of the window, and is built up of 1 by 6-in. boards to the width of the window, converging to a square flue, 6 in. square and about 5 ft. high. As the bottom of the hood is closed all the air that goes up the flue must come out of the hall, and when the upper sash is opened the warm air is quickly drawn out. It is claimed that air was drawn out at least three times as fast with these flues when installed as when the windows simply were opened at the top.—Dale R. Van Horn, Walton, Nebr.

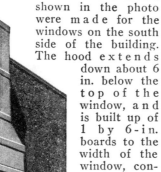

Baling Scrap Sheet Metal

What do you do with your scrap sheet steel? We used to put it in a pile or in a large box and then haul it out back of the plant. But scrap sheet metal handled in this way was of no value to us. We even had to pay to have the pile removed. This work was a miserable job, taking days and resulting in many cuts on the hands. So we built a baler to remedy the trouble. The frame was made of ⅛ by 1 by 1-in. angle iron, inclosed with No. 20-gauge sheet steel. To provide a convenient size of bale, both in weight and dimensions, we made the box 20 by 38 by 18 in. Two recesses along the side allow insertion of two baling wires, which are put in the baler before the scrap. The time saved in the process of baling easily offsets the time taken to cut long narrow strips into lengths that will enter the baler. Some man who is not busy all the time can be appointed to do the baling. We now have a clean floor space around our shears and never have to worry about moving our scrap-steel pile. The dimensions of the baler, of course, can be altered to suit plant conditions and equipment.—W. E. Gunnerson, Milton, Wis.

Drive Fit on Pins

When a pin is to be secured in a chuck wrench, or a dowel is to be made a drive fit, many mechanics flatten it slightly with a hammer or make a series of prick-punch marks around it. This makes a poor job that usually does not last long. It is much better to lay the pin in a V-block and make from one to three cold-chisel marks around it parallel to the axis. The ridges thus made keep their holding power, no matter how deep the pin may be driven and also prevent it from turning. The best method of all is to knurl the pin, but often a lathe is not available, and the above method is then the next best.—John A. Blaker, West Auburn, Mass.

Removing Cable Lugs from Car Battery

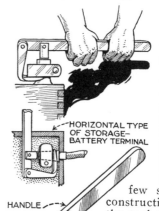

HORIZONTAL TYPE OF STORAGE—BATTERY TERMINAL

HANDLE

With only a pair of pliers and a wrench it often takes 15 or 20 minutes to remove a storage battery from a car, but with the aid of the handy tool illustrated, it takes only a few seconds. The construction and use of the tool are clearly indicated. It consists of three pieces, a handle, a plunger and a fork, the last two being pivoted on the handle. In use the fork is placed under the lug of the cable and the plunger on the battery terminal. Pressure on the handle then pulls the lug off the terminal. This is a simple tool, and the time spent in making it will be repaid many times by the ease and rapidity with which it does the work.

❡Draftsmen should remember that a little note of explanation in the corner of a drawing often helps the worker.

A Corner Workshop for Apartments

By A. C. LESCARBOURA

THE handy man who is bent on pursuing his hobby in the narrow confines of a small apartment must resort to no end of makeshifts. First of all, he must find space enough to do his work, and, in the modern birdcage kitchen, that may be no simple problem. His work completed, he must find storage space for his equipment, and that also gives the amateur mechanic furiously to think. The solution is generally in the form of an improvisation, more or less successful, generally less, although many projects of the handy man have been worked out successfully on the kitchen sink, as the radio fan knows.

The "board workshop" shown in the accompanying illustrations will help solve the problem for those who have not as yet

arrived at any satisfactory answer. The foundation of this is a plain board, about 2 by 8 in., although the size of the board can be suited to individual preference. This is held down to the kitchen table by means of two clamps, made from flat steel or iron, as shown in the detail drawing. One of the clamps serves only to hold the board to the table; the other, in addition to holding down the board, may be set and

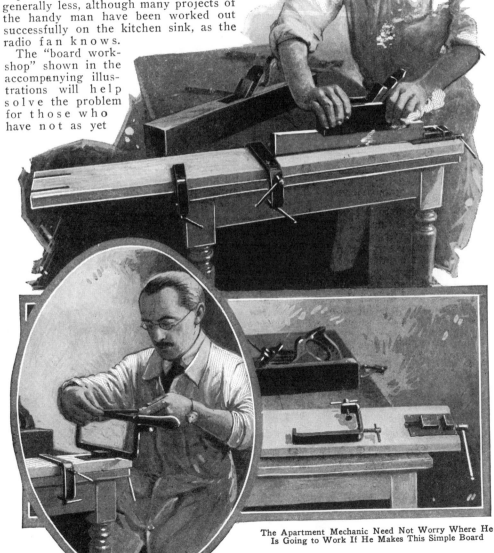

The Apartment Mechanic Need Not Worry Where He Is Going to Work If He Makes This Simple Board

clamped to the latter at any point along its length, and aids in holding boards to be planed or otherwise worked, as shown in the upper photo of the larger illustration. The drawing shows the construction of this clamp clearly enough to make further description unnecessary.

While any kind of vise that the maker desires can be used at the end of the

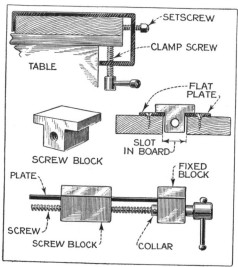

Details of the Movable Clamp for the Board and the Easily Made Vise

board, the one shown is particularly suited to the job, as the rear jaw moves instead of the front one, and it thus becomes a work clamp when used in connection with the movable flat-steel clamp. Thus, when planing a length of wood, or gluing boards together, the vise is closed, the wood placed behind the rear jaw, and the movable clamp slid along the board to the other end of the work, whereupon it is tightened.

Now, by opening the jaws of the vise, the work will be held firmly. The vise is set in a slot cut in the end of the board, and the various parts are not at all hard to make. The jaws may be castings, but the home mechanic will probably find it easier to cut them out of machine steel using the same material for the plates on which the screw block runs. The screw may be one taken from a cheap vise, or one may be made in the local machine shop at small cost.

With this workshop, there is no danger of marring the kitchen table, and the owner can work to his heart's content. It will be found advisable to place small blocks under the points of the clamp screws, below the edge of the table. Quite a lot of good work can be done with this simple outfit.

Repairing Ford Battery Carrier

Ford battery carriers often cause trouble due to loosening of the four rivets, which hold the wide band underneath. This allows the battery and band to swing from side to side with the motion of the car. In some cases the battery will drop so much that the clamps will no longer keep it in place. This will even occur when the fastening bolts are tight and the carrier is well bolted to the frame. A remedy is to remove the battery from the carrier and the carrier from the car, cut off the four rivets with a cold chisel on the outside of the carrier, and drive them out. Then holes are bored with a $\frac{5}{16}$-in. drill for carriage bolts of this size, which are placed with the heads on the inside of the carrier. These holes should be countersunk or squared on the inside of the band to fit the squared part of the bolt. Use $\frac{5}{16}$ by $1\frac{1}{8}$-in. bolts, such as those clamping the flat-iron bands about oval or round Ford gasoline tanks. These are somewhat too long, but are best suited for the purpose, as they have a shorter squared part and a flatter head than ordinary carriage bolts. Lock washers should be used under the nuts. The bolts can be tightened from under the car when necessary.—E. T. Gunderson, Jr., Humboldt, Iowa.

Homemade Hinge or Butt Gauge

An accurate and efficient hinge or butt gauge used for hanging doors can be made as follows: Take a block of hardwood, preferably maple and about 4 in. long, $1\frac{1}{2}$ in. wide and $1\frac{1}{8}$ in. thick. Into the face of the block drive a small screw, file the edge of the head so that it will cut well and set the screw to the distance that the hinge is to go back on the door. The

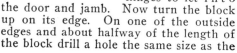

gauge can be adjusted to any depth by simply turning the screw in or out. Now, into the side of the block drive another screw, sharpening it in the same manner and turning the screw in so that the cutting edge is the same distance away from the block that you desire the hinges to let into the door and jamb. Now turn the block up on its edge. On one of the outside edges and about halfway of the length of the block drill a hole the same size as the head of the screw you are going to use for a cutter, so that only about three-fourths of the hole is in the block. Turn the screw into the hole and you will see that you have a cutter made by the head of the screw sticking out past the face of the block. This gives you the gauge that marks the distance that the hinge is to be set into the door jamb from the door stop. You never use this gauge endways as you have to use the regular metal gauges, thus there is no wabble or variation. It is very light and can be easily carried in the pocket. It can be made by anyone in a few minutes and will last indefinitely, as there is nothing to rust except the screws, which can readily be replaced.—C. E. Gardner, Herndon, Va.

Drawing Guide for Window Letterer

A simple and useful device for a window letterer, which promotes accuracy and speed, is a guide rail supported by two rubber suction cups. It is used in place of the ordinary maul, or padded stick, which most letterers hold in the left hand, with one end against the glass and the forepart of the right arm against the stick. The guide shown is about 36 in. long, having a straight edge so that it can be used as a ruler. At either end is fastened an ordinary rubber suction cup such as is used on electric massaging devices. It is provided with a threaded metal inset by which it can be fastened to the end of the stick. This guide can be placed in any desired position on glass or wooden surfaces and will provide a firm support for the hand.—Hoag & Ford, Los Angeles, Calif.

RUBBER SUCTION CUP

¶To keep the mother hen from scratching and wasting chick feed, cover a piece of 1 by 12 by 24-in. board with ½ or 1-in. mesh poultry wire by tacking it to the edge; then nail a strip of lath to the edge to form a shallow box. This will stop the waste of expensive chick feeds.

Air Blower for Curing Hay Independent of Weather

There is always an element of uncertainty in depending on favorable weather conditions when the hay is to be cured.

AIR PIPE FROM BLOWER

PERFORATED TUB

Curing Newly Cut Grass Artificially Gives Good Quality and Uniformity to the Hay

The illustration shows a method of curing it by means of an air blower that is always dependable, and the quality of hay is generally much better and more uniform than if it is left to dry on the ground before stacking. A length of pipe is led from the fan or blower, just underneath the surface or on the ground, to the center of the spot where the stack is to be made. The end of the pipe is fitted with an elbow, the opening turning upward. An ordinary metal washtub is perforated with a number of ½ to 1-in. holes through the sides and bottom and turned over the end of the air pipe as shown. The hay is piled in a medium-size stack over the tube and the blower started. By this means air will be driven through all the hay and a sweet, mellow roughage will result.—L. M. Jordan, Vredenburgh, Ala.

Safety Link in Tow Chain

When plowing with a tractor it is always advisable to use a weak link in the drawbar chain so that it will give when a large stone is struck. It can be made by using a piece of rod iron and

SAFETY LINK

bending it to the shape of an "S," as shown in the illustration.—W. R. Smith, Cloverdale, Can.

Disappearing Air Hose

Whenever an air-hose nozzle is used within a limited radius, a disappearing holder such as that shown in the drawing w i l l automatically

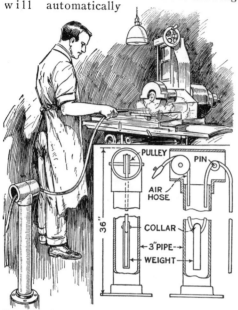

Convenient Holder for Air Hose in Woodworking Plant Disappears When Not in Use

hold the nozzle and hose out of the way when not required. It is often quite dangerous to leave a hose lying around a machine, and, aside from this, it is a nuisance to have to continually move it away or hang it up. To make the holder, a length of 3-in. tube, a tee and floor plate are assembled in some convenient place, preferably against the wall or a post. Before assembly, the tee is drilled through on both sides. On one side a pin is driven in and the hose wrapped around it one turn. The other side has a loose pin, headed over at each end to k e e p it in place, and carrying a pulley made from a shaft collar w i t h a washer on each side. A weight is made out of a piece of flat iron doubled o v e r a n d drilled t h r o u g h at the open end for a pin carrying another shaft collar, w h i c h acts as a roller. The o p e r a t i o n of the holder is o b v i o u s. When the hose is re-

quired the nozzle is pulled out, causing the weight to rise. When the nozzle is released the exposed hose disappears inside of the tube leaving the nozzle only outside. This is made certain without injury to the parts by arranging that the weight strikes the floor just before the nozzle reaches the tee. Care should be taken not to use a weight that is unnecessarily heavy but one that counterbalances.—Harry Moore, Montreal, Can.

Polishing Radius of Screw-Machine Form Tools

To polish a radius in a form tool, get it free from scratches and keep the radius true has always been one of my most difficult jobs. I now do it to perfection by turning a piece of brass to the proper diameter and using it for a lap. After the radius has been cut in with a tool and filed fairly smooth, the tool is run slowly in the lathe, while the lap, driven rapidly in an electric drill chuck, is held in the groove to be polished. The lap should be fed generously with valve-grinding compound, grade D. Grade A is used for finishing. It will be necessary to use several laps as they wear down rapidly. As there are two rotary motions at the same time, a radius is generated to perfection, which is impossible by any other method.—John A. Blaker, West Auburn, Mass.

Cleaning Sewers

Sewers, which are not completely plugged can be cleaned as shown in the accompanying drawing. A wooden ball, slightly smaller in diameter than the inside of the pipe is placed in the sewer at the first manhole above the section to be cleaned. The manhole is filled with water and the pressure from this head of water pushes the ball downstream through the sewer, the small quantity of water which crowds between t h e edges of the ball and the sewer, at high velocity, washing the deposits downstream a h e a d of the ball. The section of sewer r u n ning upstream from the manhole should be plugged temporarily to reduce the amount of water n e e d e d. — Ivan E. Houk, Denver, Colo.

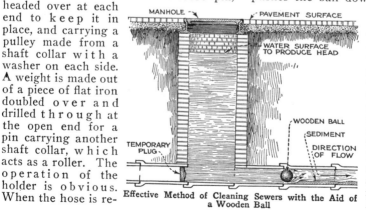

Effective Method of Cleaning Sewers with the Aid of a Wooden Ball

Sun Bath for Milk Pails

After a milk pail has been emptied and washed, there still remains a thin film of milk on the inside, and this turns into lactic acid, which hastens the souring of milk put in the pail. The film is very thin and the ultraviolet rays of sunlight, says Prof. Gilbert L. Houser, of the university of Iowa, are deadly to the microscopic bodies which produce lactic acid. So, exposing the inside of the pails to the sunlight will enable one to keep milk sweet for several hours longer than if this precaution were not taken.

Drying the Fish Line

Winding a fish line on the reel when wet and storing it away for any length of time is bound to injure it more or less as the strands, whether silk or cotton, will eventually decay from the presence of moisture. A practical little device which overcomes this difficulty is shown in the accompanying illustration. A strip of metal is cut and bent in the manner indicated to clamp around the pole just in front of the reel. Within the jaws of the clamp a folded strip of felt is placed in such a position that a setscrew passing through the clamp also penetrates and holds the felt. In use the clamp is turned to the upper side of the pole and the line is placed within the jaws. By turning the reel, the line is drawn through the felt, which removes the water. The clamp may be turned downward to be out of the way when casting is being done.—G. E. Hendrickson, Argyle, Wisconsin.

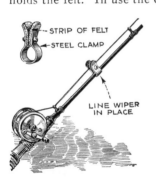

STRIP OF FELT
STEEL CLAMP
LINE WIPER IN PLACE

Pouring Lubricant into Grease Cups

In a Washington auto-service station, specializing in oiling and greasing cars, an unusually handy kink for filling the many grease cups and the grease gun, is in use. The workmen keep the grease can on the side of a small stove where the grease is heated to a fluid. It is then an easy matter to pour this into the cups and into the grease gun.

Cutting Wallboard

Cutting wallboard with a hacksaw is a tedious and time-consuming task, and valuable material is not seldom spoiled by tearing

LENGTH OF KNIFE STEEL BOLTED BETWEEN TWO LENGTHS OF ANGLE IRON

Easy Method of Cutting Heavy Wallboard with Floor Knife

or breaking it. To avoid this, a Wisconsin contractor devised the simple floor knife shown in the drawing, which cuts quickly and always with a clean straight edge. A 4½-ft. length of knife steel, about 2 in. wide, was sharpened and bolted between two equal lengths of angle iron, as shown, the knife-edge protruding about ¾ in. This device was placed upon the floor, and the wallboard cut along the desired line by placing it on the knife and pounding with a rubber-covered mallet.

Improvised Soft Hammer

If a mechanic has no soft hammer, the following suggestion for making his own will be found useful. Cut out a round piece of sheet copper or lead, and cut in four wings to the shape indicated in the illustration. As the metal is soft and pliable it can readily be bent over the head and shank of the hammer. The four projecting legs are then fastened around the neck by means of a piece of wire twisted together securely.—M. J. Quoits, Philadelphia, Pa.

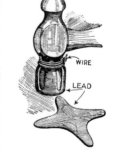

WIRE
LEAD

A Warming Pan for Your Dark Room

By RICHARD C. TARR

AN efficient and economical warming pan may be easily made from a common deep roasting pan, the total cost of which is about $1.60. The materials needed are as follows: One black-iron roasting pan (the one pictured measures 9½ by 14 in. inside, and 4 in. deep); one snap switch; one lamp socket, plain wall-type, keyless; one 100-watt lamp, nitrogen or gas-filled (may be smaller if less heat is desired); one attachment plug; 6 to 12 ft. of sadiron double lampcord (preferable to twisted cord, even though its cost is a trifle more, as it is covered with asbestos, and resists heat); two brass bolts, ⅛ by 1 in. for attaching switch to pan; screws and small nails for attaching board to pan and fastening lamp base to board; two or three rubber-tube insulators, or grommets, with nuts for same.

Bore or punch four 3/16-in. holes in one end of the pan for switch, as shown. Two are

for the bolts that fasten the switch to the pan, and the others for the wires. Bolt the switch in place, and make a hole in the opposite end of the pan, large enough to permit a hard-rubber insulator to be fastened, through which to insert the cord. Select a short piece of pine wood, ⅞ by 3½ in., for the lamp base, and saw to fit the pan, as shown. Bore two ¼-in. holes through the center, about 2½ in. apart. Screw the lamp socket between these holes, gauging the proper location, so that it will be about ¼ in. from the pan bottom and clear of a rule placed across the top. Then mark the outline of the socket base on the board, remove the lamp and screw the socket into place. When finished, the lamp should clear the pan itself and also the material upon which it rests. The socket should be about midway between the holes in the board, to permit the ends of the lampcord to pass through and be attached to the terminals of the socket. The wiring is simple. One of the cord wires is led to one side of the switch, the other to one side of the lamp

socket. The free terminals of the switch and socket are then connected to each other. As the neater arrangement of introducing the cord is through the back of the pan, a ⅜-in. hole is made through the board, so as to hold the cord to one side and prevent it from coming in contact with the lamp. Fasten the board to the pan with screws or nails to maintain the position shown. To the other end of the cord the plug is attached. The lamp, to prevent breakage, should not be screwed into the socket, except to gauge the

Views of Top and Underside of Simple Warming Pan, with Sketch of Connections

SWITCH
LIGHT

proper location on the board, until the job is finished.

Should more heat be desired than will generate from a single lamp, another socket and lamp may be readily added. In operation, the pan rests upside down on a sheet of asbestos or corrugated strawboard (cut from an old carton). The air cells in the last-named material prevent the greater part of the heat from blistering or scorching the table upon which it may rest, although two thicknesses should be used over a highly finished or varnished surface. If not sprung in the making, the pan will be light-tight, or nearly so, if for use during development of plates or printing in the photo laboratory. All light may be prevented from escaping if the pan is set on a couple of layers of weather-strip felt, glued to the strawboard, as shown.

The heat produced is steady and penetrating. A 100-watt nitrogen lamp will give a surface heat of 150° F. and more, without trouble. This amount, used intermittently, will keep a pan of developer "up to snuff" in a cool room, or maintain a good heat in a pan of toning solution.

A special print, needed in a hurry, can be dried quickly on a ferrotype tin, with the use of the pan. If not needed in the laboratory for heating purposes, it makes a pretty fair floodlight for taking photos at night, and the writer has used it as such. Also, it has uses in the kitchen.

Handy Straw or Litter Carrier

To carry straw or litter to the poultry house or stable, or wherever it is to be used, cannot be done without scattering some of it along the way unless you have a carrier of some kind. A carrier can be made at little or no cost. Get three 100-lb. bags, such as poultry and chick feed is shipped in. These usually are made of burlap or other heavy cloth, but, if not available, old grain bags will do. Rip the seams apart and sew the edges together to form a large sheet about 6 or 7 ft. square. Hem the edges so that they will not tear or get fringy. At each corner, on both sides, stitch a triangular piece of tough cloth, such as canvas, and also an old harness ring. Get a piece of ⅜-in. rope, 7 ft. long, and tie one end to one of the harness rings. Spread the sheet out, put on as much straw as you can easily carry, pass the rope through the remaining three rings and pull up until the corners come together. You can then carry three or four times as much straw as you could with a basket or by the armful and without spilling it.

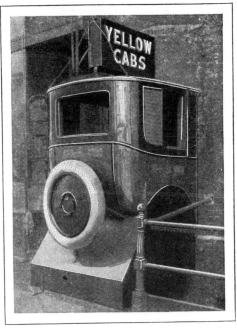

How Rear Part of Old Cab Is Used for Stand

Novel Cab Stands

Instead of disposing of their old car bodies, the Omaha Yellow Cab Co. use them as stations. Only the rear half of the body is used. It is repainted and attached to the wall of a building as shown in the photo. A desk and telephone are installed, and the rear seat gives the operator plenty of room and comfort. These cab stands are unusually attractive and with an electric sign above them can readily be located.—John T. Bartlett, Boulder, Colorado.

Boiler-Front Polish

Application to boilers is the hardest test that paint can be put to, as some parts of the steel and cast iron are only warm and other parts very hot, and most paints will blister and peel off in patches after the boiler has been used for a short time. A boiler should be out of service when it is being painted. For a number of years one plant has used graphite plumbago mixed with water to the consistency of paint, applying it with a brush. After it is dry it is polished with waste or a cloth. Very little rubbing is required and a smooth finish of a blue color will be imparted. This finish remains indefinitely and all that it requires is a dusting. Before the graphite plumbago is applied all the old paint must be scraped off.

Handy Carrier, Made of Canvas, Prevents Scattering Straw

HANDLE-- --HOLES-- ---SETSCREW

Operating Two Drill-Press Spindles Simultaneously Speeds Up Production

Operating Two Drill Spindles at Once

In many instances the output of a multiple-spindle drill press can be doubled by the simple expedient of coupling up two spindles so that they can be operated as one. The drawing shows the coupling bar and handle used in one shop for this purpose. The device consists of a straight bar drilled at each end to go over the spindle handles, tapped for screws to tighten it in place, and drilled in the center for a drive-fit handle. It will be found that the length of movement on most machines will allow of holes about ¾ in. deep. Thus, short through holes can be best drilled in this way, and the set-up will, of course, vary according to the job. Two vises clamped on the table are handy for many pieces, in other cases parallels will keep the work from turning and make for quicker production.

Beauty Clay Aids Babbitting

When bearings are to be babbitted it will be found advantageous to preheat the babbitting mandrel and also the shell to be babbitted from 100 to 250° F. However, a homogeneous bearing is not always obtained in this way. Make a mixture of ladies' beauty clay and water to the consistency of medium lubricating oil, and paint the mandrel with this after it has been heated. This will make a coating about .003 to .004 in. thick, which will draw the moisture from the metal, insuring a solid bearing.

Bracing Fence Corners

Fences can often be kept from sagging by properly bracing the corner posts. A good method of doing this is shown in the drawing. Set the corner post about 3 ft. in the ground and the next post to the same depth and about 8 or 10 ft. from the corner. Wedge a length of 2 by 4-in. wood between these posts, about 6 in. from the top. A heavy rock is to be placed in the position shown, a hole being dug for this purpose. The hole should be about 2 or 3 ft. deep and some solid earth should be left between it and the post. Now take heavy smooth wire or barb wire, loop and twist it securely around the rock so that it cannot be pulled off readily, then drop the rock into the hole, tamping the ground over and around it firmly. Cut a narrow trench in the ground between the rock and the corner post for the brace wire to rest in. The wire should be brought around the second post about 6 in. below the top. Draw the wire tight and staple it well to the second post. After this is done twist the brace wire between the two posts with a pair of pliers or a piece of steel bar; then stretch the horizontal wires. There will

Method of Bracing Corner Posts of Fences to Prevent Sagging

be no appreciable strain on either post as most of the strain is taken by the rock. I placed corner posts in this manner in loose sandy soil 10 years ago, and they are still standing just as straight as they did at first.—Wm. Bathlot, Taos, New Mex.

❡Never leave a machine after using it without cleaning it thoroughly.

You Can Make This Floor Sander

By EDWARD SHAW

MOST modern homes have either hardwood floors or parquet floors in some part of the house. If it becomes necessary at any time to refinish these, a big problem presents itself. To sand the floors by hand would involve a great deal of work and to make use of any of the acid cleaners is not entirely satisfactory. A small rotary sander, capable of doing a good job, can be easily and cheaply constructed by the man handy with tools. The material required, exclusive of the motor, should not cost more than three dollars. A hardware store, or the neighborhood repair shop, would find a machine of this type a source of considerable profit, either if rented out to home owners, or used by one of its own men to refinish floors in local residences.

The perspective drawing and photograph show the completed outfit. In the second drawing is given a general assembly of the outfit showing the driving

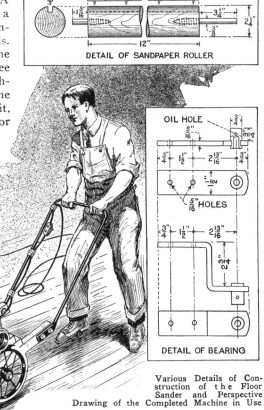

DETAIL OF SANDPAPER ROLLER

METHOD OF MOUNTING WHEELS

OIL HOLE

DETAIL OF BEARING

Various Details of Construction of the Floor Sander and Perspective Drawing of the Completed Machine in Use

motor mounted in place, power supply cord, etc. A ¼-h.p., 1,750-r.p.m. motor is used and it is advisable to use one of the

109

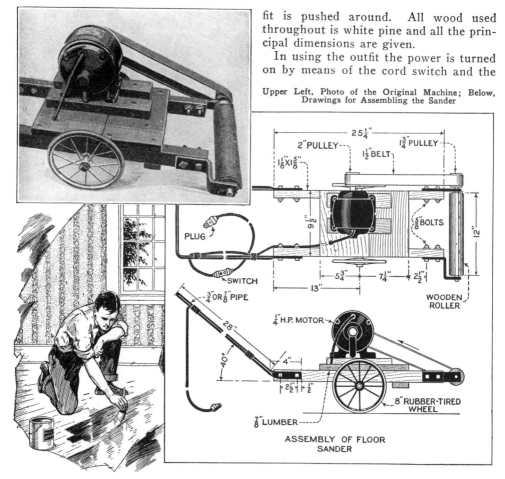

fit is pushed around. All wood used throughout is white pine and all the principal dimensions are given.

In using the outfit the power is turned on by means of the cord switch and the

Upper Left, Photo of the Original Machine; Below, Drawings for Assembling the Sander

inclosed type, or else it will be necessary to cover it up while in use in order to keep out the dust. The abrasive used is coarse No. 00 Aloxite cloth, which, at the speed of the roller, cuts well and does not easily clog. For the roller, a rolling pin was used into each end of which had been fastened lag screws, as indicated in the detail. The brackets which support the wooden rollers are provided with bronze bearings, in which the roller is free to turn. One of the brackets is offset to enable the machine to come in close to the wall when in operation. It is very important to use but a very little oil in these bearings so as not to take a chance on having it get into the floor.

These details are all shown in the drawings, as well as the means used for mounting the shaft that carries the two 8-in. rubber-tired wheels upon which the out-

handle is lifted slightly until the roller begins to cut. In going across the floor it is well not to attempt to take too large a cut. Take a medium depth cut and travel slowly over the entire floor in some uniform fashion, going over it a second time if the floor is in bad shape. It is best to watch the Aloxite cloth and if it should become clogged with the old shellac or varnish taken off the floor, it should be replaced by a new piece.

After sanding the floor, several coats of varnish or shellac and wax can be applied.

Making Phone Receiver Comfortable

The soft sponge-rubber caps used on radio headphones can be applied to advantage also to the ordinary desk-phone receiver. The cap is slipped over the receiver end, which it will grip even more tightly than it will the average radio headphone. If provided with such a rubber ear cap, an ordinary phone is much more comfortable. In addition, disturbing noises and sounds are eliminated, because the cap fits the ear much better than the hard-rubber end. Phones used in the open air, for instance, on construction work, are very uncomfortable in cold weather, and the caps will help here, because the soft rubber does not feel so cold as the hard variety.

Door Construction

Mechanical tests of doors by the forest products laboratory have shown that, if put together by the through mortise-and-tenon method, the doors will have greater stiffness and resistance to sagging than either the dowel-joined doors or the type called "blind-mortised and tenoned." The last-mentioned, in which the tenons of the horizontal members, or rails, do not go clear through the vertical stiles, showed the lowest strength, but were somewhat superior to the doweled doors in stiffness. On being subjected to a damp atmosphere the blind-mortised and tenoned doors swelled the most, and in dry air showed the largest opening of joints. The doweled doors were the least affected by change of atmospheric conditions.

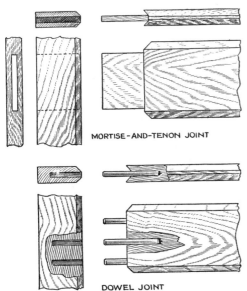

MORTISE-AND-TENON JOINT

DOWEL JOINT

Doors with Mortise-and-Tenon Joints Are Stiffer But Swell More Than Those with Dowel Joints

Extension Oilcan Holder

To oil nearly inaccessible places in machinery the extension oilcan holder shown

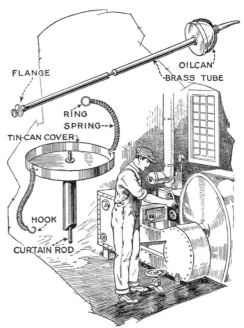

Extension Holder for Oilcan Permits Oiling Otherwise Inaccessible Places

in the illustration will be found useful. It consists of a heavy tin-can cover into which the base of the oilcan fits. A hole, slightly larger than the diameter of a metal curtain rod, is drilled in the exact center and two small holes in the rim of the cover as shown. A suitable length of ½-in. brass tubing is soldered over the center hole, at right angles to the face of the cover and a small flange to the opposite end of the tube. Two stiff coil springs, fastened to the cover and slipped over the spout, hold the oilcan in position securely. A curtain rod is slipped inside of the tube and a washer soldered to the end to act as a push button. In use the can is guided with one hand while the button is pushed with the other.

¶When winding springs on the lathe, it is a good kink to turn the spindle backward a few times in order to relieve the strain of the spring. This eliminates the danger of injuring the hands as the spring will not fly back when the wire is cut off.

Portable Desk for Lumber Yard

Wholesale or retail lumber dealers who are compelled to carry a tally book about the yards when selling lumber from the

Shelf Wedged between Boards of Lumber Pile Serves as Writing Desk

various piles, or when taking inventory of stock, are often inconvenienced by the inability to find a suitable book rest. A Wisconsin lumberman overcame this difficulty in the following way: A board upon which the tally book is fastened is provided with two flat-iron strips, which project about 6 or 8 in. beyond the end of the board. These are bent at a slight angle and, when inserted between the boards of a lumber pile, will hold the book at the height and slope desired for writing.

Welding Closed Containers

Metal tanks, barrels and drums are widely used to transport and store liquid products. When made by welding, such containers are permanently tight, but those made by other methods frequently develop leaks which the operator is called on to repair. Whatever work has to be done, the welder should never apply the welding or cutting torch to such containers until he is positive that they are thoroughly clean and properly vented. Make it a rule to clean every container regardless of what you think was in it. Thorough steaming of the container will effectively remove traces of volatile liquids, such as gasoline, and scrubbing it with a strong lye solution will remove all oily materials. Possibly the easiest and safest way to protect the operator is to flush the container thoroughly with water. Then turn it so that the damaged section is uppermost and fill up with water to the defect to be repaired. Welding is then done with the least possible space inside. This precaution applies not only to oxyacetylene welding, but to repairs by any other process as well. Even a blow from a hammer or friction, generating static electricity, may cause a spark that may ignite the gas in the tank. In welding or cutting on any type of closed container, the handhole or other fittings should always be opened before applying the flame.

Canvas-Bottom Concrete Form

Undesirable eddies that wash the cement out of concrete poured under water, even though the mixture is carefully deposited through a tremie, can be prevented by using a form with a canvas bottom. The canvas, while allowing the concrete to settle into all the irregularities of the foundation, prevents water disturbances on the outside of the box from coming under the edges and through the bottom. Such a form can be used to advantage in pouring foundations for bridges, buildings, retaining walls, head gates, and other structures, where available pumping facilities cannot completely remove the water.

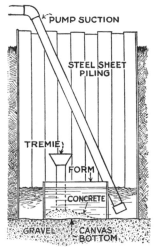

Farmer's Saw Driven by Auto

The farmer who has occasional need of a power-driven saw, grinder or similar apparatus, which requires from one to ten horsepower, can rig up his automobile to let the engine do the

ings at each end and at the center. Braces, G, which are ³⁄₁₆ by 1¼ by 10-in. flat iron, are riveted to the frame and the body part of the jack to hold the latter rigid to the frame. Two hook bolts, F, threaded to a distance of 4 in., connect the standards,

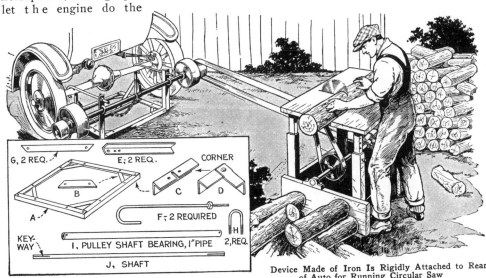

Device Made of Iron Is Rigidly Attached to Rear of Auto for Running Circular Saw

work. A simple device for transmitting the power to a saw is shown in the illustration. It consists of a shaft with two pulleys that come in frictional contact with the rear wheel, and another pulley to take the belt running the saw. The frame is about 3 ft. square and is made of 1½-in. angle iron. It is braced at each corner with a piece of strap iron, as shown at B. Four of these braces are necessary and they are ³⁄₁₆ by 1¼ by 10 in. in dimensions.

The main frame, A, is made by cutting a ¼-in. slot in one side of the angle iron, as shown at C, every 3 ft. of a 12-ft. length. The length is then bent at the slots to form a square, and overlapping parts at the corners drilled with a ⁵⁄₁₆-in. hole for rivets, as shown at D. The standards, E, for the shaft bearings are also made of 1½-in. angle iron; each piece is 14 in. long. A piece of 1½-in. pipe, I, 4 ft. 4 in. long, is attached near the top of the two standards by means of two U-bolts, H. A 1-in. shaft is put through the pipe, centered, and, after wrapping oakum or other material about the shaft to fill the pipe at a position about 4 in. from each end, babbitt is poured into the pipe to form bear-

E, to the axle of the car and hold the pulley wheels against the tires of the auto when the device is in operation. To use it, the car is backed to position over the frame, the latter being staked to the ground or attached to the floor. The car axle is lifted by means of the jacks until the wheels clear the surface. The two hook bolts are then set over the axle and the nuts turned on until sufficient pressure is given the two pulley wheels against the tires. A smaller pulley may be added to the end of the shaft for slower-speed machinery, and thus two or more machines can be driven at the same time. A chain connects the pipe supporting the shaft with the frame of the device, preventing the former from falling back beyond a determined distance. To move the device from place to place it may be inverted so that the wheels will roll on the ground and the frame then hitched to the rear of the car.—W. Mitchell, Rogers, Nebr.

¶A flat piece of aluminum, ⅛ in. thick by 1 in. wide, makes an excellent tool for cleaning files. A piece 5 in. long will be found most suitable.

Self-Closing Cover for Milk Strainer; Detail of Opening Lever in Insert

Two Kinks for the Dairyman

Anyone who has visited a dairy farm during the time when flies are numerous will appreciate the usefulness of the device shown in the photo, which prevents flies from getting into the milk strainer and thus makes for better sanitation. It is simply a cloth cover for the strainer, stretched over a wire frame. It is attached to a wall at such a height that it fits flatly on the strainer when let down, and is operated by a pedal and lever, as indicated in the photo. When a bucket of milk is poured into the strainer, the cover is lifted out of the way by pressing on the pedal, which, when released, allows the cover to drop down by its own weight. To keep an accurate record of the milk given by each cow, it is a good idea to weigh the milk on a spring scale and enter the amount on a chart. The weight of the pail is, of course, deducted.

¶A straight bar magnet greatly facilitates the job of removing valve-spring retaining pins which are hard to grasp with pliers.

Adjustable Reamers as Mandrels

Sometimes the lathe man finds it necessary to turn the outside of a small piece true to a hole already sized and finished. This means that the piece must be held by some method that will keep the hole true. I have found nothing better for this kind of work than the adjustable reamers now so common. They are always accurately centered, and the shape of the movable cutters gives them just the grip to hold the work. With proper care, the reamer is not injured in the least, and the marks left on the inside of the work are hardly noticeable. The reamer should be expanded quite firmly against the walls of the hole in order that no slipping may occur, which would injure the hole by actually reaming it. A little judgment will tell how large a cut can be taken with safety.—S. J. Gee, Montpelier, Idaho.

Speeding Up Concreting

Faced with the problem of carrying on simultaneous concreting operations requiring two different mixes, one to be conveyed by motor dump trucks and the other to be spouted, I worked out an interesting hoisting-tower tripping device, which saves much time, labor and extra equipment. To put into effect a two-mix plan it was thought advisable to use the same hoist tower and to make provision for discharging the bucket at a lower level than that at which it discharged for spouting operations. So, I figured out the arrangement shown in the accompanying illustration. It consists of two guide arms of channel iron, slightly flared at the lower end, which are pivoted to the corner posts of the tower and held, when in operating position, by supporting rods, as shown. The supporting rods

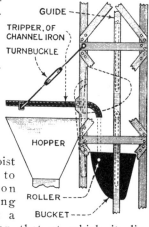

are provided with turnbuckles which permit quick adjustment to engage or to disengage the tripping device. When the bucket is to be discharged at the upper level these rods are disengaged and the tripper arms fall to a perpendicular position, allowing the bucket to pass by and up the tower. For discharging at the lower level the operator simply raises the tripping arms, pulls out the supporting rods, places the holding blocks at the lower ends of the rods in slots cut in the lower sides of the tripping arms to receive them, and twists the turnbuckles a few times to lock the arms. This operation is accomplished in a few seconds. On either side of the bucket is a small roller securely mounted on a pin. As the bucket is raised these rollers enter the flared ends of the trippers and follow along the channels, holding the lip of the bucket down while the bottom is being carried upward to the discharging position.—August Jeffers, Bedford, Ind.

Making Washers

When making several hundred small brass washers from ¼-in. round stock I found it rather troublesome to pick them out of the cuttings, which were collected in the small box I had placed to catch the washers as they were cut off. By fastening a piece of spring wire, about 10 in. long to the toolpost on the lathe, and inserting the other end in the hole drilled in the stock, the washers would slide down the wire as fast as they were cut off. This end of the wire was bent to form a hook to hold it in place, and the wire was placed in front of the tool post and slanted, to allow the washers to slide. The moving of the tool at each cut tends to stiffen the tension on the wire, holding it in place until the washers are all cut, when they are removed.—Chas. G. England, Washington, Pa.

Handy Workbenches for Garage

On each column in a San Francisco auto-service station, two handy benches for

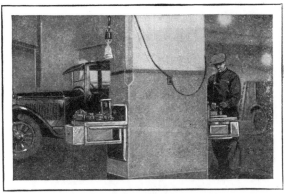

Small Workbenches Attached to Columns in Auto-Service Station Handy for Small Jobs

small jobs have been arranged as shown in the photo. The benches are provided with a vise and drawer for tools, and are narrower at the front than at the column side, so that there is no tendency for cars being driven down the aisles to catch the front edges. — Charles W. Geiger, San Francisco, Calif.

Binder Heads Make Pump Jack

The pump jack shown in the photo was made from two binder heads and a single cogwheel from the end of the trip arm, and gives a 6-in. stroke. It has been in use for a number of years and still gives excellent service. Two old bundle mechanisms from old binders were required to furnish the three wheels, two of which are alike, and the two shafts. The boxings were made of maple, soaked in oil, and oilcups are screwed down into the wood above the bearing to permit hard oil to be fed to the bearing. The pulley wheel was salvaged from a scrap heap. The pitman was a piece of hardwood, 1 in. thick, 2 in. wide, and long enough to reach the proper distance.

Efficient Pump Jack Made from Old Binder Parts Gives a 6-Inch Stroke

Easily Made Orchard Ladder Which Facilitates Picking and Can Be Moved About Readily

Convenient Orchard Ladder

Fruit pickers will find the ladder shown in the illustration of considerable utility and a great improvement over an ordinary ladder. It enables the picker to reach the top branches of the trees, can be moved about very easily and will not tip over. It is made from a ladder, two old mower wheels, or any other wheels of similar size, and some wooden braces and crosspieces. The upright braces are lengths of 1 by 4-in. stock, while the handlebars are made of 2 by 4-in. stock and fastened to the axle with iron yokes.

Asbestos for Annealing

Asbestos is used in practically every foundry for covering hot castings. This paper is torn after being used once or twice, and it is then usually thrown away, which is an expensive practice. The torn paper can be used in the annealing bin by tearing it into small shreds, which make excellent material to bury castings in. The paper will soon become pulverized and will last a long time.

Method of Locating Partitions

While doing a job of electrical wiring, difficulty was found in avoiding partitions and joists, which could be seen from an unfinished attic but were invisible in the furnished and plastered rooms below. A horseshoe magnet and a common compass overcame this difficulty. The magnet was placed close to the ceiling where it was desired to cut a hole, and the exact spot could be located on the other side by the dipping of the compass needle, which pointed to the pole of the magnet when the compass was moved in a circle around the approximate location of the magnet. This method is applicable to other difficulties of location where it is not feasible to measure, or drill test holes.—Floyd A. Meek, Rockbridge, Ill.

Turning Edges of Screen Wire

When cutting strips of screen for doors and windows the dealer is often requested to fold back the rough edges about ½ in. so that they will not unravel when tacked on the frames. Although special tools of the tin shop may be used for this purpose, the dealer in most cases has none of these and will find the illustrated method quite a timesaver. At the end of the screen counter, a straight stick, about ½ in. square, and of a length equal to the width of the counter, is nailed to act as a gauge, and ½ in. from this, toward the screen rack, a deep slot is sawed across the counter as indicated. To fold the end of a cut piece, it

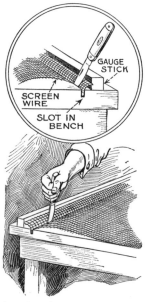

is placed against the stop gauge and a dull knife drawn across it over the slot in the counter.

Why Your Car Shimmies and How to Cure It

THERE is nothing more annoying than shimmy in a car, whether it be the slight, sudden shimmy felt when the car wheels hit a rut in the road or the violent, uncontrollable vibration sometimes encountered in a balloon-tired automobile at high speed. In by far the greater number of cases the shimmy is easily cured, and still more easily prevented. Often the owner of the car can, with an hour or two of work, cure the trouble permanently, and any owner can prevent low-speed shimmy with a little time spent on the care and proper lubrication of s t e e r i n g connections. For the cure of the violent shimmy at high speed, co-operation with the manufacturer's service station may be necessary, but, even here, the owner can help a great deal by not allowing conditions to arise that will aggravate the trouble.

The front wheels of a car, if adjusted properly, do not point straight ahead, neither are they straight up and down Here is a sketch of the front axle and wheels, looking at them ·from the rear (Fig. 1). Notice that the wheels are closer at the bottom than at the top, due to the steering-knuckle spindle or king pin being set at an angle in the axle. This inclination of the wheels is usually about 2°. The idea is to make the center line of the king pin or spindle correspond, as nearly as possible, with the center line of the wheel at the point where the tire touches the road. This permits the car to be steered more easily. Another reason for it is that the wheels have a tendency to spread at the bottom and come together at the top when speeding, and the "camber" helps to compensate for this tendency.

To offset the wearing action on the tires produced by the camber, and to make them wear more evenly, the wheels are "toed-in" at the front. Here is another sketch (Fig. 2). This is a top view of the front axle, and you will notice that the distance A is less than B. The difference between the two is the toe-in. In general it amounts to about ⅜ in., although on the Ford it is about ¼ in. The toe-in offsets a tendency of the wheels to "open up" at the front at high-speed, besides helping to equalize the wear on the tires.

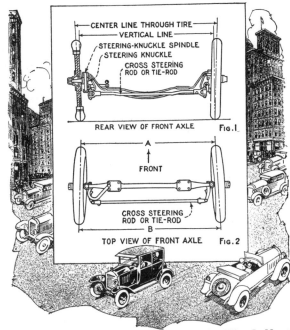

Rear View and Plan of Front Axle, Illustrating What Is Meant by "Camber" and "Toe-In" on the Front Wheels of the Car

117

Too much toe-in, however, is as bad as too little so far as tire wear is concerned, for too much will cause the tread rubber to be ground off. Toe-in is sometimes called "gather," but the first term is the one generally used.

There is quite a little more to the design of the front wheels of a car than merely sticking them on the axle ends. And this is not all; there is the "caster effect." You have noticed how easily your bed or bureau rolls on its casters, and how quickly and smoothly it is "steered" in one direction or another. Well, the reason for this is all in the design of the caster; you know how the little wheel touches the floor at a point to the rear of the caster's vertical axis, which is the center line of the pin that goes up into the foot of the bedpost. Because of this, the wheel trails, and does not tend to change the direction of motion of the bed when pushed straight, yet the bed can be steered in any direction with scarcely an effort. The same principle has been used for years in the steering wheel of bicycles; look here (Fig. 3).

Above, Checking the Camber of the Wheels with Special Gauge; Below, Checking Toe-In

A center line drawn through the steering column of the bicycle strikes the ground in front of a vertical line drawn through the axle of the wheel, so that the wheel, in effect, actually trails behind the steering axis, and, like the bed caster, the wheel tends to follow a straight line. This is why a cyclist can steer without using his hands. Exactly the same principle is used in the car. The front axle is "pitched" or tilted so as to throw the bottom of the steering-knuckle pin or king bolt forward, and thus cause its center line to strike the road ahead of the vertical axis of the wheel. Get your boy's bicycle and turn the front wheel to the right or left, then

back straight again, noticing how the front end of the machine acts. Turning the wheel actually raises the front of the machine slightly; it is the same in the car, and the weight of the body tends to bring the wheels back to the straight-ahead position. The amount of caster varies all the way from 2 to 14°, depending on the type of car.

All this is necessary in understanding the cause and cure of shimmy. There are, in general, two distinct types of shimmy; low and high speed. Low-speed shimmy generally occurs between 15 and 30 miles an hour, and is noticeable whenever the car goes over rough pavements, uneven roads, or other surfaces that happen to have just the right characteristics to start the wheels shimmying. In these cases the motion is usually not very violent, and will, in nine cases out of ten, be found due to backlash or play somewhere in the steering-gear linkage. This, then, is the first place to look when your car starts shimmying at low speeds. Go over all the joints and knuckles in the linkage thoroughly, fitting new pins wherever necessary. It is a good idea to check the adjustment of the front-wheel bearings also at the same time, and remedy any play that is found in them. Another simple cause of an annoying shimmy is too much lubrication of the springs. The springs need a certain amount of friction between the leaves, and if this is destroyed by too much oil or grease, the body may tend to "hop" or vibrate with the disturbance of the front wheels, and this aggravates the shimmy.

Shimmy at high speeds is a much more serious problem, partly because it is usually more violent and partly because a permanent cure is by no means so easy. The first remedy to apply is to watch the tire pressures closely. Balloon tires especially are sensitive to underinflation, but even high-pressure tires will cause a shimmy if they get very soft. So keep your tires at the pressure recommended by the maker of the car, even if it does involve checking two or three times a week, and see especially that the front-tire pressures are kept equal.

The next thing is to check the toe-in of the front wheels. Set the right front wheel straight ahead, then tie one end of a long, stout string to a spoke on the front of the wheel, pass it around the back of the forward part of the tire, then around the front and lead it back to the rear wheel, keeping it as near the center of the wheel as possible. Pass it across the back of the car, around the rear side of

Above, Gauge That Automatically Registers "Pitch" of Axle; Below, Diagrams Explaining Caster Effect

the left rear wheel, then forward to the left front wheel and make it fast temporarily. Go back to the right side and see that the right front wheel is pointed straight ahead. This will be seen if the string touches both sides of the tires on the right wheels equally. Now take the free end of the string, keeping it taut, and hold it so that it touches the rear side of the front tire, at the center. Measure the distance from the string to the front side of the tire, and this will give the toe-in. This may be adjusted by means of the cross steering rod or tie-rod, and the maker's specifications should be followed closely. There are special gauges made for checking the toe-in and camber, but the string method is a good one for you, provided care is taken.

If the axle is not properly pitched it can be remedied by using an iron wedge between the front spring and spring seat

(Fig. 4). Since the amount of caster has been determined by experiment by the manufacturer and varies in almost every car, you will have to find out what yours should be before you can check it. A clever gauge is now being made that is attached to the front-wheel spindle and which, when the wheel is swung to the left and then to the right, automatically registers on a dial the amount of pitch on the front axle.

Balloon tires have caused much head-scratching on the shimmy problem. Many manufacturers have found it advisable to reduce the amount of toe-in to about ⅛ in. and this puts the owner under the necessity of keeping very careful check, to see that play in the steering mechanism does not alter it. Another maker has found that reducing the amount of caster, and consequently causing the car to steer harder, tends to dampen out the wheel wobble, and still another has found that. while wheels themselves are usually balanced, vulcanizing on tires or putting in heavy repair boots causes unbalance and induces shimmy.

The things to do, then, in a case of high-speed shimmy are: Keep the tires inflated to the proper pressure; keep the wheels in balance; keep the steering linkage free from play; check the toe-in of the front wheels and the pitch of the axle; keep the front-wheel bearings adjusted, and don't allow too much play in king bolts or bushings before replacing them.

Large Oil Tanks on Lanterns

One construction company, which has considerable road work to do, saved much labor by providing the red lanterns with oil tanks of 1-gal. capacity so that they required attention only about once a week instead of daily. The tanks were made of galvanized iron, with a hole in the top slightly smaller than the bottom of the original reservoir, and the lanterns were soldered over this hole after the bottom of the small tanks had been cut away. After putting in an extra-long wick, the lanterns were ready for use.

Enameling over Putty

Every one who has tried to put on white enamel over newly puttied holes has noticed how persistently the putty shows through the flat white coats. If, instead of regular putty, a thick paste made of white lead and ordinary flour is used, the filled holes will cover as readily as the wood. A child's box sled, finished in this way, has stood hard usage and all kinds of weather for over two years.

Cleans Typewriter Quickly

Typewriter operators find it a difficult matter to clean their machines, because the dust and dirt from erasures enter every crack and corner and often remain there until the machine is taken apart. However, there is a simple solution to this problem, if a bicycle pump is used in connection with the other cleaning tools. It is quite an easy matter to blow the dirt out with the pump. A stiff brush is commonly used to clean the type, but it will be found that, if the bristles are covered with a soft cloth, the work will be greatly simplified. The bristles merely stir up the oily dirt without removing it, but the cloth, backed by the stiff bristles, will make the type look like new. When the platen roll begins to look shabby and rough, it can be renewed by smoothing it with very fine sandpaper. Most typewriter rolls can be removed quickly and easily and it is then a simple matter to do this.

Rubber Stamp Attached to Thimble

In canning factories, cold-storage plants and other places, where numerical or other identification and grading stamps are used, the thimble stamp shown in the drawing will be found very useful. The small round rubber stamps are removed from the original wooden handles and are mounted on thimbles, the ends of which have been flattened for this purpose. The stamps are fastened with glue or rubber cement. The op-

erator then provides himself with a pad, strapped to the hand as shown, for inking the stamps. This is made from a cross section of an old inner tube with the ink pad glued to it. With a little practice he can ink and stamp much more rapidly than in the usual manner, and both hands are practically free to move or turn boxes and crates.—G. E. Hendrickson, Argyle, Wis.

Remedy for Run-Down Pump

A pump that persists in "running down" can be remedied in a short time in the following way: Remove the leather check valve and cut a piece of rubber from an old inner tube, or piece of rubber-patching stock, the same size and shape as the worn-out flap; attach this on the underside of the flap with the screw already in the latter. Put the pump together again, and you will have no more trouble of this kind. The rubber is more flexible than the leather and will not allow sand to collect on it.—Clyde Brindel, Yorktown, Ind.

Markers for Centering Short Work

A method of marking off the centers of short round pieces which is quicker than any of the various tools generally used for this purpose, is shown in the drawing. The complete set-up comprises two lengths of straight, round rod, two thin tool-steel cutters or markers, and a couple of clamps of suitable design. Both markers are ground to a central sharp edge on one side, this edge being also slightly convex. In assembling, the markers are placed between the rods at each end and all are held together by the

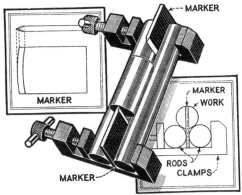

Handy Tool for Center Marking Short Round Stock Quickly and Conveniently

clamps. The piece of short stock is placed between the rods and driven sharply first against one and then against the other marker. After giving the piece a quarter turn the operation is repeated. Thus a cross mark is produced in each end and in practically the same time required to mark one end with the ordinary method.

Outside Chute in Haymow for Feeding Stock in the Yard

Outside Hay Chute

For feeding cattle in the yard, the outside chute illustrated herewith, which was built by an Oklahoma farmer, will be found convenient. The barn had a haymow of average size. At one end, the yard came up to the barn and the owner wished to feed the outside stock direct from the haymow. To do this it was necessary to build a chute with a floor at a 30° angle. The chute is 10 ft. from the ground and consequently the hay falls well away from the barn.

To Strengthen a Magnet

A permanent U-magnet may be strengthened in the following way: Place a keeper of iron or steel on the side of the magnet, from pole to pole and as near its ends as possible. Lay the magnet, keeper side down, on the bench, with the ends projecting over the edge. Hold the magnet firmly in place and, with a hammer or like object, strike the keeper sharply to the floor. Turn the magnet over and repeat the process. Do this several times.
—Dexter W. Allis, Everett, Mass.

Tattooing Hogs Is New Marking Method

A S the ballyhoo man at the circus might say, "Step right this way, ladies and gentlemen, and see the new curiosity, the tattooed hog—just discovered by

Upper Left, Tattooing the Hog; essary; Below, How Blocks

Upper Right, the Materials Nec-Can Be Changed in Holder

science." And while the subject of tattooing hogs may be new now, it probably will be so familiar within a few years as to be accepted as a matter of common procedure.

Tattooing hogs, as conducted experimentally by scientists of the federal bureau of animal industry during the last five years, is a promising means of tracing tuberculosis, hog cholera and other ailments of swine to lurking sources of infection. Instead of fighting these microscopic foes in the dark, as one might say, the tattoo method of marking hogs enables one to determine just where the diseases have their strongholds.

The new method, in keeping with modern times, speeds up the process. The work must be done quickly to be practical, so the method provides for applying a full set of tattoo marks at one stroke of the marker and takes only a second. The instrument used in tattooing is a metal holder slotted to receive babbitt-metal blocks in which, when molten, phonograph needles are imbedded. The needles may be arranged to form figures, letters or other symbols. The blocks can be used in any desired combination, so it is possible to obtain a great variety of characters. The illustrations show the appearance of

the device and the method of using it. The application of the marks causes no material pain or discomfort. "While the hogs sometimes grunt or hump their backs," Dr. Murray, the inventor, states, "very few squeal, and that is generally from excitement. An animal near a hog that is tattooed is just as likely to squeal as the one marked." This comment is based on experimental work with about eight thousand head.

The pigment found to be best adapted for the work is ordinary black automobile enamel, preferably a thick, sticky grade. It is applied to the points of the tattoo instrument with a small brush, a stencil brush being especially good for the purpose. The mark should be applied on the shoulder or fore part of the back. In that part of the body there is nearly always a thick layer of fat free from nerve ends and as the points are only a quarter of an inch long, the hog scarcely notices the operation. When a hog is tattooed in the manner described, the numbers or symbols used are plainly visible on the dressed carcass, even months afterward. Extensive inquiry among various branches of the live stock trade has failed to show any objections to the tattoo marks on carcasses. It is advisable, however, not to tattoo hogs on the hams. In developing the method, the investigators found that hogs could be successfully tattooed also without any pigment provided the animals were slaughtered within the next 36 hours.

This phase of the work has a very practical application when hogs are shipped for immediate slaughter. The marks in that case are pink, due to slight capillary hemorrhages, instead of black which is the obvious result when the black pigment is used in the manner formerly described. Of course, the ability to tattoo hogs without any pigment greatly hastens and simplifies the work. But, as already implied, the mark in that case lasts only a short time unless the hog is slaughtered. Persons familiar with packing-house procedure know that hog carcasses receive very rigorous treatment, including immersion in the scalding vat and later under the beaters and scrapers which remove the hair. That is why a good tattoo mark, being below the surface of the skin proves satisfactory, while tags, paint marks, chalk and similar marking devices are undependable under packing-house conditions.

The principal use for the device appears to be systematic disease-control work, as conducted by state organizations and the U. S. department of agriculture. In this connection the tattoo method is sponsored by the federal bureau of animal industry, which about 15 years ago gave the swine industry the preventive serum treatment for hog cholera and more lately has been responsible for administering the nationwide campaign to eradicate tuberculosis. The bureau also conducts federal meat inspection and has charge of suppressing such plagues as foot-and-mouth disease. With such an organization actively interested, stock owners are assured that the use of the tattoo device will mean prompt and systematic action in getting the greatest benefits from it. The device can be made and used by anyone.

⁋In a loose-pin hinge, the pin often will work up and out. Removing it and driving it in from the bottom, will save trouble.

Depth Gauge for Sawing

There are many instances when the woodworker has to have a depth gauge and a miter box is too small. An easily

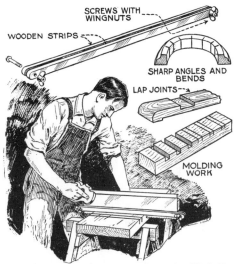

Useful and Easily Made Depth Gauge for Work Too Large for a Miter Box

made depth gauge is shown in the accompanying illustration. It consists of two wooden strips, about 2 in. longer than the saw and drilled at both ends for screws and thumbnuts. The strips are attached to the saw as shown, so that it will cut to the desired depth, then tightened again.

Converting Driveways into Walks

The accompanying photo shows how a western city changes its driveways into walks when the pedestrian traffic becomes more important than the vehicular. Iron posts, about 3 in. in diameter and painted white, were set across the roadway at intervals of 3 ft. The white paint makes them stand out against the dark road, at night as well as in the daytime, thus showing that the way is blocked, while the spacing permits the pedestrian to pass through easily.

White-Painted Posts on Driveway in a Western City Insure Safety for Pedestrians

DOING YOUR OWN CONDUIT WORK

by E.R.Haan

WHERE wiring has to be done in damp places such as basements or outdoors along the sides of buildings it is advisable to use rigid metal conduit, which protects the wires from mechanical injury and reduces the possibility of short circuits or grounds. This method of installation is especially recommended for service lines so that they can be run along the outside of the building as shown in Fig. 2. We have previously shown other methods of service-line installation where conduit is not available, but the conduit method is far superior and should be followed if possible. The fittings used are shown in the details. Ordinary pipe clamps are used to hold the conduit securely to the wall. In case of brick or concrete walls these clamps are screwed into wooden plugs driven into small holes made in the concrete. A pipe cap of the type shown, or any other kind which will not permit water to get into the pipe, is fitted at the top. At the bottom the conduit can be bent to a right angle or an L-fitting can be used as shown. Any electrical store and many hardware stores in the smaller towns handle conduit of the ½ and ¾-in. sizes which are most commonly used. Conduit is either lined or unlined. Lined conduit has a paper tube inside, treated with an asphaltic or similar compound and unlined conduit does not have this. Single-braided conductors can be installed in the former but double-braided conductors must be used for the latter. Where conduit is to be brought through a brick or concrete

PIPE CLAMP

wall a star drill, obtainable at any tool store, should be used to make a hole as shown in Fig. 1. The length of conduit is measured, cut off, threaded and bent if necessary.

Bending is accomplished in different ways, Fig. 4 showing how a "hickey" is used for this purpose. This tool merely consists of a 4-ft. length of 1-in. pipe with a tee screwed on one end. It is advisable to make one before starting the work of installing the conduit as it will be necessary to use it constantly. This tool is used by placing the conduit on the floor and slipping the tee over the end. The worker then places one foot on the conduit close to the tee and pushes down on the handle. Care should be taken to move the tee to different points while bending to prevent the conduit from buckling. Other methods of bending conduit are shown in Figs. 6 and 7, the latter being especially adapted to bending heavy conduit, as a considerable leverage is obtained with this arrangement. When bending conduit one should always take care not to make the bends too sharp or the conduit may buckle, which will make it useless, as the wires cannot be run through it.

After the conduit has been completely installed, the wires are pulled through. This is done with the aid of a "fish" wire, a length of flexible wire, which can readily be pushed through the conduit. One

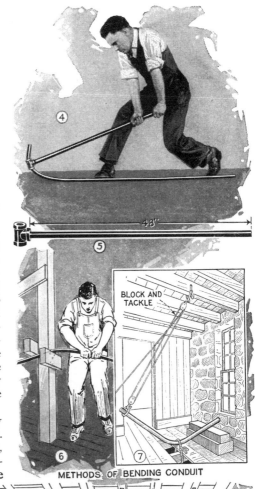

METHODS OF BENDING CONDUIT

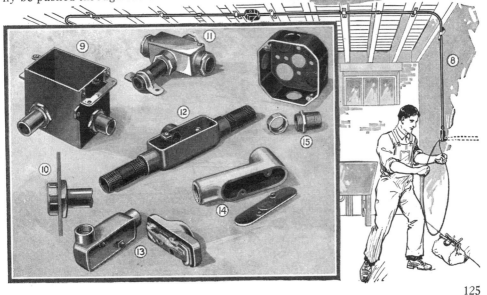

end has a hook formed so that the bared ends of the wires can be attached and pulled through. Do not attempt to pull the wires through the conduit separately but pull them through together. It will be found, especially during hot weather, that the wires are apt to stick in the conduit. To reduce this friction to a minimum, dust soapstone on the wires, or if this is not available use ordinary flour.

Conduit usually comes in 10-ft. lengths, threaded at both ends. Do not attempt to fit a coupling between two 10-ft. lengths because it will be too hard to pull the wires through a 20-ft. length of conduit. Always screw in a special fitting with a removable cover of the types

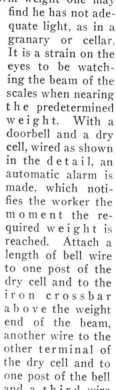

Cross Arm and Frame of Scale Wired to Ring When Correct Weight Is Reached

shown in Figs. 11, 12, 13 and 14. This enables the worker to pull the wire through the 10-ft. lengths separately and he can also tap off for other outlets by using a 4-outlet fitting shown in Fig. 11 or a 3-outlet fitting as shown in Fig. 12. Fig. 13 shows a fitting having a porcelain cover for a drop light, in cases of open-conduit work, and Fig. 14 shows an L-fitting. In Fig. 8 the worker has pulled the wire from the ceiling outlet to the L-fitting, where the conduit projects through the concrete wall, and he is pushing the wire through the horizontal length of conduit.

Fig. 9 shows a switchbox to which the conduit is screwed by means of two nuts as shown in the detail Fig. 10. A ceiling outlet, having a number of perforations, which can be easily punched out to accommodate the conduit on any side, is shown in Fig. 15. A neat conduit job in a farm workshop, equipped with a lighting plant is shown in Fig. 3.

Bell Alarm on Scales

When using scales to sack vegetables or grains to a uniform weight one may find he has not adequate light, as in a granary or cellar. It is a strain on the eyes to be watching the beam of the scales when nearing the predetermined weight. With a doorbell and a dry cell, wired as shown in the detail, an automatic alarm is made, which notifies the worker the moment the required weight is reached. Attach a length of bell wire to one post of the dry cell and to the iron crossbar above the weight end of the beam, another wire to the other terminal of the dry cell and to one post of the bell and a third wire from the other post of the bell to one of the bearings that support the beam of the scale. The iron crossbar below the weight end of the beam, on which the beam normally rests, must be insulated from the beam. A wrapping of paper or tire tape will serve this purpose. The sliding weight is set at the number of pounds desired in the sacks or crates. When the weight that the scales are set for is reached the beam will rise and make contact with the crossbar above and ring the bell. When the full sack or crate is removed the beam drops to the insulated crossbar and breaks the circuit.

Test for Leaky Tire Valves

A common method of testing tire valves for leakage is to hold the stem in a can of water, with the wheel turned to bring the valve stem to the upper side. If the car is standing in a poorly lighted garage, or one of the angle valves or disk wheels is being used, this is difficult to do. A better plan, in this case, is to turn the wheel until the valve is at the top, in the case of ordinary straight valves, put a few drops of water in the small valve cap and turn it back in place. Any air leakage past the small cap will be shown by a sputter that can be heard several feet away from the valve. Often the sound will be irregular. The air leaking past the valve inside builds up pressure until a defective valve cap will no longer hold it, when it escapes with a hiss. After the test has been made, remove the cap and shake out the water.

Record Form for Checking Pipe Fittings

Here is an ingenious and simple method of keeping a record of pipe fittings, which was developed in a large eastern engineering company's shop. Where reducing tees have three different sizes of openings, as often happens, the problem of recording these openings in an orderly manner was always more or less difficult. The accompanying reproduction of a blank used by this engineering concern shows how easily it can be done. Reducing el-

REDUCING	TEES						
NO.							
⊢							

REDUCING	ELBOWS						
NO. 90° C							
NO. 45° ⌐							

Blank Used by Engineering Company for Recording Pipe Fittings

bows and return bends can be checked or recorded on the same blank. The blank tells the whole story without the necessity of explanatory remarks such as are often found written on records pertaining to fittings of this character.

Countersinking Machine for Drilling Brake Lining

In a San Francisco auto-repair shop an old drill press has been used

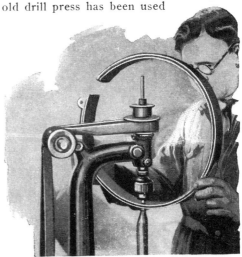

Homemade Machine for Drilling and Countersinking Rivet Holes in Auto Brake Bands

in building a brake-lining countersinking machine at a saving of $85. The countersinking tool is put in the chuck and the guide arm is clamped in place on the drill table, the plate being operated by a foot lever, leaving both hands of the operator free to handle the work. In operation, the brake band is held over the guide and the lever pressed down, which lowers the drill. This drills and countersinks the lining in one operation. There is a shoulder on the tool, which prevents it from drilling too far. After drilling and countersinking, the rivets are placed in the holes and clinched by a foot-operated rivet machine.—C. W. Geiger, San Francisco, Calif.

Starting Gasoline Blowtorch

When starting a gasoline blowtorch, it is customary to place the hand over the nozzle to catch the fine stream of gasoline and direct it down to the generating pan. Of course, there will be gasoline left on the user's hands after doing this, and if a match is used to light the torch the gas on the hand may become ignited. The user must be careful to hold the match in the other hand while lighting the torch, or use a cork of the proper size in the nozzle of the torch to deflect the gasoline.

Homemade Tools for Small Concrete Jobs

By G. A. LUERS

WHERE there are only occasional calls for a small concrete job, and the amount of work does not seem to justify

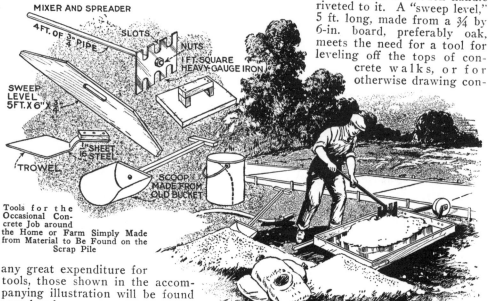

Tools for the Occasional Concrete Job around the Home or Farm Simply Made from Material to Be Found on the Scrap Pile

made from ¾-in. pipe, will be found a very useful tool, as is also the trowel of the same material with a wooden handle riveted to it. A "sweep level," 5 ft. long, made from a ¾ by 6-in. board, preferably oak, meets the need for a tool for leveling off the tops of concrete walks, or for otherwise drawing con-

any great expenditure for tools, those shown in the accompanying illustration will be found very handy.

The first thing for which one usually has to hunt is a mixing board. It will be found to save time in the end to make a board, as shown in the drawing, and keep it for future jobs. This consists of a shallow box, about 4 ft. square, fitted with a small roller or wheel and two handles, like a wheelbarrow, to facilitate moving the board about, and to aid in carrying the other tools and materials to the job. A mixer or hoe, of heavy sheet iron or steel and provided with a handle

crete rapidly to an even surface. A wooden float, about 12 by 14 in., will work up a wet top surface on the concrete, and may also be used as a mortar board for small jobs. The scoop measure is made from an old bucket, in the manner shown in the illustration. The size of this being immaterial, it may be chosen to suit individual taste and can be made from any suitable article on hand.

Locking Motor-Support Bolts

Some automobiles have front motor-support bolts, which are often difficult to tighten unless the radiator is removed, as it is impossible to place a wrench on the bolt heads, while tightening the nut from below the supporting frame. The idea shown in the illustration remedies this trouble. The bolt heads are drilled with as large a drill as the head will safely accommodate, and after the bolts are in place, a steel bar is inserted in the holes in the heads, the bar having cotter-pin holes outside each bolt

head. The bolts are easily tightened whenever desired as they will not turn and are as easily removed by sliding the locking bar out of the holes in the heads.—Edwin Kilburn, Spring Valley, Minn.

Ducks Keep Ditches Clean

A western farmer has found that the mosslike plants which grow in irrigation canals during the summer months, sometimes to such an extent as to interfere seriously with the flow of irrigation water, can be kept down in the small shallow lateral ditches by ducks. The ducks swim back and forth along the ditches, eating the moss as fast as it grows, thus feeding economically and keeping the ditches open.

Shop Power Plant Has Many Uses

By D. R. VAN HORN

THERE are many small garages and repair shops where the volume of work does not warrant the installation of a regular automatic air-compressor system, but where the necessity for pumping up heavy tires arises often enough to make the hand-pump method a nuisance. One small shop, where this was the case, solved the problem in the manner shown in the illustration. A ¼-hp. electric motor was obtained and attached to the top of a tool box.

tor, of course, is belted to the compressor. The box, being full of tools, is heavy enough to permit the motor to be belted to any other small machine within its capacity and to serve as a power plant. The upper left-hand photo shows the compressor belted to the motor, and also the large pulley on the former. This was made of wood, and is necessary to reduce the speed of the motor to one suitable for the compressor. A slot is cut in the top of the tool box to accommodate the pulley and belt. The other photo shows the compressor pumping up a truck tire 8 in. in diameter; it will inflate these tires to a pressure of 105 lb. per sq. in. without any difficulty, and those who have attempted

For All-Around Use in the Small Shop with No Power, This Portable Unit Will Pay for Itself in a Day

In line with it, on the box top, was bolted a small air compressor or tire pump of the type fitted to many automobiles several years ago, and which can often be picked up at a wrecker's for next to nothing. The mo-

to pump up a tire of this size by hand will appreciate the advantages of the outfit.

Besides doing the chores of pumping tires, the motor is pressed into service for doing other work around the shop. One use to which it is adapted is shown in the sketch. The forge in the shop is of the hand-drive type, but the

129

motor is now used, permitting the workmen to handle the work to better advantage. To reduce the excessive draft caused by the motor drive, pieces of cardboard are set on each side of the forge air inlet to restrict the opening. The motor may also be used for driving scratch brushes and tire buffers by means of a flexible shaft, or operate a small sensitive drill or a bench grinder. In fact, any tool in the shop that is within the capacity of the motor can be made into a power tool by simply setting the motor and box in position and belting it to the drive pulley.

Rig for Rolling Veneer Blocks

Rolling huge veneer blocks, by means of a cleverly contrived rig, is the novel method used by a western factory to get

Rolling Huge Blocks from Forest to Mill with a Tractor Linked to Their Centers

its raw material from forest to plant. Although logs of great diameter are well suited for conversion into veneer, they are difficult to load onto flat cars, motor trucks or wagons. But by driving axles into the big blocks at their centers, the cut logs, like mammoth cheeses, are readily rolled to the mill with a tractor. The system operates independently of roads and one man and one tractor have demonstrated ability to transport more veneer blocks than two men and two teams of horses.

Cutting Off Piston Rings

After turning and boring a piece of cast iron to make a few piston rings for a repair job, I found that I did not have the proper tool to measure the width before cutting them off. However, the following plan proved very successful: The width of the parting tool and the thickness of the scale were first measured carefully, and the parting tool was then set approximately in the position for cutting, with the scale held across the open end of the work in line with the parting tool. The micrometer was placed in the position indicated, over the tool and the scale, and the parting tool shifted around until the micrometer reading corresponded to the total width of the parting tool and the thickness of the scale. The parting tool was then tightened and the ring cut off.
—L. Christensen, Hoboken, N. J.

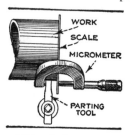

Stand for Tailors' Goose

In most tailor shops where pressing is done by hand considerable space is taken up on the work table by the pressing iron or goose. To make the handling of the heavy iron more convenient and at the same time keep the pressing board free of the iron, one tailor devised the holder shown in the drawing, which is set up a short distance from the end of the board. The legs of the holder are lengths of pipe of the proper height, so spaced that the feet on the cast-iron plate, furnished with the iron, can be inserted in their upper ends. The lower ends are fitted with flanges screwed to the floor.

Quick Way of Lapping Bushings

A few days ago I made a bushing for a boring-bar guide that had to be a running fit without shake, to avoid chatter. In taking my measurements I found that I had a tight fit when the bushing was tried. I was going to chuck it over and scrape it slightly, but my foreman said he would take care of it. He took a piece of emery cloth, wrapped it around a length of broom handle, slipped the bushing over the emery cloth and forced the bushing against a belt running perpendicularly so that the bushing would revolve several hundred times faster per minute than any lathe spindle in the shop. The bushing was lapped out in a few moments, with a high polish, and it was more accurate than could be done in a lathe. The closer the polishing stick fits the hole, the better the work will be.—F. W. Schrader, Woodstock, Ont., Can.

Electroplating Lead

Before plating lead, it is advisable to give it a coating of copper as other metals adhere more readily to the copper. The surface of the lead is scrubbed thoroughly with a hot solution of potash and water, using a coarse brush, then rinsed and dried with a clean rag. It will then take a coating of copper by electroplating, and another metal can be applied later.

Knob Makes Acetylene-Tank Wrench

It seems that no matter how many acetylene-tank wrenches are around the welding plant, there will be some operator who cannot find his wrench. Recently we missed a door knob from one of the inner doors of the welding room; the knob was replaced, but disappeared again in the course of a few days. This occurred several times and finally the foreman saw one of the missing knobs lying on the top of an acetylene tank. He picked it up, and in doing so noticed that the square hole in the knob was just about the size of the stem on the acetylene tank. He tried it— it was a perfect fit. All the operators are now equipped with "wrenches" of this type.—A. S. Jamieson, Springfield, Mass.

Roof Protects Outdoor Air Press

This 15-ton air press, used to shape steel of various sizes and contours, was con-

Roof Attached to Framework of 15-Ton Press Protects It from Elements and Reduces Repairs

tinually getting out of order, because snow penetrated into its moving parts and froze. To house it would have caused serious difficulty in getting long and heavy steel to the press and was, therefore, out of the question. The problem was solved by bolting the framework for a shed to the upper portion of the heavy steel columns of the press, so that nothing would be in the way of the workmen on the ground.

Fixed Line Gauge

One inconvenience frequently experienced when operating a linotype is the absence of a line gauge at the moment when it is urgently needed. To be sure to have one handy at all times, one may be made of brass and graduated in picas and half picas along one edge, the opposite edge being drilled for screws, which hold the strip on the keyboard, as shown in the illustration. A small stop should be fixed at the zero graduation in order to facilitate the measurement of the slugs still further.

FIXED LINE GAUGE

Line Gauge for the Linotype Operator Is Handier When Fixed on Keyboard

Sawbuck Helps Raise Log

Sometimes it is troublesome to lift a large log up on a sawbuck, but with the  buck shown in the drawing the task will always be easy. It has a 7-ft. base made of 2 by 4-in. stock, and the other members are 1 by 4-in. In use the device is placed so as to straddle one end of the log and by pulling the base down, as indicated by the arrows, the log is raised with little effort. — Luther Strosnider, Onago, Kans.

Clamps for Welding

It is often difficult to get a clamp to suit a specific welding need; sometimes the right size is not available, or else the clamp is not sturdy enough to withstand the strain. The clamp shown in the accompanying illustration is strong enough to stand any strains to which it may be put, and is adjustable. In making it, a ring, 1 in. wide and cut from 2-in. boiler tubing, is flattened on the sides to an oval shape. A reinforcement made from a section of a similar ring is fitted snugly around one end of the oval, and the ends of this strip welded to the sides. A ⁵⁄₁₆-in. hole is drilled through the top of this reinforced section and the top of the ring, and then tapped for a setscrew. The shoe of the clamp is a piece of ring, 1 in. wide, and is also cut from boiler tubing, bent to fit. A spot countersink is  made in the top of this shoe to receive the point of the setscrew. Because of its adjustable feature, this easily constructed

clamp comes in handy for many special purposes about the shop or plant.—A. G. Wikoff, New York City.

Inside and Outside Coatings for Smokestacks

There is no oil-mixed paint that gives good service when applied to the inner surface of a smokestack or breechings. The best covering is three or four coats of cement mixed in small quantities at a time to the consistency of thick paint and applied with a brush. A wire brush should be used to remove all soot and rust from the crevices before the cement is applied. For the outside, asphalt paint is best and this, also, should be applied only after a thorough wire brushing of the surface.

Quick-Acting Marking-Off Blocks

For holding medium-length round pieces when marking off positions on opposite sides or at right angles, the device shown in the illustration will be found to be a great convenience. Once it is made, the center is known, and, unlike V-blocks, where the height center varies with the diameter of the work, it remains the 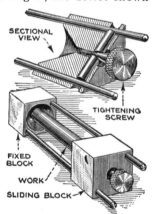 same for all sizes within its capacity. To make it, two square blocks are cupped out on one side, clamped together, drilled and reamed at opposite corners to take two guide bars. The bars are a tight fit in one block and a sliding fit in the other. The latter is drilled through cornerwise to receive a tightening bar, which consists of a piece of cold-rolled stock drilled and countersunk in the center and sawed in two. A special screw with a tapered point, entering a tapped hole in the block, expands the two halves of the tightening bar against the guide bars. With this device the blocks can be adjusted very quickly to hold the work. The piece is inserted in the cupped end of the fixed block, and the sliding block pushed up against the other end. One turn of the screw then tightens it in place.

Oil in Boilers May Cause Blistered Tubes

The practice of using oil in boilers to loosen scale and prevent them from rusting, when allowed to cool off or for other purposes, is not good unless care is taken to remove all particles of it with some grease dissolvent afterward. If this is not done, the oil adheres to the tubes or plates and prevents water from coming in contact with the metal. Thus the heat is not carried away from this point and the tube or part may become so hot as to blister and weaken.—Geo. G. McVicker, North Bend, Nebr.

Waterproofing Shipping Tags

Shipping tags bearing order numbers, addresses and other essential information can be waterproofed to prevent the writing from "running" by the simple method indicated in the drawing. Get an open glass jar, about 8 or 10 in. in height and large enough to allow your hand to enter freely. Suspend a 60-watt lamp in the jar as shown. Turn the current on and shave enough paraffin so that, when melted, it will come up to the top of the lamp. It is then an easy matter to dip the tags in the melted paraffin, and this will effectively waterproof them. After use, the lamp is turned off and the paraffin is allowed to harden around it. When ready to use it again, just turn on the lamp and in a few minutes the paraffin will be melted so that tags can be dipped in it. The tags also will be strengthened by the treatment.—E. V. Wills, Chicago.

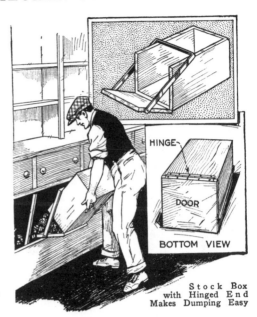

Stock Box with Hinged End Makes Dumping Easy

Stock Box with Hinged End Saves Time in Store

A useful box to have around a storeroom, where small parts are kept in bins, is one with a hinged end like that shown in the drawing. For dumping a boxful of parts into a bin without loss of time nothing could be handier. With ordinary boxes the user must tip them up to empty the contents, with the not uncommon result that some of the pieces are scattered on the floor. The other way is to ladle the contents out by handfuls, which, of course, is slow. We took an ordinary wooden box and knocked out one end of it, then made a new endpiece, the full over-all width of the box, and hinged it at the bottom. Next we bent an iron strap, to fit close over the box lengthways, and attached the ends to the hinged lid with a screw on either side. It is quite easy to unload this box into a bin even at shoulder height from the floor. It is lifted up and the hinged end is pushed a little way into the bin. The strap is then raised and pushed forward to open the lid. Tilt the box slightly, shake it, and the contents will slide out.—H. Moore, Montreal, Can.

¶Taps should never be screwed down hard; if this is done, their washers wear out quickly, and the taps begin to leak.

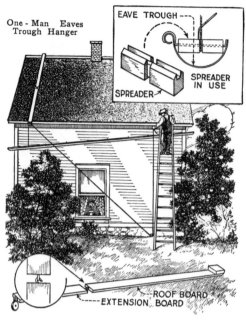

One - Man Eaves Trough Hanger

EAVE TROUGH

SPREADER IN USE

SPREADER

ROOF BOARD
EXTENSION BOARD

Hanging Eaves Troughs

Hanging eaves troughs is generally considered a two-man job, but with the arrangement shown in the drawing one man can easily do the work. In addition to a ladder, a ¾ by 6-in. board of convenient length is used. It is rounded at the top edge so that it can be pushed over the shingles easily, and has a 2 by 4-in. cleat nailed on one end, which is hooked over the ridge, and a screweye in the other. If a board of sufficient length to reach from ridge to eave is not available, an extension board can be hooked to the first, as shown, and a screweye driven into its lower end. The little wooden spreader shown in the insert is also required. The device is used in the following way: The board is hooked over the ridge of the roof so as to project a little over the drip edge. A pulley is attached to the screweye for a rope, as shown. The spreader is placed in position under a trough hanger, and one end of the rope is attached to it. The rope is threaded through the pulley, then through another pulley at the side of the ladder, which is then set up at the other end of the house. The worker now attaches the free end of the rope to the trough and climbs the ladder, taking the trough with him, and, in doing so, also lifts its other end. After fixing a hanger

at his end, he raises the trough to the proper slope and sets the remaining hangers.—H. A. Freeman, Willimantic, Conn.

Stamp for Dimension-Line Points

When inking in a drawing, I found that much time could be saved and a neater job done, if the dimension-line arrowheads were put in at one time with a rubber stamp. I cut it on the end of an eraser with a very sharp knife. The inside of the V was cut out first, and then the outsides. For an ink pad I used a small piece of blotter saturated with ink. After I had marked all the ends of the pencil lines, the latter were inked in.—Dexter W. Allis, Everett, Mass.

Attachment for Calipers Makes Precision Tool

Any mechanic can make a precision tool of his inside caliper by fitting it with the attachment illustrated. The indicating arm can be long enough so that accurate measurements can be obtained. The leg of the caliper is upset to make it thick enough for a slot to be cut in it for the indicator arm. The plunger comes in contact with the work and exerts pressure on this arm, and the spring keeps

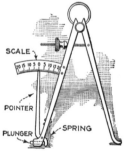

SCALE

POINTER

PLUNGER

SPRING

it tight against the plunger. For making shrink and forced fits the caliper is set at zero and the allowance can then be read on the scale. As this tool does not depend on the sense of touch of the operator, the human element is eliminated and accurate results are assured. The scale should be made accurately, which can readily be done with a dividing head.—Charles Kugler, Philadelphia, Pa.

Using Lacquer

Never apply lacquer over a coat of ordinary paint as the ingredients of the two are so different that the finish may be ruined due to chemical interaction. The solvent in the lacquer attacks the paint and c a u s e s bad checks which m a k e the surface very rough, necessitating the removal of the paint, and resanding. If the lacquer is too thick to use, and no thinner is available, use wood alcohol. This should also be used to clean the brushes. Lacquers made by different concerns can sometimes be mixed if they have similar solvents, but ordinary paint and lacquer cannot be mixed. Turpentine should never be used to thin lacquer. After lacquer has dried thoroughly a coat of varnish can be applied if necessary, but usually lacquer has a gloss finish and the more it is rubbed the more it will shine. It is unnecessary to use a wood filler before applying lacquer as it fills the wood and gives a nice even finish if put on properly. Do not use too much lacquer or the surface will be uneven and it will run. Apply it quickly and evenly and do not attempt to brush it out for the reason that it sets in a very few moments and gets tacky at once.—E. R. Haan, Chicago, Ill.

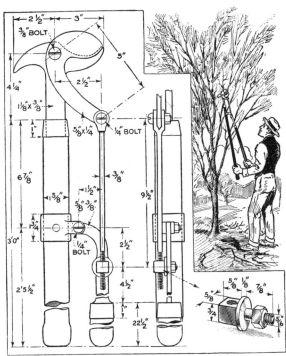

Handy Pruning Shears for the Gardener and Orchardist Can Be Made by Any Blacksmith

Magnet for Removing Chips

Having a number of holes to drill and tap in a solid block, which could not be turned over easily to remove the chips, I found the magnet a very handy tool. After drilling the hole to the required depth I took the magnet and a capscrew that would slip into the hole easily. After letting the screw to the bottom of the hole, I applied the magnet to the head, which caused t h e chips to cling to the end of the screw so that they could be removed easily.—Ralph Hanenkratt, Albany, N. Y.

Effective Pruning Shears

An almost indispensable tool for horticulturists and gardeners, is a pair of pruning shears. A good one, which can be made in any blacksmith shop, is shown in the illustration. The constructional details of the shears and the dimensions are clearly given. One particular advantage of this style is the hook part of the shear blade, which enables the user to pull the pruned limb or vine down without touching it with his hands. The shearing blades are forged from 60-point carbon steel, hardened in water and drawn to a dark blue, while the other parts are forged of ordinary machine steel. The handles are turned of ash.

Cleaning Files

One of the best methods of cleaning files, whether fine or coarse, is to rub them with a piece of coke. If the coke becomes full of grease when used on fine files, rub it on a rough file. This will make the coke clean again and the file will be cleaned at the same time.

Forming Corn Stacks

One man can stack corn with the simple "horse" shown in the drawing. The center pole is light enough to be dragged

With This Wooden "Horse" One Man Can Stack Corn Easily and Quickly

around with ease. It has two legs, preferably braced, near one end. A hole, large enough to allow a broom handle to pass in and out freely, is drilled at the point indicated. The stack is built up, tepee-fashion, by standing the stalks in the four corners of the crosspiece. When the stack is finished the broom handle is pulled out, which permits the horse to be removed easily.—H. Faller, New York City.

Removing Steel-Wool Shreds from Crevices

Steel wool is an excellent substitute for sandpaper in many cases, particularly on paint jobs between coats. It has the disadvantage, however, that small shreds of the wool break off and lodge in cracks, corners and crevices, from which it is hard to remove them with the dust brush, yet they will often be dragged out of these places by the bristles of the paint brush and disfigure the work, especially on white or other light-colored jobs. As a help to the dust brush, a horseshoe magnet, such as a magneto magnet, solves the difficulty, for it pulls out the bits of wool easily. As the shreds are so light in relation to the strength of the ordinary horseshoe mag-

net, just a sweep along the cracks and in the corners will remove all the steel-wool shreds.—L. I. Thomas, Oak Park, Ill.

Rotary Punch for Felt

In an attempt to punch 2-in. blanks from $\frac{1}{2}$-in. felt, I found that an ordinary arch punch had a tendency to cut through the felt obliquely, even though the punch was held vertically. There being a large number of punchings to do, I turned down the shank of the punch to fit the chuck of a drill press, and used it in the press in the manner of a drill, bringing it down onto the felt while revolving at moderate speed. A board was first placed on the drill table to save the edge of the punch. I found there was now no spoilage, and the work could be done faster than when using the punch with a mallet.—Dexter W. Allis, Everett, Mass.

Automatic Oiler for Line Shaft

Frequently an engineer or oiler will come across a bearing that never gets enough oil. This trouble can be remedied by providing an oil pump that will take care of three or four bearings. A cam is made with a 1 or 1½-in. throw, depending on the stroke one wants to give the pump. A lever, having a small roller in contact with the cam, is pivoted to a bracket at one end, and the other end is attached to the pump piston. A strong compression spring is placed under the piston to make the return stroke. The cylinder is made from a length of brass tubing. Two holes

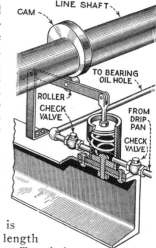

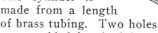

are provided for the inlet and outlet, and check valves placed in the pipe run to the bearings and from the source of supply.

You Can Fix That Dripping Faucet

Worn-Out Washers and Fuller Balls Can Be Replaced in Five Minutes When You Know How the Faucet Comes Apart

THERE is nothing more annoying around the home than a dripping faucet, and yet the trouble can be cured in five minutes with the aid of a monkey wrench and a new washer or ball, which costs about a cent. Faucets are common-

FIG. 1

FIG. 2 — COMPRESSION FAUCETS

SEAT WASHER — BODY — PACKING NUT — STUFFING BOX — HANDLE — CAP NUT — STEM — SEAT WASHER — SCREW — BODY

HANDLE — STEM — ADJUSTABLE CONE — CUTTER

SPINDLE — ECCENTRIC STEM NUT — RUBBER BALL

FIG. 3 — FULLER FAUCET

How Common Compression and Fuller Faucets Are Taken Apart for Renewal of Balls and Washers or Redressing the Seat

will be found fastened to the bottom of the spindle by means of a round-head screw, and it is only necessary to remove this screw and the small iron washer under it to replace the seat washer. Be sure to use the proper size of seat washer for the faucet. If the screw has rusted in place and is difficult to start with the screwdriver, place a drop or two of kerosene on it and allow the liquid to soak in for a few minutes before trying again. The screwdriver blade should be square across and a

ly of two kinds, the compression and the fuller type. In the first the stem of the faucet, carrying a composition washer at the bottom, is screwed down against a seat in the body of the faucet to stop the flow of water. In the fuller type the seat is horizontal, and the flow of water is controlled by a rubber "ball" which is moved toward and away from the seat by a small crank or eccentric on the end of the spindle.

To replace the seat washer on a compression faucet, shut off the water in the basement, or under the sink if there is a cock or valve there, then unscrew the cap nut on the faucet (see Fig. 1). A piece of heavy paper between the jaws of the wrench and the nut will prevent scoring or otherwise marring the nut. The washer

good fit in the slot of the screw head. If no regular composition washer is at hand, cut a new one of the same size and thickness as the old, from rubber, if the faucet is used for hot water, and from leather if it is for cold water. When replacing the spindle, be sure that it has not been screwed down hard on the seat before the cap nut is tightened. Screw the spindle in, down to the seat, then back it off the seat a full turn and screw down the cap nut.

Compression faucets used on washstands are often slightly different in construction from the regular sink compression faucets, although the mechanism is the same. If the top of the spindle looks as shown in Fig. 2, and there seems to be two cap nuts, then the upper, smaller one is a packing nut, and the lower one (marked stuffing box) is the one that must be turned with the wrench to remove the faucet. If, in a faucet of this type, any leakage is found to occur around the upper small nut, tightening this will usually remedy the trouble. If it persists, unscrew the packing nut and wrap a turn or two of asbestos cord, candle wicking or even common string rubbed with soap, around the spindle, then screw down the packing nut again.

The seat of a compression faucet often becomes nicked, scored or worn, and new washers will not stop the leakage. When this happens, the seat can be made as good as new again by means of a seat-dressing tool, shown in Fig. 3. To use this, the stem of the faucet is removed as described before, and the threaded cone of the tool screwed down into the body of the faucet to center it. The handle at the top of the tool is then revolved several times and the cutter on the bottom of the tool spindle squares the seat. The cuttings are then washed out of the faucet and the stem replaced. These tools come with several cutters for faucets of different sizes.

The method of removing a fuller faucet for renewal of the ball is shown in Fig. 3, the wrench being applied to the hexagonal part of the faucet body. It is not necessary to remove the spindle, as the ball is exposed when the front part of the faucet is unscrewed. Use one wrench on the body of the faucet and another, pressing in the opposite direction, on the tailpiece of the faucet, to prevent unscrewing the latter. The ball is held on the stem by a nut and cup-shaped washer. Re-

move the nut and washer, replace the ball, put back the nut and washer, screw the faucet body back into the tailpiece, and the job is done. Be sure to use the same size ball as the one removed. If, when tightening the faucet back into place, it turns over too far, or if the joint leaks when the water is turned on, screw the body back half a turn and wrap one turn of string around the joint, between the body shoulder and the shoulder on the tailpiece; then tighten.

Feed Box on Manger Front

The feed box shown in the illustration is mounted on a barn-door carrier track in front of the horse mangers. The carrier cars are bolted to the back side of the box, while two flat-faced wheels are mounted on the same side but below, to take the side draft of the box. They roll along the front of the mangers. The box is shown in position receiving grain from one of the two overhead chutes, sliding doors being provided on

Sliding Feed Box Mounted on Manger Front Is Filled from Chutes

the spouts to control the flow. The wooden flange on the top of the box prevents wasting any of the grain.—Dale R. Van Horn, Walton, Nebr.

Ball Punches Spring Steel

I often have occasion to punch strips of $\frac{1}{16}$-in. Swedish blue-tempered steel with a $\frac{1}{8}$-in. hole in each. These holes must be absolutely uniform in size, and must be put through with little expense as to time and tools. After unsuccessfully trying all ordinary methods, including use of the mercury-hardened drill, I hit upon the following plan which proved successful: On an anvil I placed a flat piece of steel having a $\frac{1}{4}$-in. hole through it. Over this I placed the strip to be punched, and with a round-end prick punch made a depression in the strip directly over the hole, using a heavy hammer. Then I dropped a ⅛-in. bicycle ball into the depression, and over that placed a strip of soft steel, that held it in place while I pounded on top of the soft strip. Three or four blows forced the ball through, making a clean hole.—D. W. Allis, Everett, Mass.

Electric Knife for Opening Storage Batteries

The novel electric knife described in this article consists essentially of an old spatula blade slotted to within ¾ in. of the end, as shown in the drawing, the slot being ⅛ in. wide. The blade is fitted with a fiber handle, made in two pieces. Between the blade and the fiber block on each side, are four brass terminal plates, made as shown in the lower detail, and rounded on the projecting portions to fit in the tubes of the plug connector. The latter consists simply of a fiber block drilled for two brass tubes, which should be a tight fit in the block and are drilled and tapped for small round-head screws to fasten the ends of the line wires.

About 2 volts are sufficient for most purposes, although for very rapid heating from 4 to 6 volts may be employed. Number 10 wire, rubber-covered, is used for the leads. The knife can also be used on a.c. current by using a step-down transformer, 3 volts being about right.—Arthman C. Capron, Athelstan, Can.

Self-Measuring Wood-Turning Tool

Many wood-turning jobs can be done more quickly with the aid of the novel turning tool shown in the drawing. It is used for finishing wood plugs and, by its shape, renders unnecessary any measuring tools. To make it, a steel ring is bored to the finished size of the work. The ring is split eccentrically and a hole drilled through the center of the smaller part to take a handle. After roughing, the tool is used until it cuts no more.

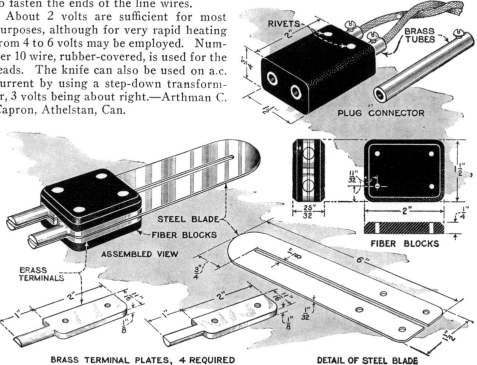

STEEL BLADE
FIBER BLOCKS
ASSEMBLED VIEW
BRASS TERMINALS
BRASS TERMINAL PLATES, 4 REQUIRED
DETAIL OF STEEL BLADE
RIVETS
BRASS TUBES
PLUG CONNECTOR
FIBER BLOCKS

A Knife for Use in Opening Storage Batteries That May Be Heated from Another Battery or from an A. C. Line; About Two Volts' Pressure Is Sufficient

Knurling in the Vise

In the home workshop or garage, where one has only a few hand tools and a vise, a good knurling job can be done the following way: The work is pinched between two mill files, placed in the jaws of the vise as shown in the illustration. The files must be parallel and the work set perfectly vertical. A moderate pressure should be applied, and the end of one of the files is carefully tapped with a hammer so that the work rolls between them.—Allan B. Shaw, Prescott, Ariz.

Homemade Milk-Bottle Washer

Washing milk bottles by hand is out of date and the small dairy, which cannot afford a commercial machine, will welcome the washer shown in the illustration. Its construction is simple, only one casting being required and that for the mouthpiece, which should be of some non-corrosive metal, such as brass. This piece is drilled a sliding fit over a ½-in. pipe and is fitted with a rubber washer, as shown. Use soft rubber, which will conform to the shape of the mouth of the bottles. A push-pin bracket is screwed on the bottom. A piece of ½-in. pipe is screwed into a ½-in. tee, and in the bottom of this tee, is screwed a brass plug, made as shown, while into the outgoing hole of this plug is screwed a short length of ¼-in. pipe, connecting with the two small water-inlet holes, drilled into the sides of the plug. A ⅜-in. button-head steam valve is fitted into the side branch of the tee and is operated by the push pin, which is carried in alinement by the bracket and a hole drilled in the tank cover. The top plate is made of ⅛-in. sheet metal and should be drilled with small ¼-in. holes to allow the water to drain back into the tank. The whole outfit rests on a ½-in. flange screwed to the bottom of the tank. A coil spring lifts the mouthpiece and supports its weight when empty. When a bottle is set into the mouthpiece and a weight is put on the bottom of the bottle, the mouthpiece descends and the pin pushes the valve open. Live steam shoots up through the ½-in. pipe sucking up a quantity of water by its whirling action, which cleanses the bottle. For the first washing a quantity of caustic or cleaning powder is added to the water in the tank, which is heated by the condensing steam. In rinsing, only clean water and steam are used. Control of the steam jet is made possible by placing a shut-off valve in the ascending line against the wall. A washer of this type will pay for

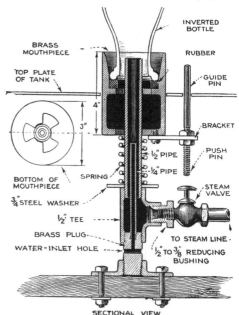

SECTIONAL VIEW
Inexpensive Milk-Bottle Washer Lightens Labor on Small Dairy Farm

its cost in a few days and will speed up the cleaning considerably.

¶ A piece of canvas, cloth or light leather, about 12 by 24 in., with the apron string along the longer edge, makes a good protection for the clothes when leaning against the drafting table for long periods.

Filing Piston Rings

When filing piston rings it is not necessary to use a vise. The rings can be filed more easily and quickly in the following way: A hole is drilled horizontally at a convenient height in the bench or stand close to the work, and the shank of the file is inserted in the hole as far as it will go, which will leave its cutting surface projecting horizontally. The operator should stand in front of this and bear down sufficiently on the projecting end to hold it firmly while filing the ring, which is done with both hands, moving the ring back and forth with the file between its ends. A neater and quicker job of filing can be done in this way and if the motor block is out and lying on its side on the bench, a hole for the file need not be drilled, as it can be stuck in a capscrew hole and, of course, much time will be saved in doing the job, for there will be no running back and forth to the vise, as is necessary with the common method.— Glen F. Stillwell, Collinsville, Ill.

Test Distinguishes Steel from Iron

A few years ago I was employed by a large manufacturing concern that purchased a quantity of surface-rusted large-diameter shafting which was supposed to be cold-rolled steel but later was found to be only iron. If a simple test had been made of this material previous to purchase, this error could have been avoided. Such a test, which can be performed by anyone, is the following: A spot on the material to be tested is ground or filed bright and then brought to a polish. Onto this spot diluted nitric acid is placed and allowed to remain until the surface is well etched. The acid solution is then washed off and the surface dried. If iron, the surface will have a fibrous appearance, but if cold-rolled or other ordinary steel, it will appear honeycombed. If the spot shows a fine, frosted surface, the metal is a high-grade steel.—W. J. Edmonds, Jr., Whitehall, N. Y.

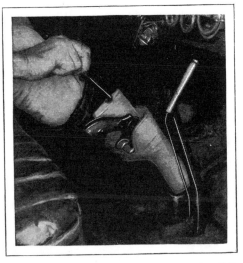

Convenient Method of Carrying Revolver on Gear-Shift Lever of Car

Handy Holster for Revolver in Auto

When a revolver is needed while driving, it will be found very convenient to have the holster attached to the gear-shift lever for quick action. A western fish and game warden carries his revolver here while traveling in his car. The method of mounting it is clearly shown in the photo.

Improved Crates Cost Less

The crate on the left in the accompanying photo was used by a manufacturer of steel pulleys for the export shipment of his product. The crate on the right is an improved type designed for the shipper by the U. S. forest products laboratory. Some crates carry a load of four 36-in. and twelve 8-in. pulleys. The improved crate occupies a trifle less shipping space than the other one. It requires 13.5 per cent less lumber for its construction, 33⅓ per cent less strapping and weighs 5 per cent less. One drop in the tumbling drum used to test boxes was sufficient to bring about the failure of the original crate. The improved crate withstood 100 drops before breaking.

Left, Old Crate for Holding Heavy Iron Castings; Right, Improved Crate

Compact Sling Loads Broken and Spread Evenly in Loft by Suspended Chain

Chain Scatters Hay in Mow

An objectionable feature of the ordinary hay carrier is that the fork or sling load is so large that the hay becomes too compact in the mow, which necessitates the use of a hay knife to get the hay out for feeding purposes. This difficulty can be prevented by suspending a chain between plates or studdings in the hayloft, as shown in the drawing. The sling load is tripped over the chain so that the hay is scattered loosely and can later be pitched out with an ordinary fork.—Tud Garver, Huntingdon, Tenn.

Cutting Off Spiral Springs

In an attempt to cut to length a quantity of ¼-in. diameter spiral springs, made of No. 20 gauge piano wire, I found the use of cutting pliers out of the question and the cold-chisel, hammer and anvil method inconvenient, because the lengths of spring would fly away and be lost as I cut them off. I did the job by clamping the cold chisel, edge up, in a vise, placing the spring on the edge and using the hammer to cut it. A gauge was set up on the bench to make the pieces of spring equal in length. With this method of cutting I had one hand free to hold the spiral and prevent the cut-off ends from flying away. —Dexter W. Allis, Everett, Mass.

Spring Compressor for Ford Clutch

It often happens, in overhauling a Ford transmission, that it is necessary to remove the clutch spring. While this is not difficult to do, with the proper equipment, the task may become burdensome with makeshift apparatus. The job can be performed on the arbor press or on the garage press, but the spring compressor shown in the photo makes it still easier. A ring or collar, large enough to clear the spindle of the driving plate, is turned out of ⅛-in. stock. Two holes are drilled into the rim, just far enough apart to allow the side members of the puller to pass over the spring and through them. A discarded transmission throw-out collar yoke is used for the grip, which enters the clutch throw-out collar. This is its normal position so that it is a nice fit. The side members of the studs are made from ⁷⁄₁₆-in. cold-rolled steel. One end of each is heated and forged flat. Holes are drilled in this flat portion to receive the lugs on the collar yoke. With the side members in place, the lugs are then riveted over. The upper ends of the studs should be threaded for a distance of about 5 in. and nuts and washers supplied. The spring is readily compressed and held while the parts are moved about and the pinholes lined and

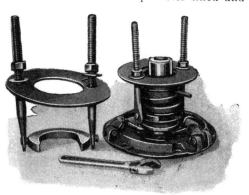

Spring Compressor for Ford Clutch Simplifies Task of Removing Spring

the pin driven out or in, as the case may be, without any awkward manipulation of punch and hammer.—Ray F. Kuns, Cincinnati, Ohio.

Leaks—in Walls, Pipes and Purses

By ROBERT TAYLOR JONES

MOST of our home-building efforts are directed toward the prevention of leaks. The walls we build must not leak heat, cold, wind or rain. The roofs we place over our heads—if they leak, then malediction on the roofer! Then there are the pipes that the plumber puts in. He is supposed to do work of such quality that we never again shall be reminded of him, and if the plumbing leaks, it violates our confidence—besides ruining the plas-

a crack so large that through it we could actually read the numbers on the license plates of passing automobiles. No wonder the basement was cold and the cost of heating the house high! The easiest way for the home owner to remedy a condition like that is to get a bucket of damp clay and mix with it a small quantity of hair, which can be obtained from any dealer in supplies for plasterers.

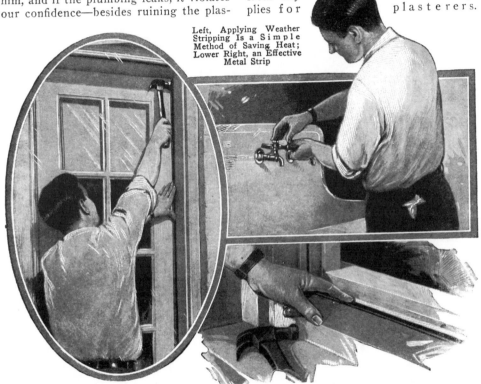

Left, Applying Weather Stripping Is a Simple Method of Saving Heat; Lower Right, an Effective Metal Strip

ter. There are smoke leaks, spark leaks, leaky flues, leaky cellars, leaks in electric wires and heat leaks from uncovered piping, all leading directly to a large leak in the pocketbook. All of these can be stopped, however, with a little work and a little horse sense. Perhaps not everyone can tell what causes a leak, but certainly everyone can find it after it starts. Sometimes they exist from the time the house was built, sometimes they grow up as the house wears down. The other day a friend took me into his basement, and there, between the sill and the foundation wall was

Then fill in the cracks in the walls of the basement and joints with the mixture. Chink up every place where a ray of light can be seen, and then, on the first cold, windy day, see if any cold air can be felt coming in around these places. If so, fill in with some more of the homemade plaster. In many houses, warm air can pass up from the basement between the studs of the walls. If such is the case, it is advisable to close the openings between the joists with old brick, tile or other suitable material. Also, in houses where there is no fire stopping between the studs, cold air can pass freely from the attic to the basement. In such cases, if the plaster goes down only a little below the top of the baseboards in the rooms, much air enters the rooms under the baseboards, where they do not fit closely. Such cracks should be closed. Basement doors and windows should be examined and made as wind-tight as those in the other parts of the house, as cold air entering the cellar cools off the furnace pipes and the floor above.

The covering of the furnace and the heating pipes in the basement is usually advisable, although a little judgment should be applied here. In one case, where the basement was always comfortably warm, with the furnace and the heating pipes uncovered, it became too cool for the housewife to wash and iron in comfort, when the j o b was done. This was remedied by

Look to the outside doors. These are often poorly fitted, and cold air can pass easily above and below them. The crack below the door is often so large that cold air sweeps across the floor, keeping the room cold. Good weather stripping, applied all around the door, will remedy this, of course, but a better job, and a permanent one, may be had by the use of metal weather strips on all doors and windows. This is more expensive than the wood-and-felt type, but it pays in the long run. Leaks around window casings and baseboards can be stopped with strips of paper, soaked in water overnight and then driven into the openings tightly. This can be stained, painted or varnished to match the trim, and will stay in place for years. The wallpaper around the casings should be protected while the wet paper is applied.

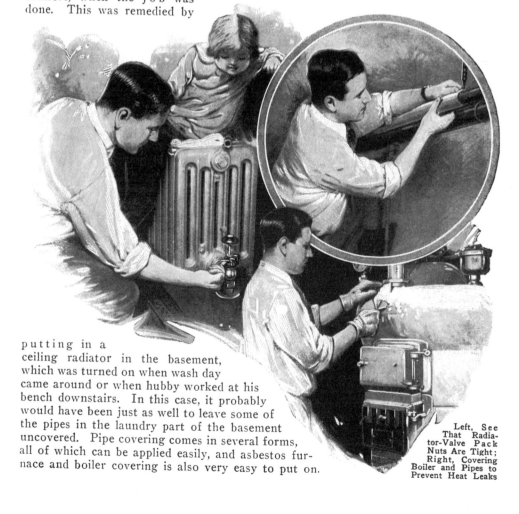

putting in a ceiling radiator in the basement, which was turned on when wash day came around or when hubby worked at his bench downstairs. In this case, it probably would have been just as well to leave some of the pipes in the laundry part of the basement uncovered. Pipe covering comes in several forms, all of which can be applied easily, and asbestos furnace and boiler covering is also very easy to put on.

Left, See That Radiator-Valve Pack Nuts Are Tight; Right, Covering Boiler and Pipes to Prevent Heat Leaks

There are some things that will save heat that cost no money at all, only a little time. Locking the windows when closed, drawing down shades all the way so as to provide an air space between the shade

linings cost so little that they can scarcely be found in the masonry bill, yet they pay dividends year after year in protection.

Left, a Leak around the Chimney Flashing; Center, Repairing Eaves Trough Leak; Right, What Happened When the Trough Leaked

and the glass, turning off heat in an unused room, or at night when the windows are open, periodical care of the heating equipment, all take but a little time, but will save a lot of heat.

Another part of the heating plant, the flue, is a prolific source of leaks. There should be two openings in a flue and no more. The flue should be lined with tile from the point where the furnace or stovepipe or fireplace throat joins it to the top of the chimney stack. Think what happens in that flue when the soot accumulates and takes fire, as it often does. If there is an opening somewhere along the stack between the bricks, due to mortar falling out, what is to prevent the blazing soot from going through this opening rather than out of the chimney top? Fire starts and the house is ruined. Flue

Then there are roof leaks. These can be prevented only in one way: by using good material, properly applied. See that the flashing around the chimney, for example, is built right into the brick, and that no light shows around the chimney opening from inside the attic. Get after any little leaks that do show up, before rain and snow get a chance to rot the wood in the roof, and perhaps the attic floor and the ceiling plaster. Watch the gutters on the eaves and repair any small holes that develop in them before they make rusty marks on the sides of the house, or allow water to seep in around the window casings.

Learn to fix the small leaks in the plumbing equipment of the house. Faucets and toilet flushes are easy to fix when they go wrong, and many a plumber's bill will be saved by a stitch in time. A can of "smooth-on" cement will fix the majority of piping leaks. If the pipes can be unscrewed and the new joint made up with this cement, the repair will be permanent. If not, one or two applications of the cement to the outside of the joint will make a repair that will last for a long time.

¶Plenty of exercise in deep-litter scratching keeps hens in a healthy laying state.

Water-Cooled Meat House

The claim is made by the owner and builder of the water-cooled meat house shown in the illustration that the meat chilled in it will keep from two to three times as long as meat chilled in an ice house. The owner of the house is a cattle trader and butcher of Princeton, B. C., who operates his own slaughter house in connection. After being killed and dressed the carcasses are taken to the meat house for chilling, cutting and weighing. They are kept there from 24 to 48 hours and sold. The house consists

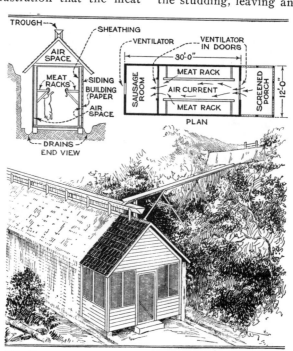

Thin Sheet of Cold Spring Water from Near-By Hillside Flowing over Roof Keeps Meat House Cool

of a 30 by 12-ft. frame building with two rooms and a porch. It is built in an excavation in a hillside, placing it partly below the level of the ground, and a V-trough is built over the ridge of the roof as shown. The trough has holes drilled in the sides to allow a steady flow of water to pass over the roof and down off the eaves. The building is shaded by close-growing cottonwoods and alders, although this detail was intentionally omitted in the drawing. Of the two rooms back of the porch, the rear one is used for a sausage room, and the front one for meat storage. The weighing, cutting and wrapping of meat for delivery are done on the porch, which is fitted up with tables, scales, chopping blocks, etc., in true butcher-shop style. Excellent insulation against the heat is obtained by air spaces in the walls and ceiling, as shown in the end view, and a double floor with building paper between the boards. The walls

are built of 1-in. ship-lap lumber nailed to 2 by 4-in. studdings with building paper on the inside. The inner walls are of 1-in. sheathing nailed to the inner face of the studding, leaving an air space for insulation between the inner wall and the building paper. The cross beams between the walls are covered with a ceiling of 1-in. sheathing, making an air space between the roof and the ceiling. The roof rests on 2 by 4-in. rafters over which 1-in. sheathing is nailed; and over this, in turn, red cedar shingles are laid, 4 in. to the weather. Over the peak is a V-trough made of 1-in. fir. A 4-in. insulated door, in which is a small trap window, separates the porch from the chilling room, while an ordinary door of 1-in. lumber separates the two inner rooms. At the back of the building, near the floor level, is another trap window, 12 by 20 in., leading to the space between the building and the earth bank at the rear. Two sets of horizontal bars serve as racks for hanging the meat in the chilling room. The sausage room is fitted up with tables, choppers, sausage machine, etc. Back on the hillside, about 50 ft. distant and about 10 ft. above the level of the roof of the meat house, there rises a small spring of ice-cold water which has an even, year-long flow. This has been dammed and the water led to the roof of the meat house in a V-flume. The flume is directly over the peak of the roof and runs to within 4 ft. of the front. Small holes are drilled about 4 in. apart in the sides of the flume to allow the water to run down over the roof. They are close enough together to make a solid sheet of water over the whole roof. The water drips off the eaves into the space between the building and the earth bank and is carried away in drains. The coolness of the water, as well as its evaporation, keep the building exceptionally cool. The flow of water in the flume is controlled by a slide gate in the dam. Dirt and leaves are kept out by screening in the outlet gate. A current of cool air is arranged for by small trap windows in the front door and rear of the building. This is a very important part of the chilling process.

Lathing Hints

Lath shrink most when they first dry out, and therefore only well-seasoned, clean lath should be used. Less contraction, however, takes place when the lath are wet on installation. Hence, they should be thoroughly soaked before they are nailed on to prevent cracking of the plaster. To make this wetting most effective, the plaster should be put on as soon as possible after the lath are placed. They should be spaced about 3/8 in. apart and a space of 1/4 in. left at the joints. Regular lathing nails should be used, and the lath should be nailed to every stud, breaking joints every six or eight laths. It is objectionable practice to allow lath to run in behind partitions, and ends in corners should always be supported.

Convenient Rack for Holding Saws on Wall above Workbench

Handy Saw Rack

To have your saws out of the way and handy at all times you will find the illustrated saw rack of considerable convenience. It consists of a 1-in. board, about 6 or 8 in. wide, the length depending on the number of saws. A space of 3½ in. is allowed for each with an inch extra at each end. Shape a number of pieces of 2 by 4-in. stock as shown in the illustration, and nail them to the board on 3½ in. centers. Place a 2-in. roller in each space and nail on a 2-in. strip, as indicated, to prevent the roller from coming out.

Substitute for Dry Cells for Ignition

Dry cells used on a gasoline engine running a concrete mixer were worn out, and to replace them meant a trip to town, which would delay the work considerably. Electric-light lines were near by and a toy transformer was obtained as a substitute for the dry cells. This was hooked up, and the engine started with a bang and kept on running in a satisfactory manner.

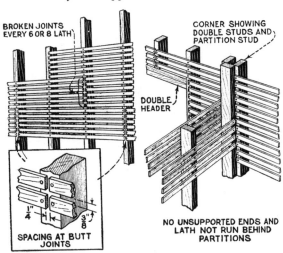

Proper Method of Applying Lath and Supporting It at Corners

Fixture for Lathe Refaces Brake Drums

In a western auto-repair shop the foreman has rigged up a lathe attachment for

Lathe Attachment Trues Up Automobile Brake Drums without Removing from Wheels

truing up and refacing brake drums on auto wheels, which does the work as well as a special machine made for this purpose. There are three attachments for different models of cars, consisting of duplicates of the axle shafts of the cars, on one end of which the wheel may be mounted, while the other is held in the lathe chuck. The axle is supported at the outward end by a special bearing on the lathe ways. The auto wheel is fastened to the end of the attachment as shown in the left-hand photo, and the machinist then refaces the brake drum. The right-hand photo shows the attachment, the bearing and a brake drum which has just been refaced.—Charles W. Geiger, San Francisco, Calif.

Tile Trenches Dug with Tractor and Plow

We were tiling 40 acres this spring and instead of digging the trenches by hand we used a tractor to remove most of the dirt. First a walking plow was run just as deep as possible, that is about 10 in., and with it a furrow was thrown each way. A lister with long extension moldboards on each side was hitched to the tractor. The latter straddled the trench and the lister was run about 12 in. deep. A long hitch was made with a chain and a guide wheel was attached to the front end of the beam. As the soil was heavy and wet at this depth, it was pushed out along the extensions of the moldboards far enough

so that it would not roll back into the trench. The rest of the depth and the leveling were done by hand, which was not more than one-fourth of the digging. Where the trenches are to be extra-wide, the plow is again run along one side, throwing the dirt into the trench made by the lister. This leaves it loose and it can then be easily thrown out by hand.—Geo. G. McVicker, North Bend, Nebr.

Saving Cement

When a bag of cement is dumped out, a good deal of the material is left in the bag fibers. A simple and effective method of removing this is to put a few stones in the bag and then shake it vigorously. The amount of cement thus shaken loose from the fibers is surprising. This method is better than beating the bags, as, in the latter case, the wind carries off a good deal of the cement.

Attachment on Ferryboat Holds It to Dock

Designed to hold the boat to the dock without the aid of ropes, the ferry attachment shown in the photo has been found extremely satisfactory. One man can run the boat and make a landing, whereas otherwise two men would be required, one

Attachment on Ferryboat Permits It to Be Moored to Dock without Ropes

to steer and the other to tie it to the dock. The attachment consists of two iron rails fastened to the side of the boat by means of heavy supports, as shown. The boat is steered so that the rails catch the mooring post on the dock.—Carlton Groat, The Dalles, Oreg.

Shop Notes

Blowtorch Made from Gasoline Lamp

By L. B. ROBBINS

MANY modern gasoline and kerosene lamps operate on the principle of the plumber's blowtorch, the gasoline in the fount being projected into the burner in the form of vapor, where it is ignited and consumed in flame. A lamp of this type can be converted into a useful soldering outfit as shown in the illustrations. As the fount holds 1½ qt. of gasoline and the burner is small, one filling of fuel will last a long time.

First remove the air chamber at the top of the lamp, the mantles and the generator. Leave the vertical air-intake tube standing. Saw off the generator about 3 in. above the locknut and force the shredded asbestos out of the tube. Then replace it and attach a length of thick-walled rub-

Novel Soldering Torch, Made from a Discarded Gasoline Lamp, Is Useful for All Kinds of Small Jobs and Can Easily Be Made in the Home Workshop

ber tubing, wiring this on. A few turns of stiff wire near the metal tube will prevent the tubing from kinking at this point.

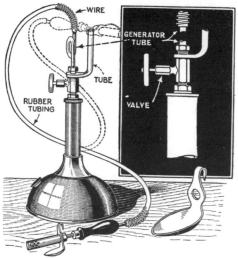

Construction Details and Assembly of the Blowtorch

Straighten out a second generator in the vise so no kinks are left. Saw off the spread end, reverse the direction of the locknut and push it up near the tip. Then drill a hole, the size of the tube, lengthwise through a wooden tool handle and drive the tube through it, leaving a couple of inches projecting to which the rubber tubing should be wired. Get a piece of thick-walled brass tubing, about 3 in. long and with an inside diameter that can be tapped to take the generator locknut. Drill several small holes through this tube in the unthreaded end as indicated. A heavy spoon, with a wide shank, should be fashioned as shown and a hole drilled in the handle of such size that the generator tube will be a force fit in it, while leaving sufficient material outside to cover the end of the large tube completely. Now assemble the parts. The generator tip should rest about a third way down the length of the perforated tube, the spoon shank should bear against the threaded end of the tube, and the locknut should be screwed up tightly against it. If the generator tends to slip or air spaces show, fill these with hard solder. The top end of the spoon shank is bent to form a hook so that the burner can be hung up.

To start the outfit, pump air into the lamp fount, burn a little gasoline in the spoon to heat the tube, turn on the gas valve and light the burner. If the tip is in the right position in the burner tube and the holes properly placed you will get a nice blue flame, hot enough for any light soldering. Experimenting in enlarging the hole in the tip and in varying its distance from the burner end will get you the best results. When found, a drop of solder will hold it permanently in position.

Assembling Bendix Drive on Ford Starter

When assembling the bendix drive on a Ford starting motor, take care to see that the stop nut or bearing, which enters the mounting bracket on the starting motor, is not too tight, and that the bearing is in proper alinement with the bracket. The bearing should be oiled and then fitted so that it can be readily turned with the fingers. If the bearing is too tight, dress it down with an oilstone, as too tight a fit will cause the bearing to freeze to the bracket, which will result in serious damage to the starter.

Planks Keep Trench Openings Smooth

Keeping pavements smooth at trench openings, where the pavement cannot be relaid until the back filling has settled properly, and where the tires of passing vehicles keep pulling out the backfill, has been solved in one city by placing planks in the trench. Two or more 3-in. planks, wide enough to fit the opening in the pavement and cut to the proper length, are placed in the opening, the backfill being graded so that the plank surfaces are flush with the top of the pavement. The planks are lifted out at intervals and more backfill is added as the trench settles.

Planks Used to Cover Trench Openings in Pavements

How to Braze Band Saws

The proper way to braze band saws is to make a lap joint by beveling the ends for a distance equal to about two teeth. The blade is clamped so that the ends overlap in the center of the clamp. After applying a little powdered borax in the lap, a small piece of silver solder, about the size of the braze, is inserted. Heat the brazing tongs to a red heat and press them against the joint firmly, holding them there until the tongs cool to a dull red. The tongs are then slid back and forth along the blade a few times to insure a uniform braze. Then the cooled joint is carefully filed down to a uniform thickness.—William C. Thomas, Chicago, Ill.

Brace Keeps Heavy Posts Upright While Tamping

When he had to set a number of heavy fence posts in concrete, a mid-west farmer found the task seemingly impossible without the aid of an assistant to hold each post perpendicular while the concrete was poured and tamped into the hole around the post. As help was not available, he devised the simple brace shown in the drawing. A length of ½-in. round iron was bent to the shape of a horseshoe with loops at each end and one at the center. To each of these loops a pointed standard of the same material was attached, the points being bent slightly inward. To support a post set in the hole the brace is placed as indicated and the hook points of the three standards are forced into the sides. The post is safely and securely held in this position and the operator is free to tamp the cement and gravel around it. If made in a larger size, the same kind of support could be used to brace telephone poles as very little support is necessary to hold a pole in position when it is once erect.

Grooved Roller for Glaziers

To simplify the application of putty to window sash, a Wisconsin glazier devised the illustrated grooved roller. The putty is placed on the mixing board and rolled out to the desired thickness, after which it is cut into V-shaped strips with the roller. A strip, 8 or 10 in. in length, is used each time and can then be smoothed on more readily than when applied with a putty knife.— G. E. Hendrickson, Argyle, Wis.

Cutting Holes in Thin Sheet Copper

Having occasion to cut a large circular hole in a tank of thin copper and having no tool on hand for this purpose, the one shown in the illustration was improvised in a few minutes and found entirely satisfactory. All that is needed is a drill and bit, a machinists' C-clamp, two short pieces of wood and an old hacksaw blade. These parts are assembled as shown in the illustration, the center hole first being drilled so that the drill fits in it and serves as a center. A cut is made in the end of one of the blocks of wood to hold the saw blade securely. The teeth prevent it from sliding up in use when the pressure of the clamp is applied and the grooves on the drill keep it from turning in the blocks when the device is used. The jaws of

HACKSAW BLADE

the C-clamp must be placed between the drill and the saw blade.—W. N. Lurcott, Weehawken, N. J.

Lathe Rigged Up for Use as Rotary Metal Shears

Nearly every day the average small machine shop that depends on rapid production for work and profits has need for a device that will cut a piece of sheet

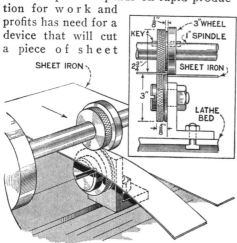

metal of medium gauge. We were recently called upon to make four ventilators using about 20-gauge sheet iron. As we had no tools except ordinary hand snips, and I knew that the job would be a tiresome one, I did some figuring, which resulted in the rotary shears shown in the drawing.

Rotary Shears Run by Lathe or Milling Machine Are Useful for Small Shops

The outfit consists of two circular cutters, each of which is mounted on a suitable shaft and is partly knurled to grip the metal while cutting it. The device is set up in a lathe or milling machine and one man can easily operate it. The upper cutter is made of tool steel, turned down to 3 in. in diameter, and has a 1-in. hole to fit on an arbor to which the cutter is keyed. The smooth part is $3\frac{1}{4}$ in. in diameter. I did not grind the cutter, as we were in a hurry, but it was hardened in oil. Do not forget to undercut it as shown, or you will be unable to sharpen it. The lower cutter is turned to 3 in. in diameter, but only three-fourths of the face is knurled. It is held in place and rotates on a stud driven into an angle-iron bracket, which in turn is clamped down securely. When assembling the device, care should be taken to bring the rolls together firmly but not tight in a horizontal direction. One-half the thickness to be cut is

the proper space between the knurled parts of the cutters. The lower cutter should, of course, be lined directly under the upper cutter. In using the shears no pressure is required to follow the line. It took about three hours to make them, and they saved considerable time.—Omar Fluharty, Sciotoville, Ohio.

Simple Method of Protecting Railroad Ties against Fire

One of the hazards troubling the railroads is firing of ties, piled along the tracks, by sparks from passing locomotives. Those made from fat pine, which are desirable for their lasting qualities, or those treated with creosote to prolong their life, are very easily ignited. A roadway supervisor has adopted a successful plan of preventing these fires by covering the piles with a 4-in. layer of earth which is jammed down tightly, so that no cracks are left between the ties. Any projecting ends of ties at the sides of the piles are similarly protected, a shovelful or so of earth on each piece being sufficient to give ample security against fire.—L. M. Jordan, Newton, Ala.

Handy Ladder Support

Getting the ladder out of the shop or putting it back is much simplified by using the device shown in the drawing.

A wire is stretched from one end of the shop to the other and a pulley is placed on the wire with a hook heavy enough to hold the pulley vertically. When the ladder is withdrawn the pulley and hook will be at the entrance of the building where the ladder may be hung on and pushed back in place readily.—F. E. Poister, Morrill, Kans.

Removable One-Man Truck Body

A wrecking company in San Francisco has equipped one of their lumber trucks with a removable body for hauling bricks bent to form hooks. These catch the rear roller, holding the body in the position shown. When this has been done the driver slowly backs up until the empty body stands vertically on end and the

Special Body Built by a Wrecking Company for Hauling Brick; It Can Instantly Be Removed or Attached to Truck by One Man

because the limited extent of their trade in this commodity did not warrant the expense of a special truck for this purpose. There are two rollers provided on the bed of the truck to facilitate moving the body. To remove the body from the truck, the rear roller is turned by means of a bar until the body is moved to the position shown in photo No. 1. The rear end is lowered to the ground, as shown in photo No. 2, but the body is kept from slipping off the truck by means of two steel straps

truck is ready to be used for hauling lumber. In placing the body on the truck again, the driver backs the truck up to the body, which is standing vertically, pushes the body over, until it strikes the roller on the rear of the truck, then drives forward until the roller on the rear engages with the two steel straps. Now he can easily lift the rear end of the body and push it forward on the rollers. All the operations are easily and quickly performed by one man.—C. W. Geiger, San Francisco, Calif.

Graduating a Six-Foot Scale in the Lathe

A small jobbing shop had only a lathe, drill press and shaper. A tailor brought in a piece of brass, 7 ft. long, 2 in. wide and ⅛ in. thick. He wanted a 6-ft. length of this marked in ⅛-in. graduations to be used for measuring cloth. We first fastened the brass with screws to a piece of machine steel, 7½ ft. long and 1½ in. square. This was placed in the lathe, as shown, and an indicator was used to line it up on the top and side. The 1-ft. graduations were measured off with an ordinary scale, and the 1-in. and the ⅛-in. graduations with a 1-in. and ⅛-in. length of steel, used between the edge of the carriage and a clamp stop on the bed. The cross slide and the scribing tool shown in the upper detail were used to do the marking. This method, of course, will not make a precision scale but the job was quite sufficiently accurate to serve the tailor's requirements. — C. Moran, Philadelphia, Pa.

TOOL FOR SCRIBING LINES

TOOL

C.R. STEEL ⅛" THICK

SCREW

CLAMP

Graduating a 6-ft. Metal Scale in the Lathe for Use as Tailor's Measure

Spring Clamp Facilitates Laying Out of Blocks in Pairs

In cases where it is necessary to mark off a large number of blocks in pairs, the

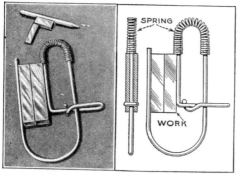

Spring Clamp Facilitates Marking Off Blocks by Handling Two at a Time

spring clamp shown in the illustration has been found to be of considerable assistance. The clamp is made of two pieces of 3/16-in. wire held together by a coil spring as shown. The tendency of the spring to straighten out holds the clamp tightly against the work. One wire is bent at right angles and looped around to inclose the other, in order to keep both in line opposite each other.—Harry Moore, Montreal, Can.

Felt Washer Protects Painted Surface

When drilling through a painted or highly polished surface such as the dash or

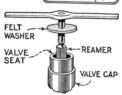

fender of an automobile, the drill frequently breaks through and the chuck mars the finish. A piece of leather or felt put over the bit and against the chuck as shown in the illustration will prevent this trouble. Similarly when using a tap or reamer the tool will go through the work suddenly and the handle will strike the work. On gears, valve cages or wristpin bushings, where the teeth may be marred, the valve seat

bruised or the face of the piston scratched, such a leather or felt washer put between the tool and the work will prevent this objectionable bruising.— G. A. Luers, Washington, D. C.

Set Your Own Wagon Tires

Wooden carriage and wagon wheels often lose so much of the natural moisture in spokes, hubs and especially the felloes that the steel tires become loose, and the wheel is soon ruined if used in that condition. Instead of taking it to the blacksmith, soak the wood parts in water until the tire is tight and the wheel, when tapped, gives the sound of solidity. Now, the important thing is to make this setting last at least one season, and this is done with oil or paint as follows: As soon as the wheels are surface-dry, give the wood a coat of kerosene, and again let it, too, become surface-dry. This allows the oil or paint to penetrate deeply enough to hold, as keeping moisture in the wood depends on a cover of paint or oil. Now apply a good wagon paint, or linseed oil of which one-third is drier.—Louis Murback, Poultney, Vt.

Device for Changing Spring Shackles on Ford Cars

When fitting new spring shackles and bushings on a Ford, either on account of wear or failure altogether, do not jack up the body to take the weight off the springs. They can easily be changed by using a C-clamp of suitable size and a strip of

hardwood, say, 1 by 2 by 8 in. in dimensions, and clamping it in position, as shown, recessing it to fit over the oiler in the spring perch to avoid damage to the oiler. Screwing up on the clamp will cause the shackle bolts to slip out. With the usual type of coil-spring shock absorbers, a clamp can be used without a wooden strip.—C. S. Bartless, Dallas, Tex.

Portable and Collapsible Tool Table

Mechanics often carry their tools along to a job and when they get there they may have to work for long periods on their knees or standing on a stepladder. Where several tools are used, convenience and a considerable saving of time can be accomplished by having the tools at all times readily accessible on a small portable and collapsible tool table of the kind shown. It is adjustable to any range of height up to the worker's head, and the top revolves, so that any tool can be brought within easy reach. The music stand, which can be obtained for a few dollars. With the iron rod deep in the stem and

the legs folded upward against the stem, it makes a neat bundle, about 2 ft. in length, weighing less than 4 lb. The flat top consists of two semicircular pieces of heavy sheet metal, hinged together and reinforced underneath by light wooden ribs, as shown. A hole in the center of these ribs fits over the upper end of the stand.

Collapsible Workbench, Which Is Light in Weight and Can Readily Be Carried in the Tool Chest, Facilitates Work of a Mechanic

table is durable and exceedingly light, and can be carried in a tool box, when collapsed. It is made from an ordinary metal

The table can be adjusted to any height from 18 to 60 inches.—P. C. Grose, McComb, Ohio.

Welders' V-Blocks

Most welding shops possess some kind of V-block arrangement for lining up broken shafts, rods, etc., or butt-welding pipes and tubes, but the one shown in the drawing has a few advantages not commonly known. In the first place the lining-up member is well away from the heat of the torch, and is not underneath the work as in ordinary extension V-blocks, where it soon becomes scaled and difficult to move. Secondly, there is no limit to the length to which the vees can be extended. As no machinery is required to make a pair of these blocks, smaller repair shops can adopt them profitably. Take a piece of ¼ or ⅜-in. flat stock, bend it to the double V-shape shown and then cut the piece in half. In use, the work to be welded is laid in the vees on one side and any suitable piece of round stock is laid in the others to line them up. The alining rod should be placed in the vees first and these slid in or out until the two portions of the pieces to be welded are balanced.

¶A good auto-top dressing consists of 2 lb. lampblack in oil, 1 gal. pure boiled linseed oil and 1 pt. pure turpentine, with a small amount of drier.

Tools for Applying Pebble Dash to Stucco

Temporary Stair on Loose Dirt

Framing for Niche in Living-Room Wall

Fireplace for Gas Log with Air Vent

Scaffold for Street Does Not Block Traffic

Wedging Bricks Makes Good Arch

Roofers' Nails Hold Stucco to Old Wall

Support for Column Facilitates Handling It

Holding Stone Veneer to a Brick Wall

Glass for a Surface Plate

The other day I needed a surface plate; something that would be fairly accurate. I looked over the workshop but could find nothing that would answer the purpose. Precision surface plates are expensive and for the little use we have for them yearly, it really does not pay a farmer to buy one. I needed the surface plate badly and had about given up when I happened to think of a broken windshield which we had left from an auto accident. We never dreamed that it would be of any use whatever, but, while it was not perfect, it served as a dandy surface plate and will answer for pretty fine jobs in any farm or other workshop. In going over the matter with a mechanic recently, he decided to get one for himself after he had examined it.—H. W. Swope, Danville, Pa.

Protection against Corrosion of Battery Terminals

On automobiles where battery terminals are subject to considerable corrosion, it is a good idea to tin the terminals. This can be done best by dipping them in melted solder or lead up to

MOLTEN SOLDER OR LEAD

the insulation on the cables. The clamp screws and nuts should also be tinned. A method of doing this, which has been found practical and satisfactory, is to melt the solder or tin in a ladle and then dip the terminal in it, as shown.

Belt-Saving Trick

A great saving can be made in a shop where there are many belts, if the following method is used: When the belts are to be laced, punch out holes large enough to insert eyelets in the holes. It will be found that the holes, especially in rubber belting, will not become worn so quickly.

Washing Parts in Gasoline

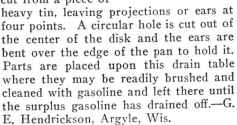

In the garage or machine shop, when engine or machine parts are placed in a pan of gasoline to be cleaned, the liquid often becomes so dirty that it is difficult to locate the pieces when wanted. To overcome this, one mechanic employs the novel drain table shown in the illustration. A disk, somewhat smaller than the diameter of the pan top, is cut from a piece of heavy tin, leaving projections or ears at four points. A circular hole is cut out of the center of the disk and the ears are bent over the edge of the pan to hold it. Parts are placed upon this drain table where they may be readily brushed and cleaned with gasoline and left there until the surplus gasoline has drained off.—G. E. Hendrickson, Argyle, Wis.

Printers' Emergency Furniture

It sometimes happens in printing offices that there is no metal furniture of the required size. This makes it necessary to resort to numerous emergency methods, the most usual of which consists in filling up the space with lead slugs. The drawing shows a convenient and simple method of filling large spaces by making furniture of the proper size from pieces of rule or slugs. Pieces of the proper length to fill the space are cut and notched on a saw trimmer, which is found in nearly every plant. These notched pieces are put together and then placed in the space to be filled,

PIECES OF RULE

as shown in the illustration.—A. C. Cole, Chicago, Ill.

Safety Guard on Power-Line Poles

Children frequently climb telephone and power-line poles and serious accidents have often resulted from contact with live wires. To prevent this, the Louisville Gas and Electric company provided guards made of sheet metal and attached these to the poles, as shown in the illustration. This was found to discourage the children from using the poles for climbing.

Cutting a Radius Corner

Cutting a corner on a given radius is something many machinists consider impossible without the liberal use of a file, and this is more or less difficult where a high degree of accuracy is involved. A good method of accomplishing this job with ease is shown in the drawing. The edge of the cutter is first ground to produce a radius about one-tenth smaller than the finished radius of the piece. This will make the actual radius of the tool even smaller on account of the angle at which the upper surface of the tool is tipped. With the shape of the corner roughed out with other tools, begin to use the special cutter on one side, then on the opposite side, and then at the center, shifting the tool as soon as more than one-third to one-half of its lip starts to cut. This work is done best with the

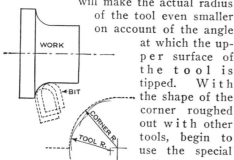

power shut off and the belt operated by hand. The result of cutting in this manner is to remove a fine chip of metal at each cut, which eliminates chattering as the tool never gets a grip on much metal. A series of small shallow ridges will be left, but these are so slight that they disappear after a few light strokes with a fine file. The completed job will be well finished and accurate. It is also possible, with this method, to merge the arc of the corner exactly with adjoining surfaces.

Electric Alarm Indicates Unwound Clock

One of the janitor's duties in a large manufacturing plant is to see that the master clock is kept wound and running on time each day. After several lapses of memory, when he allowed the clock to run down, he devised the following simple method of warning when the spring was nearing the end of its operating power. He drilled two holes in the side of the case, one near the bottom and the other directly opposite the side of the spring. An insulated electric wire was run through the lower hole and bolted to the metal frame of the clockwork. The top hole was reamed out just large enough so that a spark-plug porcelain could be forced tightly through it. This porcelain was connected to a

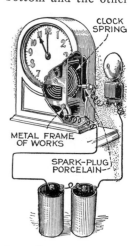

second wire and the wires were connected to a battery and doorbell in series. The contact point in the porcelain was adjusted a certain distance from the spring so that, when it was nearly uncoiled, it would touch the point and close the circuit, ringing the bell.

¶To make a battery box acid-proof, melt 8 parts of wood tar and 14 parts rosin in an iron kettle, then stir in 10 parts fine brick dust; apply solution warm after the box has been cleaned and sandpapered.

KINKS THAT HELP THE BUILDER

Hood over Pulley Protects It from Debris

Hot-Air Vent Held Securely by Ears

Framework and Bracing for a Rubble Pier

Sturdy Hanger for Heavy Soil Pipes

Stone-Filled Barrels for Temporary-Line Poles

Pipes Held on Floor to Prevent Moving

Strap Irons on Plank Ends Prevent Splitting

Quickly Erected or Dismantled Wooden Derrick

Convenient Platforms for Cornice Builders

V-Block Centering Device

One of the quickest methods of marking the center of short lengths of round work is to use the handy V-block attachment

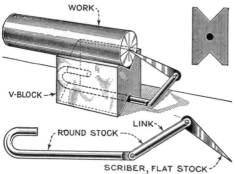

Convenient Scriber Mounted on V-Block Centers Round Stock

shown in the drawing. It consists of three pieces: a block having a "V" cut on two opposite sides; a length of rod fitting in the bottom "V" and bent over so that when put in place the end slips into a hole drilled in one end of the block; a length of the same-size rod pivoted to the end of the first piece, and a scriber, made of flat stock, pivoted on the end of the link. Any size of work can be marked off and a further advantage is that the work need not be square on the end, as the scriber readily accommodates itself to irregular surfaces. In use, the scriber is moved downward and the shaft turned and marked in two or more places, the point of intersection being the center.—Harry Moore, Montreal, Can.

Hulling and Scarifying Clover Seed

We have grown our own sweet-clover seed for several years and thresh it with our grain thresher. It does not hull the seed, but this work and the scarifying are done in one operation in the following way: A quantity of coarse, sharp sand or gravel is obtained; this is dried, and then run through a fanning mill so that all sand particles smaller than a clover seed are screened out. A bushelful of the coarse gravel, which passes through the fanning mill, is placed in a barrel-type concrete mixer and a bushelful of the un-hulled clover seed is put in with it. The two are tumbled together for about 15 minutes. Both are passed through the fanning mill with a screen that will allow the clover seed to screen from the gravel. The wind blast removes the loosened hulls and the seed is clean and well scarified by the scratching the sharp gravel gives it.—Wendell N. Mitchell, Rogers, Nebr.

When to Paint Vacuum Equipment

New pipes or cylinders in which a vacuum is to be maintained should not be painted until after the plant is set in operation and a vacuum is being maintained within the parts. The reason is that all metal is more or less porous, and when it is new, it allows leakage. If painted before using, the thin coating on the outside soon gives way. It should be painted while in use with a thin-mixed paint as this allows the pores to become filled, and the result will be a very noticeable increase in the vacuum.

Trailer Carries Concrete Mixer

Having a number of widely scattered jobs to do, a western construction company built a heavy trailer for one of its trucks to carry a big concrete mixer, in order to transport it faster than it could travel on its own power. Four wheels with solid rubber tires were used. They were put on axles fastened to a triangular framework of iron beams, a small beam being placed at the front end to keep the mixer from running onto the wheels at this end, which were very close together. Iron plates were used as a runway, and the mixer

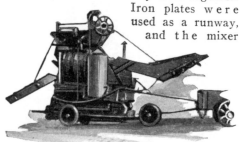

Large Concrete Mixer Transported from Place to Place on Heavy Trailer

run up on the low framework under its own power.—A. Flinner, Wichita, Kans.

¶Paraffin rubbed on woodwork with a soft cloth will remove all dust and dirt.

Novel Sliding Door on Drain Pit

By DALE R. VAN HORN

ONE of the objections to the open drain pit usually found at gas-filling stations is that there is no convenient method of keeping out the rain and snow. The accompanying illustration shows an installation which embodies this desirable feature in a practical, efficient

is set into the side of the pipe and a cable runs over the pulley. The end inside of the pipe is connected to an iron weight

Counterbalanced Sliding Door over an Oil-Drain Pit at a Gas-Filling Station Is Convenient and Safe, and Keeps Out Water and Snow

way. With this sliding door, the pit is kept closed at all times except when a car is to be drained. It is a matter of a few seconds for the operator to raise it to an upright position and attend to the car in the usual way. Since the door is counterbalanced with a weight inside of a vertical pipe (indicated by the dotted lines) only a little effort is required to open or close it. The pipe should be about 4 in. in diameter and extend 5 ft. above the ground, its total length being sufficient to allow it to be solidly set and give the weight freedom to run the necessary distance. A pulley

which pulls up and down freely, thus counterbalancing the weight of the door. A cap is screwed on top to exclude moisture. The door itself is made in two sections. Each section is of the same length and slightly wider than the pit. One section is hinged to a piece of 2 by 4-in. wood, which is mounted on the end of the pit by means of bolts whose heads are imbedded in the concrete. The other section of the door is hinged to the first section by means of ordinary hinges. Both sections are covered with matched lumber, with cleats on the inside, and the edges are trimmed with material, 1 in. thick and 3 in. wide.

When the door is down these hinges fit along the edge of the concrete pit. A handle is provided on one section of the door. To facilitate opening and closing the door it will pay to attach small casters to this half of the door so that they will ride on the concrete edge, which is built in the usual way. Steps lead down to the bottom of the pit for the worker. No dimensions are given as these are hardly necessary because each filling station proprietor has his own ideas about a pit. The installation shown is used in a number of cases in and around Kansas City and is proving entirely satisfactory.

Handy Radiator-Filling Funnel

Simple Funnel Facilitates Filling Auto Radiators

By soldering a tin funnel, which had lost its neck, to a cap of a glass jar it was made into a very satisfactory radiator filler. A hole, a little larger than the small opening of the funnel, was cut in the cap and the latter was soldered in place, as shown in the right-hand figure.

Test for Foul Air in Wells

Inexperienced well workers often lose their lives by going into wells without first testing them for foul air. This can be done by lowering an ordinary lantern into the well, as far as possible. If there is any foul air the flame will get dim and if there is much of it the light will go out entirely. The foul air can be removed in the following way: Lower to the bottom of the well an old pail filled with burning charcoal, holes being punched through the bottom of the pail to permit sufficient draft. As the foul air is heated it rises out of the well and fresh air enters to take its place.

After the fire has burned for about 10 or 15 minutes it can be removed, and the workers can go down safely. Even if the well is very dirty, carbonic-acid gas or foul air will not collect again for a considerable time, at least not for several days. A pail, a sufficient length of wire attached to the handle, and a long cord or rope, can nearly always be obtained, but a blower and a length of hose are not always procurable. Furthermore, the blower method is not quite reliable. Fresh air can be forced down into the well but a layer of gas may still remain at the bottom. One breath, enough to fill the lungs, may cause almost instant death. The easiest and surest method is the use of a charcoal fire as described.—James E. Noble, Toronto, Canada.

Profile Planing

In machining large, cast-iron forming dies of the kind shown in the detail, the method indicated in the illustration was found especially convenient. We made a template out of ½-in. machine steel and clamped this on the planer table. It was a duplicate of the dies, but about 1 ft. longer because the stroke of the planer must be greater than the length of the job being planed. The roller and the arm, which holds it, are screwed to the planer head and the latter is kept against the template with a rope and weight, the rope being fastened to the planer head and sliding over a pin, as shown. The depth of the cut is regulated by moving the clapper box. It is evident that the tool will move in a path that exactly duplicates the template. The operator feeds the tool by hand.—Charles Kugler, Philadelphia, Pa.

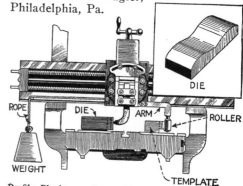

Profile Planing on Large Dies Was Done in Record Time by Using Template

Drill-Spindle Screwdriver

When a large number of long screws have to be driven, a fixture permitting the driver to be used in a drill press will be found a timesaver. By running the press at a reasonable speed, the work can be done much more quickly than by any hand method. The device consists of two round stock bearings, a length of steel tubing, a slotted screw and the special driver. The driver head is finished with a tongue in the center to fit the slot in the screw. These two parts are finished first, then, with a washer behind the head of the screw, the two bearings in which they turn are driven tightly into the ends of the tube. Another washer is placed on top of the bearing containing the driver screw, and two locknuts on top of this. These nuts are adjusted so that the screw will drive the screws into the work but will itself turn when the head touches. This forms a friction-slip drive and can be adjusted nicely with just enough tension to drive the screws. The tool is gripped in the drill-press chuck and the work, with the screws started a thread or two by hand, placed on the table. The screw to be driven is brought beneath the tool and the spindle fed

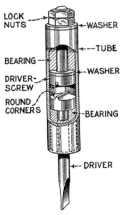

LOCK NUTS
WASHER
TUBE
BEARING
WASHER
DRIVER-SCREW
ROUND CORNERS
BEARING
DRIVER

down until the slot and tongue engage. The screws are then driven into the work by operating the drill press. The connection is maintained until the screw is finally driven, when the driver screw turns or rather ceases to turn with the machine.

Homemade Heat-Proof Paint

Where a heat-proof black paint is required, the following easily prepared mixture will be found practical. It consists of graphite, 2 parts; Fuller's earth, 10 parts; sodium silicate, 11 parts; glucose, 1 part and enough water to make the mixture applicable with a brush.

To Increase Capacity of Saw

When it was necessary to cut a large quantity of 5-in. pipe, the handsaw was found just a little too small, both in stroke and depth of cut, making it necessary to turn the pipe three times. To hasten the work and make smoother cuts, a piece of ⅜-in. rod was bent as shown in the illustration, and a pin to hold the blade was set

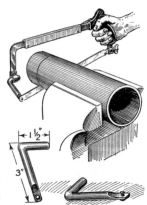

in the flattened lowered end. By using a longer blade, the pipe could be cut through with one setting. The attachment has been left on the saw permanently, as it does other work just as well as before the alteration.—Harold E. Benson, Boulder, Colo.

Factory Foreman's Call Bell

When there is need in the shop or factory for a loud gong, such as is used to call the foreman to the office or announce the starting and quitting time, the installation shown in the drawing will be found useful. Remove the small bell and substitute a brake drum taken from an old auto wheel. Fasten this on with a large screwhook or a bolt bent to L-shape. There should be about ¼ in. clearance between the clapper and the gong shell. Drive three nails into the wall round the edge of the drum, to make it stand out from the

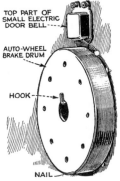

TOP PART OF SMALL ELECTRIC DOOR BELL
AUTO-WHEEL BRAKE DRUM
HOOK
NAIL

wall as indicated. This will prevent muffling of the sound and the bell will give a clear signal.—Earl E. Moffat, Pasadena, California.

Quantity Production of Automobile Name Plates of Type Metal Is Easy Work for Anyone and Only a Few Tools Are Required to Do It

Profit from Making Auto Name Plates

By BRONALDO MURRAY

MAKING automobile name plates for autoists is a profitable spare-time business. Anyone can make a mold, pour the metal, and finish a large number in a short time. The only equipment necessary for this work is a gas plate, or other heating device, a small melting pot, a ladle and a polishing wheel upon which a wire brush and a cloth buffer are mounted.

The material used to make the name plates is ordinary type metal such as printers use in their linotype machines. A little metal antimony is added for hardening. The melting pot should be of iron and the type metal can readily be melted over an ordinary gas flame, or if this is not available, over a gasoline or kerosene-stove flame. A blowtorch can also be used for this purpose. After the metal has been melted, it is poured into a plate-steel mold with a ladle, as shown in the accompanying illustration. The mold is made from two steel plates riveted together. The lettering is cut in one plate with a metal-cutting scrollsaw, which plate is

then riveted to the second. After the metal has been poured and hardened, it is dipped in water to cool it. Shrinkage of the metal then takes place, which makes it comparatively easy to remove the name plate. This is done by laying the mold, with the name plate in it, face down on the bench top, and tapping the back side with a light hammer to loosen the plate. The work is finished nicely on a buffer, and dipped in a transparent varnish.

To facilitate fastening of the name plate to the radiator it is advisable to drill two or three small holes through the letters at different points. Bolts, a little longer than the thickness of the radiator, are pushed through the holes and washers and nuts on the other end hold it in place securely.

Emergency Grain-Drill Tube

While using the wheat drill this spring one of the rubber tubes dropped down and wound around one of the wheels, which ruined it. A length of old bicycle tire was found, and a length of strap iron was placed in it to hold the section straight. This was attached in place of the damaged tube and answered as well for completing the spring seeding as a regular tube.—Geo. G. McVicker, North Bend, Nebr.

Novel Road-Marking System

Road commissioners in St. Joseph county, Mich., have found that they can save labor and material in dividing county highways into two lanes of travel by using white-painted squares every 10 ft. apart instead of applying a solid white band the whole length of the highway. The new method has proved entirely satisfactory.

Method of Measuring Angles

When no protractor head is available, an angle can be accurately measured by the method shown in the illustration. The dimension B is always the same and the distance C is read directly from the scale. First see that the surface plate is level,

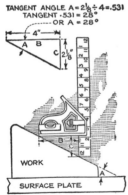

TANGENT ANGLE A = 2⅛ ÷ 4 = .531
TANGENT .531 = 28°
OR A = 28°

4"

A B

C 2⅛"

WORK

SURFACE PLATE

A

then mount the square on the work as shown and move the scale up or down until the bubble in the level is in the center. Now two sides of a right-angle triangle are known, and the angle A can be calculated by dividing the length of side C (2⅛ in.) by the length of side B (4 in.), the result in this case being .531, which is the tangent of the angle A. A table of natural functions will show the corresponding angle to be 28°. The application of this method is unlimited, and if a micrometer depth gauge is used to get the exact measurements of B and C very accurate results can be obtained.

❡A good method of curing egg-eating hens is to punch tiny holes in each end of an egg, blow the inside out and then fill the shell with mustard.

Clamp Holds Pliers to Bench

Considering the facility with which parts are held in the jaws of large pliers and tongs for such work as splicing and fitting thimbles to wire cables, holding bar stock and electric conduit, the bench fixture shown in the illustration should appeal to all mechanics having such work to do. It is made of fairly thick flat iron or steel, and its construction and use are shown

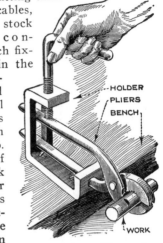

HOLDER
PLIERS
BENCH
WORK

with sufficient clearness in the illustration to make any more detailed description unnecessary.—G. A. Luers, Washington, District of Columbia.

Fitting Connecting-Rod Bearings

Frequently, upon examining connecting rod bearings, it is found that the bearing shells are floating loose in the connecting rod and in the cap, even though they had originally been riveted in place. After re-riveting the bearing shells it may happen that their edges are lower than the surfaces of the rod and cap. To remedy this by filing is difficult and tedious work, necessitating repeated checking on a surface plate if an accurate job is to be done. An easier way is to make a number of shims, with the inner edge folded over, so as to press directly upon the bearing shells. If the number of shims and their thickness are correct, the bearing shells will be held permanently in place.—Richard P. Cole, Paterson, N. J.

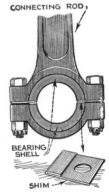

CONNECTING ROD

BEARING SHELL

SHIM

Shortening Ford Valve Stems

After grinding Ford valves or installing new ones, one is usually found too long, and it is then necessary to file it down or shorten it in some other way to get the required minimum of 1/64-in. clearance between the end of the stem and the top of the push rod at its lowest point. But filing the end of the stem by hand, even when the valve is held in a vise, is a somewhat troublesome process. An easier method is to place a sharp file, flat side down, on the top of the push rod and insert the valve in its correct position in the cylinder block, allowing the end of the valve stem to come in contact with the file as it rests on the push rod. The end of the stem is rotated on the file by turning it with a valve grinder and the stem will be shortened as desired, the speed depending on the pressure exerted upon it and the number of revolutions given to the stem. Removing the file from the push-rod top allows measurement of the clearance without the necessity of withdrawing the valve stem. After grinding the stem in this manner, care should be taken to wipe away all the filings that have dropped into the valve chamber.

Double Track for Narrow Bridge

On a two-track electric line there are a number of viaducts which it was not deemed advisable to build to double-track width. Instead the two tracks were run over the bridge in the manner shown in the illustration. With this arrangement one track forms the guard rail for the train on the opposite track. Automatic signals on each side of the bridge were provided. In addition to saving in first cost, this construction permits the trains to cross without stopping while a switch is thrown, which could not be done if a single track were used to cross the bridge.

Convenient Method of Turning Coil Springs by Hand

Spring-Wire Coils Wound by Hand

An easy method of winding a coil spring is shown in the drawing. Bend a length of steel rod, equal in diameter to the inside diameter of the coil spring, to a crank shape and drill a hole through it for the end of the wire. Take two blocks of wood and set them up in the vise with the crank between as indicated. Set the wire so that it will make a thread in the wood when you start winding. The wire will then follow this thread as it is fed from the top. A little oil may be used to avoid excessive friction.—C. D. Fredericksen, Detroit, Mich.

New Use for Large Clips

A large office that sends a number of telegrams every day has worked out a new use for large 2-in. clips. Just to one side of the door that leads into this office from the corridor, one of these large clips is attached to the wall, the flat piece at the top of the clip being fastened to the jamb. Whenever a telegram is ready the telegraph signal is rung and the message put in the clip. There it is safe until the boy comes around, and he knows just where to look for it.—Russell Raymond Voorhees, Jacksonville, Fla.

Shop Notes

Use Your Outboard Motor for Power

By LAWRENCE B. ROBBINS

AN outboard boat motor is seldom used for more than three or four months of the year, but the man who likes to tinker and build things during the winter days can utilize it as a serviceable power plant for his basement or barn shop. It will function perfectly in driving small machinery, such as drills, bandsaws, bench lathes, etc., and if properly installed and operated can do the motor no harm. The only accessories needed will be an automobile radiator and fan and some garden hose; also a bit of blacksmith work and simple pipe fitting. This latter may be hired done, but the handy man should be well able to prepare every part himself.

A solid wall should be selected upon which to build the motor support. It should be at right angles to the countershaft or machine to be operated. Cut out two wide planks, about 1 ft. taller than the height of the radiator and 1 ft. wide. Slightly taper them and spike or bolt them to the wall and floor with the smaller end

View of the Outboard-Motor Power Plant Assembled and Running a Feed Grinder; Many Other Uses for the Handy Unit Can Be Found

down. Place them at least 2 ft. apart, parallel and vertical, and then spike solid planks horizontally across the front. Let

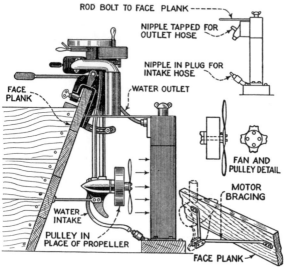

ROD BOLT TO FACE PLANK

NIPPLE TAPPED FOR OUTLET HOSE

NIPPLE IN PLUG FOR INTAKE HOSE

FACE PLANK

WATER OUTLET

FAN AND PULLEY DETAIL

MOTOR BRACING

WATER INTAKE

PULLEY IN PLACE OF PROPELLER

FACE PLANK

Side Elevation, Showing the Various Construction Details; There Is Very Little Work Necessary

the top edge of the uppermost plank project somewhat above the ends of the upright boards so the motor can be clamped to it without interference. If wide planks are unavailable, smaller ones can be used as in the drawings, in which case corner posts are necessary.

Place the motor in position and clamp it solidly in place. Then plumb the vertical shaft from all sides and fasten temporarily in place with small battens and cords. Next, drill two small holes through the end of the fin or skeg under the propeller and fashion two angle irons of solid round stock, as indicated. These should be heated and flattened at each end and bent at angles which will allow two ends of the irons to be bolted to the fin. Then the two other ends of the iron can be bolted near each side of the face planks of the support, as shown. Be very careful that the motor shaft is absolutely plumb when this is finished. It will be noted that the steering handle should clear the wall and the depth of the top of the support should allow for this.

Next remove the propeller and substitute a small-diameter solid-iron pulley. To conform with the particular motor being used, it may be necessary to rebore the pulley hole and cut a new keyway, or it

may mean that the entire propeller and pinion pulls out. In this case, a new pinion must be fitted to the pulley and the complete installation made. In either case, the work will not be found difficult. Then drill the pulley hub to match the holes in the fan and bolt the latter to it, as shown. Twist or arrange the vanes to blow air away from the motor when the pulley is revolving in its proper direction.

Plug the inlet and outlet pipes of the radiator so no leaks can occur and then drill and tap the pipes in suitable places for two $\frac{1}{2}$-in. nipples. Spike blocks to the floor in front of the fan and mount the radiator on them with lag bolts. Then make a long tie-rod, to secure the top of the radiator to the face planks in a solid manner. The hose connections are then made to the two nipples on the radiator as follows: Tap the water-intake opening at the bottom of the shaft housing and insert a short piece of pipe or a nipple, and do the same to the outlet opening at the cylinder water jacket. Then clamp a hose from the inlet to the bottom of the radiator and from the outlet to the top of the radiator. This completes the circulatory system. The revolving fan blows air through the radiator and prevents the water from becoming overheated as it is pumped around through the engine, pipes and water jacket.

Belt up the pulley to the machines, fill the radiator with water, the gasoline tank with fuel, and you will be ready to run the plant. Crank it just as if it was on a boat, and regulate the speed by the usual spark and throttle controls. See that the running parts are well oiled, and this little outfit will be found to do good work. Of course, a small pulley belted to a large one on the machine will allow the motor to run at near normal speed and develop its maximum power.

If such an outfit is used in a shop with doors and windows open, the exhaust gases will not be noticeable. If the room is tight, on account of the weather, the gases should, by all means, be carried off. This can be easily done by the placing of a tin funnel over the muffler opening and connecting it to a line of common rain pipe, 2 in. in diameter, and leading it outdoors through a window or the chimney.

Comb for the Shop-Sweeping Brush

One of the minor annoyances of machine-shop life is the way steel cuttings stick in the brush when the floor is swept. A nail or a piece of wire is often used to clean the brush, but this takes so much time that we decided to make up a regular comb for the purpose, and this is shown in the accompanying drawing. Two end-pieces, sharpened at one end, are attached to the brush loosely with screws. These two pieces hold a rod, drilled with a row of holes to take short pointed wires, which form the teeth of the comb. The pieces should be securely soldered or welded together. Have the comb laid back on the handle when the brush is in use. When the cuttings have been swept into a pile ready for removal, the brush is cleaned by turning it over to allow the comb to fall down, so that the pointed ends can be dug in the floor and the brush rocked back and forth. This causes the comb to pass

Comb Attached to Brush Cleans It of Metal Cuttings

through the brush and clean it thoroughly of all sweepings that may have stuck in it. —Harry Moore, Montreal, Can.

Handy Drill-Press Accessory

Adjustable Stand near Drill Press for Holding Long Work Reduces Labor

The adjustable steel horse shown in the photo has proved a valuable accessory to the drill press in a Denver steel shop, where it was originated to hold up the back end of long work being drilled. Two sections of ½ by 1½-in. steel bar, about 6 ft. long, are bent to form the ends of the frame, and two pieces of the same material, 16 in. long, are riveted across the end of these, to serve as braces. Four sections of the bar are also riveted lengthwise to the legs. The two uprights, which support the roller feeder, are perforated with numerous holes so that the top can be adjusted to any height desired by simply moving two cotter keys up or down. —Jos. C. Coule, Denver, Colo.

How You Can Guide Your Tractor with a Door Spring

When plowing with a tractor, where the one front wheel runs in the furrow, no guiding is necessary. But when the steering wheel is thrown partly around by the front wheels striking a depression or a bump on the surface, the former will not return to the straight-ahead position. To remedy this, a short leather strap, with a ring attached, was buckled around the rim of the wheel and a screen-door spring was attached to a point on the frame directly opposite to this ring. One end of the spring is snapped to the ring and each time the wheel is thrown either to the right or to the left, the spring returns it.

Increasing Usefulness of a Saw

The saw shown in the drawing should be used before its merit can be fully appreciated. It is a crosscut saw of the usual

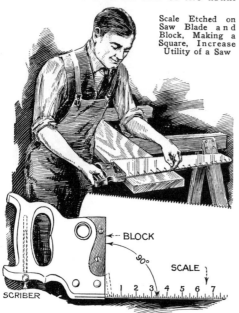

Scale Etched on Saw Blade and Block, Making a Square, Increase Utility of a Saw

kind, but with the back edge ground straight, and the handle set so that its inner edge forms a right angle with the back of the saw. Instead of a new handle, filler pieces may be fitted to the original handle, as indicated by the shaded section in the sketch. Further convenience may be had by addition of a scriber and a brass tube for holding it in the handle, and by etching a scale on one side of the saw at the back. The saw can be used as a square, having double the range of the generally used universal square. It is much easier to handle than the large carpenters' square, and it saves one tool to carry around and look after when working on a staging.—Herbert A. Freeman, Willimantic, Conn.

Safety Rules for Working around Ammonia Pipes

When opening a pipe joint where ammonia has been carried, care should be taken not to open the joint wide instantly. Fumes linger in such pipes in sufficient quantities to become dangerous when liberated in a room suddenly. Flanged joints should be loosened and very slightly opened by means of a thin wedge or screw jack and, if any fumes are detected, the joint should be closed immediately until they are drawn off or it may be left slightly open so that the fumes may pass off gradually. It is best not to loosen the bolts of a flange joint more than barely enough to separate the joint in case there might be pressure within the pipe, which would cause disaster if liberated suddenly. Screw joints should have the union slightly loosened and the joint broken loose before the union nut is entirely unscrewed. A towel saturated with vinegar held over the face should be used when loosening or working with ammonia-pipe joints especially in confined rooms.

Can Saves Varnish

A varnish can which preserves the contents, is used in a vehicle factory. It had been found wasteful to pour the varnish into small cans as it rapidly deteriorated if not used up within a short time, and as the cans must be carried around the factory some of the varnish was spilled. The special can shown in the illustration holds about 4 gal. of varnish and is made of fairly heavy metal. It is round in shape with a cover piece, soldered about 2 in. below the top, and a handle on the side. A cowl-shaped trough is soldered inside of the top of the can. A cork is fitted in a hole in the cover. When the varnish is required, remove the cork and tip the can until enough liquid flows into the cowl. The cork is replaced and the can placed upright

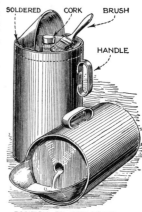

POSITION OF CAN WHEN POURING LIQUID

so that the varnish floats on top of the cover. As soon as the work in hand is finished, the cork is removed to allow any unused varnish to run back into the can.

Winding Lengths of Fence Wire into Rolls on Pegs Attached to the Rear Wheel of a Tractor, Which Is Jacked Up for This Purpose

Tractor Used to Wind Up Fence Wire

I built the small farm tractor described in the August, 1917, issue of Popular Mechanics, and it has been of considerable use to me for several years. Last year I conceived an idea about a device on the tractor for winding up barbed wire. Winding it by hand is a mean job, but with the aid of this attachment the work can be done in a short time. To each spoke of one of the rear wheels a short length of iron rod is clamped to extend outward as shown in the drawing. In use, the tractor is set at one end of the fence and is jacked up. The wire is loosened from the posts and one end is attached to one of the winding pegs. The wheel is then revolved, which winds the wire around the pegs. You can wind a length of wire about a half mile long in this way. When the roll is completed, tie it up with short lengths of wire, loosen a few pegs and slip them toward the center of the wheel, which will permit you to remove the roll of wire. When using

the tractor for this purpose, guide the wire with a 5 or 6-ft. length of iron pipe as indicated and keep one hand on the clutch at all times so that if the wire gets caught or tangled the winding can be stopped at once before the wire breaks or other damage is done. — Luther Strosnider, Onaga, Kans.

Saving Time in Testing Air

The time required to test the air on railway cars has been shortened by a method devised by an employe of a western road. He attached a short length of hose to the tester, mounted as usual on the triple-valve exhaust port, and connected the other end of the hose to the retainer pipe. By the use of a small petcock between the hose and air gauge both cylinder and retainer may be tested without the necessity of moving the gauge.

Method of Testing Air Cylinder and Retainer on Railway Car

¶To prevent chickens from catching cold, put some spirits of camphor in their drinking water, 10 drops to each quart of water, about once a week.

Two-Man Jobs Are Speeded Up by Swiveling Work Holder

Many shop operations could be finished more easily and quickly with the help of

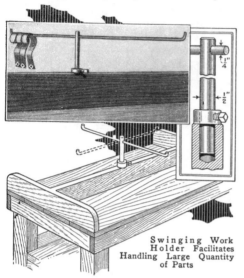

Swinging Work Holder Facilitates Handling Large Quantity of Parts

a holder similar to the one shown in the illustration. It is used in connection with a job of brazing nuts on the ends of flat-spring hooks. Removing the surplus metal and retapping the hole are the next operations. These are done on the same bench at the opposite side. The holder is used to facilitate the passing of the work from one operator to the other. The center board is drilled with a ½-in. hole to a depth of about 6 in., to take a piece of steel the same diameter, this piece being drilled through near the top to take a rail made of ¼-in. rod, which is driven tightly into the swivel post and then turned up slightly at each end. A collar with a set-screw is fitted to the post and, when assembled, it rests on a couple of washers placed on top of the board, to protect it from wear as the holder is turned. The method of using the holder is as follows: The operator engaged in brazing the nuts hangs each piece

when finished on the part of the rail at his side of the bench; the first being placed at the extreme end, as shown in the photo, so that by the time this side of the rail is full, the end pieces are cool enough to be handled by the operator on the opposite side. Both operations consume about the same time; by the time one side of the rail is filled, the other is empty and all the second operator need do to get another batch is to swing the holder around a half turn when the empty rail is again presented to the first operator ready for filling. It has been found that by working this way there is no possibility of mixing up the work as often happened before. When the holder is not required, the post is lowered and the rail laid parallel with the center board out of the way.

Acid Test for Oil

The presence of acid in lubricating oils is detrimental and the following simple test to discover it is recommended. Dip blue litmus paper in the oil, and if the color changes to red, there is acid present. The litmus paper should be soaked in rain water before the test, for if the water happens to be alkaline, it will neutralize the acid absorbed by the paper and the oil will show a neutral condition when it really contains considerable acid.

Winter Shelter for Pump and Engine

The farmer who finds difficulty in keeping his pasture engine and pump protected against severe cold, will find the idea illustrated in the photo serviceable. The shed used to protect the pump consists of a framework inclosed and roofed with corn stalks, bound together in bundles and held in place with a wire both inside and outside. With the wind thus kept out, the interior will get quite warm when the engine is running, thus making for more efficient operation.—Dale R. Van Horn, Walton, Nebraska.

Corn-Stalk Shed Shelters Pasture Pump and Engine during Cold Weather

How to Build the Form Work for a Concrete Cistern

By ROY M. SINGER

THERE are many localities where it is necessary to store water. Generally some arrangement is used whereby rain water falling on the roof of a house is let into a cistern and pumped from the cistern as it is needed. The cistern may be made either of wood, steel, or concrete. Concrete cisterns are meeting with a good deal of favor because of the fact that the materials are to be had in practically every locality and because nearly anyone can build them.

Where deep cisterns are built, the form work is simple, because such cisterns are generally built with wide mouths. For shallow cisterns, however, the situation is different. It is easy enough to erect the forms for a shallow cistern, but taking out the form work is quite a different matter. The sketches shown here illustrate a type of form work designed especially for shallow cisterns with narrow mouths, and it is especially adapted to withdrawal from a narrow space.

In building a cistern of this type, the bottom and walls are put in place first, then the form work for the top is set, as shown in the sketches. The form work consists of a central post to which a barrel head is attached by hooks; spanning the space between the cistern wall and the barrel head are set 2 by 6-in. pieces cut

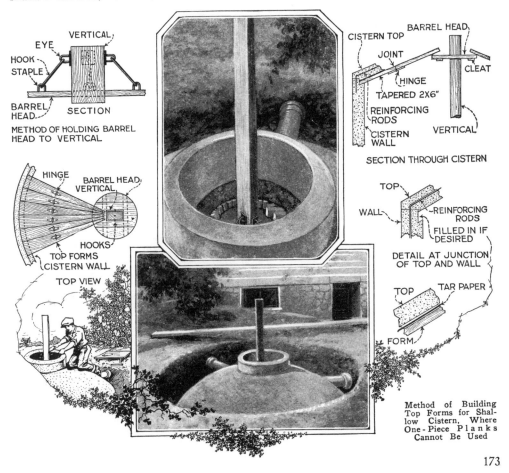

EYE
VERTICAL
HOOK
STAPLE
BARREL HEAD
SECTION
METHOD OF HOLDING BARREL HEAD TO VERTICAL

HINGE
BARREL HEAD
VERTICAL
HOOKS
TOP FORMS
CISTERN WALL
TOP VIEW

CISTERN TOP
BARREL HEAD
JOINT
HINGE
CLEAT
TAPERED 2X6"
REINFORCING RODS
CISTERN WALL
VERTICAL
SECTION THROUGH CISTERN

TOP
WALL
REINFORCING RODS
FILLED IN IF DESIRED
DETAIL AT JUNCTION OF TOP AND WALL

TOP
TAR PAPER
FORM

Method of Building Top Forms for Shallow Cistern, Where One-Piece Planks Cannot Be Used tapered to fill the circle. These pieces are hinged in the center and it is the hinges that permit the easy withdrawal of the form from the cistern. After the form work has been set up and the top of the

mouth of the cistern is wider than the barrel) and removed from the cistern, the post then withdrawn, and the job is done. Where a shallow cistern is built it would be impossible to withdraw the forms from

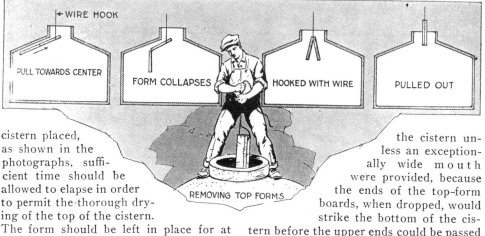

WIRE HOOK

PULL TOWARDS CENTER

FORM COLLAPSES

HOOKED WITH WIRE

PULLED OUT

REMOVING TOP FORMS

cistern placed, as shown in the photographs, sufficient time should be allowed to elapse in order to permit the thorough drying of the top of the cistern. The form should be left in place for at least ten days.

When it becomes time to remove the forms, a wire is attached to the barrel head and the hooks holding the barrel head to the post are loosened. The barrel head is then allowed to slide down on the post until it falls free of the tapered pieces. It will be found that the 2 by 6-in. lengths will stick to the top of the cistern, due to the fact that they are held in place by the notch at the cistern wall and by the adhesion between the underside of the top of the cistern and the wood form. This adhesion may be overcome by placing tar paper upon the form before the top is poured; thus there will be a layer of tar paper between the form and the top of the cistern and the form will not stick.

Now attach a wire to one of the tapered pieces so that it can fall into the cistern, then work it out of the notch in the cistern wall by jiggling it back and forth. It may then be pulled toward the opening. The manner of removing it is best illustrated by the detail drawing. It will be seen here, that as the piece is pulled toward the opening, it collapses at the joint, and the wire may then be pushed farther along until the joint is reached, whereupon the form may be removed. After all the top forms have been taken out, the barrel may be pulled up (be sure that the

the cistern unless an exceptionally wide mouth were provided, because the ends of the top-form boards, when dropped, would strike the bottom of the cistern before the upper ends could be passed through the top opening. This method of hinging overcomes the difficulty.

Time-Saving Device Administers Capsules to Poultry

Every poultry raiser finds it necessary at times to treat his stock for worms. The usual remedy is nicotine sulphate in 2-gr.

Improvised Injector for Administering Capsules to Poultry Does the Work in a Short Time

capsules and the usual method of administering the capsule is to insert it into the bird's beak and then work it down with the fingers. Frequently the operation is not successful and the bird ejects the capsule to be picked up by another already treated and then the result is at least one dead bird. To avoid such accidents and to make the operation quick and easy, a California poultryman has improvised an instrument, with which a hundred or more birds may be treated in the same time as five by the old method. The instrument is a slightly curved hard-rubber tube, or nozzle, about 5 in. long. Cut into the end of the tube so it will fit over a No. 2 capsule. A wire injector fitting the top of the hole for the capsule is placed in the tube. The top of the wire is attached to a button, while a spring is provided around the wire. Press the button to move the injector and release the capsule. Release the pressure on the button and the spring around the wire will pull the injector back into place. To use the instrument the capsule is put in place, the tube is inserted through the open beak of the bird, the injector is pressed out and the tube is then withdrawn. The operation requires about five seconds, while, without the device, it sometimes takes five minutes.—Geo. B. Bowers, San Diego, Calif.

Side Hitch for Motor Truck

There are many other than just hauling jobs that the truck will perform when equipped with devices adapting it to these jobs. The drawing and photo show how a side hitch can be attached to a truck. It can be used, without damage to the truck, for jobs that do not require too heavy strain, such as stretching fence wires where the line of posts prevents a direct pull from the rear end of the truck; pulling a plow along a bank, ditch or gulley, when filling these openings; pulling a road blade to trim off the side of the graded road, etc. The pieces required and their forms are shown in the drawing. The pulling bar is made of a piece of ½ by 3-in. machine steel, forged with the eye at the inner end around a U-bolt. The bolt passes through the side of the frame of the truck with two nuts on the inner side. A right-angle bend is given the pulling bar to allow the front wheel to clear both the bar and the chain, which connects it to the front end of the truck

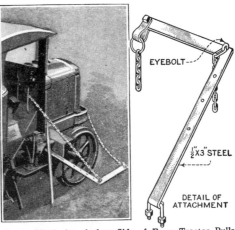

Handy Hook Attached to Side of Farm Tractor Pulls Light Implements

frame. The chain, attached to the dash and bar by means of the eyebolt, allows adjustment for height such as the tool being pulled, or as the work may require. It also allows the bar to be folded and hooked in a vertical position when not in use.—G. G. McVicker, North Bend, Nebr.

Eliminating Air Leaks in Stone Foundations

It is rather difficult to make a really air-tight job at the top of stone foundations. The heat loss caused by such leakage is considerable and causes cold floors in spite of all that is done to prevent it. A good method of preventing this trouble is shown in the accompanying illustration. A 2-in. board is nailed to the plate, as indicated, the top of the foundation having been cut back to permit this. The sealing board is set in grout, and after

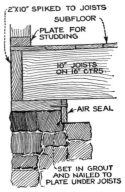

it is in place one or two coats of paint should be applied, as this will help to close all small cracks.

A Serviceable Homemade Grinder

As can be seen, the grinder and buffer shown in the drawing is built up almost entirely from pipe fittings and old Ford connecting r o d s. A floor flange and a tee, screwed to the flange with a short nipple, form the base. The tee is reamed out to t a k e a short length of pipe and

setscrews are used to hold the pipe C in place, on which four connecting rods are fitted to hold the grinder arbor and the driveshaft. The lower bearing surfaces of the connecting rods are screwed up tight on the pipe C, to make the arbor and driveshaft parallel. The upper bearings are fitted with grease cups. The driveshaft is provided with tight and loose pulleys and also a drive pulley. Another pulley is fitted on the arbor in line with the drive pulley, and also two collars having an overhang to inclose felt dust washers, which are placed as shown in the detail. The arbor shaft $\bar{I}$ is turned down for the grinder and buffer, and the ends are threaded for nuts with which the wheels are held on the shaft securely.—Geo. H. Cappel, Wilmer, Ala.

DRIVE SHAFT
CONNECTING RODS
COLLAR
DRIVE PULLEY
COLLAR
PIPE C
FLOOR FLANGE AND TEE
DRIVE SHAFT
SHAFT I
H
FELT
OIL HOLE
I
PIPE

Old A u t o Connecting Rods, a Few Pipe Fittings and Two Shafts Make a Good Grinder and Buffer for the Small Workshop

Installing New Belt in Factory

In a factory where I was doing a small job, a long and heavy leather belt, about 18 in. wide, was being installed. The method used to get the belt in position was novel to me as it removed most of the

difficulty usually encountered when doing such a job. Both ends were cut square and one end was fastened to the old belt. The roll of new belting was placed on top of the old belt so that it would unwind when the latter was turned. The shafting and pulley were turned over slowly, allowing the new belt to run over the pulley on top of the old belt. When the new belt was run out, the clamps were put on, the rods tightened and the old belt cut off, leaving the new one in place with a perfectly tight joint, ready for the joint fasteners.—J. E. Noble, Toronto, Can.

Metal Float for Special Fuels

Special fuels for automobile use are frequently compounded with benzol. The

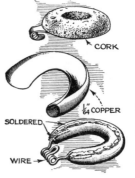

CORK
64 COPPER
SOLDERED
WIRE

benzol dissolves the shellac from the cork float of the c a r b u r e t o r and the cork becomes saturated. A clogged float and a constantly dripping carburetor are evidence of this c o n d i t i o n. L o s s of gasoline is expensive and also a possible source of fire. To prevent this trouble a metal float should be used in the carburetor. The method of making this float is shown in the drawing. The copper used should be approximately ⅟₆₄ in. thick; this is cut semicircularly and formed around a bent rod, working from one end around the circle. The ends are brought together and the seams held by overlapping and soldering them. The hinge is also soldered to the float. After completion of the float it is a simple matter to bend the wire until the gas reaches the proper level.

Lightening the Task of Handling a Heavy Air Hammer by Burlap Padding and Heavy Rubber Tube

Jig for Center-Drilling Keyways

Many machine parts, like gears, cams, sleeves, etc., are held to shafts by means of setscrews bearing on the key itself. In such cases it is imperative that the tapped hole is central with the keyway, or else part of the locking effect is lost. We use a very simple jig for this work. It consists of three parts; the body, a bushing and a screw. The body is made of ¾-in. round stock, bent as shown; the bushing is ½ in. in diameter and is sawed up the center and spread out to form a V-shape. The jig is slid into the keyway and the bushing is pushed

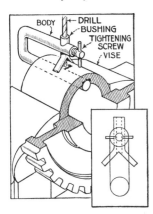

down to draw the body up in the keyway firmly; then the screw is tightened. Only one-size hole can be drilled, of course, but as this is always central, it can be enlarged with another drill to the size required. We hold such work in the vise and square it up with the side of the jig.

¶ Take 8 oz. canvas and stretch it on a frame with galvanized tacks. After painting the underside and allowing it to dry, wet the upper side with water and then paint it while damp. This insures good waterproofing.

Absorbing the Shock of an Air Hammer

Holding a heavy air hammer, driven by 40-lb. pressure, and cutting rivets with it all day is no light task for three men, yet there is a method of making the work easier than it would be with the naked hammer, as turned out by the manufacturer. To soften the jar and rub of the machine, it is wrapped thickly in burlap, while the wearisome jar of the butt, against the operator's body, is lessened by a 6-in. section of air hose, such as is used in coupling railroad cars, which is held by two small bolts through the hose and the butt of the hammer.—Jos. C. Coyle, Denver, Colo.

Pulley Guard Saves Hands

To prevent workers from getting clothing and hands between a pulley and the belt, the novel guard shown in the illustration has been found practical. It is a good precaution especially if the belts have to be thrown off frequently or the belt is used as

a safety device and throws itself off when the machine is jammed.—Auguste Mathieu, Chicago, Ill.

Broken Water Jacket Repaired without Welding

With the coming of an unexpected cold snap, many motorists discover a cracked

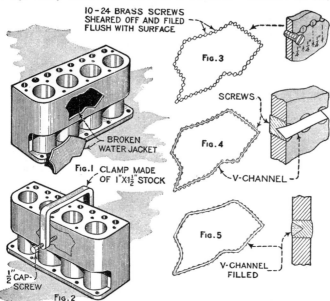

10-24 BRASS SCREWS SHEARED OFF AND FILED FLUSH WITH SURFACE

FIG. 3

BROKEN WATER JACKET

FIG. 1 CLAMP MADE OF 1"X1½" STOCK

SCREWS

FIG. 4

V-CHANNEL

FIG. 5

V-CHANNEL FILLED

$\frac{1}{2}$ CAP-SCREW

FIG. 2

Cracked Water Jacket on Automobile Repaired by Simple Method Using Screws and Solder

water jacket. This usually means a new block or an acetylene weld, a costly job in either case. However, any external break can be permanently repaired by the following method. Fig. 1 shows a cylinder block with a section of the jacket broken out entirely. Fig. 2 shows the piece restored and held in place with a specially made, strong clamp. Around the entire crack, drill and tap holes about ¼ in. apart for 10-24 screws. Next tin a quantity of 10-24 brass screws and screw them in so they will be flush with the inside of the water jacket. Tinning the threads of the screws will prevent the possibility of a leak around the threads. Chisel off all the screws flush with the surface and remove the clamp. Now make a fairly deep V-channel with a diamond chisel along the entire line of the crack. If your motor has a removable cylinder block, place it in an oven or over a slow fire until pure lead just melts, or apply the flame of a blowtorch evenly around the casting until the metal sizzles under a wet finger. Then fill up the V-groove with half-and-half solder,

using zinc chloride dissolved in distilled water as a flux. Use a hot iron and make sure that the entire surface of the "V" is tinned before filling it up flush with the surface of the jacket. Scrape away the surplus solder, file smooth and enamel, and you will have a permanent and invisible repair job. If welded, either electrically or with acetylene, the finished job would be lumpy. This method can also be used to repair an aluminum crankcase when a rod has gone through it, if you can recover the pieces. In the case of aluminum, make the screws from a piece of aluminum rod and finish the job with a good grade of aluminum solder.

Proper Application of Baseboards

Defects in plastering are frequent, and when the plaster has been "dubbed off" a few inches above the floor, the carpenter has to adopt some means of holding the baseboard straight. A good method is shown in the illustration. A 16-penny spike is driven into the 2-in. plate on which the studdings are set, so that the head is flush with the surface of the plaster, as shown at the right in the drawing. The baseboard can then be nailed on, care being taken not to drive the spike in any farther. The incorrect method is shown at the left for comparison.—H. H. Siegele, Emporia, Kans.

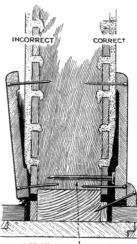

INCORRECT   CORRECT

LARGE NAIL

You Can Do Hammered-Copper Work

By DICK HUTCHINSON

THERE are few amateur mechanics who have not at one time or another looked at a pretty piece of hammered-copper work, and wished that they could duplicate it. Not that the thing looked hard, but that it was apparent that there must be some "tricks of the trade" that were necessary to know before tackling the job. It is the purpose of this article, which is the first of several, to teach the amateur how to wield the ball-peen hammer in the most effective manner. Of course, the hammering of sheet copper into any desired shape requires skill, and this demands diligent practice and effort, but the actual fundamental operations are really simple enough.

While it is the general impression that a large assortment of expensive tools is required for this kind of work, such is not the case. The following tools will pretty thoroughly cover the requirements for any ordinary work, and might as well be acquired at once: A small anvil or a block of steel with a smooth and true surface, an 8-oz. ball-peen hammer, a small bench vise, a pair of tin snips, a good cold chisel, an assortment of punches (nail sets are best and cheapest) which can be ground to suit the work at hand, an assortment of small files, 10 cents' worth of liver of sulphur, a small bottle of transparent lacquer, a good camel's-hair brush and a few sheets of jewelers' emery or polishing paper from a supply house.

Before beginning work, lay a sheet of the emery paper over several thicknesses of blotting paper, emery side up, and proceed to polish both faces of the ball-peen hammer by rubbing back and forth over the emery. The blotters afford a cushion for the emery paper, and make a better surface on the hammer face. A good surface is necessary, since the smallest scratch on the faces will show on the finished piece of work.

The first operation to be described is the shaping of a copper bowl, or what is termed cupping. The general impression, I have found, is that a bowl is shaped by hammering over the outside. This is not the case, as will be seen in a moment.

Obtain a piece of 16-gauge soft sheet copper, and from it cut a disk 5 in. in diameter. Hold the disk in the left hand

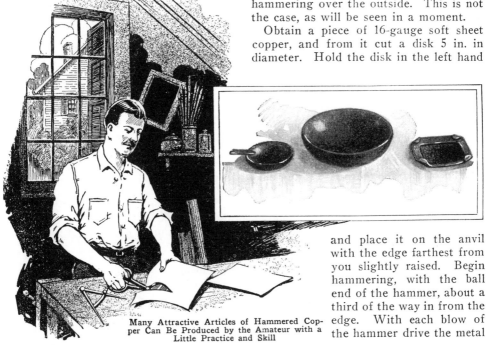

Many Attractive Articles of Hammered Copper Can Be Produced by the Amateur with a Little Practice and Skill

and place it on the anvil with the edge farthest from you slightly raised. Begin hammering, with the ball end of the hammer, about a third of the way in from the edge. With each blow of the hammer drive the metal toward the edge. Go completely around the disk in this manner, hammering over a strip about ½ in. wide. Starting inside the first strip hammered, go around the disk again in the

The Type of Hammer Used, and the Method of Starting the Cupping of the Copper Disk

same manner, and then, laying the disk flat on the anvil, circle around the inside until the center has all been hammered. Now tip the disk up on edge and hammer the part outside the first strip and up to the edge, this time driving the metal toward the center. Care must be taken not to strike the very outside edge, as this will expand the top of the bowl and make it lopsided.

The bowl should now be placed over a fire and heated to a cherry-red, then immediately plunged into a pail of cold water. This anneals the metal, which becomes hard and brittle under the hammer. The piece is now ready for the second hammering, which is done in exactly the same way as before. Repeat the hammering several times, or until the bowl is about 1 in. deep. The piece must be annealed between each hammering. The bowl can be trued by placing it over a ball of the correct size, and hammering it very lightly on the outside. When the edge has been trued by means of a file the bowl is ready for coloring.

Dissolve about ¼ oz. of the liver of sulphur in a quart of water, and, after cleaning the metal thoroughly with soap and water, immerse the bowl in the solution and allow it to remain until the desired color is attained, then remove, wash under running water and allow it to dry. This solution will produce colors running from a reddish-brown to a deep blue, depending on the time the article is left immersed. Burnish the high lights (the raised portions) with a piece of fine jewelers' emery paper, polish with a piece of clean, soft rag; then, with the camel's-hair brush, spread a thin coat of lacquer over the entire surface, and the bowl is completed.

The ash trays shown in the accompanying photos are produced by this method, and a little experiment and practice will enable the amateur to turn out many original designs along this line. The beginner must not be discouraged if his first attempt does not look as good as the work of the professional. In this work, as in all where manual skill is necessary, patience and perseverance are essential. More elaborate pieces will be described in subsequent articles.

Bumpers for Bottles

For several years I have been annoyed by the occasional breakage of stain, shellac and acid bottles when handled by the boys in the shop. I have now solved the problem by cutting sections of old inner tubes to fit the bottles. Some of the larger bottles often had the bottoms cracked by being dropped into the cases or by being set down with too great force. They are now

RUBBER BANDS

RUBBER PAD

fitted with rubber pads, the same size and shape as the bottom of the bottle, and these are shellacked or cemented on.—A. S. Peterson, Lihue, Kauai, T. H.

Light-Proof Door for Photographers

A door that really shuts out the light from one room to another is always sought by photographers, laboratory workers and others engaged in work where daylight is not desired. Most light-excluding doors depend upon interlocking systems that shut one door while the other is opened, but for simplicity,

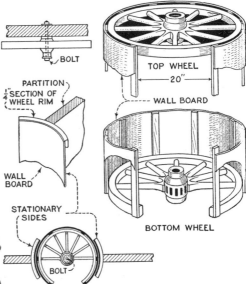

Excluding Light Effectively from a Photographer's Dark Room by Using a Revolving Door, Which Is Pivoted on Wagon Wheels

the one shown in the drawing will be found highly satisfactory. Any man handy with tools can build it.

It is of the revolving type and is made by arranging light-excluding material on a frame built on two wheels. Its construction is as follows: Get two light wagon wheels of the same diameter, and a third wheel slightly larger, so that one of the smaller wheels will just turn clear inside of it. Arrange the door opening so that it is 1 in. wider than the diameter of the smaller wheel plus twice the thickness of the rim of the larger wheel. It is best to run it from floor to ceiling. If not, a ceiling will have to built above the door to shut out the light from the top. Remove the spokes and saw the large wheel in four equal parts. Nail one section to the door jamb at the top and bottom on each side of the door and cover the inside surface with light wallboard.

If the latter does not conform to the curve, it will be necessary to insert two or three upright strips vertically, mortising them into the concave surface of the rims. When covered, these walls will be at right angles to the wall of the room and somewhat concave. Start the door by pivoting one wheel to the ceiling with a heavy lag bolt and the other to the floor. They must be centered exactly between the side walls so that they will turn with equal clearance between the walls. Connect them with wooden uprights, 1 ft. apart and mortised into the rims. One upright is left out to provide the door opening. When the frame is completed and revolves evenly, cover it with wallboard, letting the edges come as close to the ceiling and the floor as practicable. Saw out the section of the rim, between the door-opening uprights, from the bottom wheel and remove half of the spokes. Cover the edges of the revolving door with felt weather strip. A strip of this, run vertically on each side of the door opening in the revolving section, will also help exclude the light as the door revolves. The door is operated by turning the cylinder until the opening shows, then step in and push the door around. Painting the interior or the sidewalls and the revolving section black will also help to eliminate the light.

Attaching Packer to Tractor When Plowing

When plowing the stubble ground for fall wheat, time can be saved by attaching the packer behind the plow as shown in the photo. Usu-

Saving Time When Plowing Stubble Ground for Fall Wheat by Attaching the Packer behind the Plow, Both Being Drawn by a Tractor

ally a side draft is caused by hitching another implement to the side of the tractor, especially with a two-plow outfit. However, with a three-plow outfit, or a larger one, the side draft may be largely equalized by running the tractor closer to the furrow, or even in the furrow. The two right wheels may be operated in the furrow and the plow hitch set over so that the proper draft line is obtained. A timber of 2 by 8-in. oak is attached rigidly to the frame or drawbar of the tractor, and is allowed to extend over to the plowed side some 5 or 6 ft. outside of the drive-wheel. The outer end is attached to a point near the front of the tractor frame with a chain, or cable, so that the draft will not come on the attaching bolts at the rear. The packer is equipped with an extension tongue, and it is better to have a front truck. This extension tongue allows the packer to follow behind the plow and to one side. Various holes in the draft timber will allow the hitch of the packer to be made so that it will not interfere with the plow when turning corners. The greatest draft is needed for the plow, and thus, to equalize the side draft, the plow has to be hitched over to the left of the center much less than the packer is hitched to the right. The more plows the tractor operates, the farther over the timber draft bar should extend, and thus the more

packers can be attached. The whole attachment may be constructed at home with a few simple tools.

Glue for Cardboard

When gluing cardboard, attention must be given to a condition of flexibility, which is desirable in this work. To any quantity of flake glue add sufficient water to soak up the glue well, pour off some of the water and add a small quantity of turpentine. Then add 2 parts of starch powder to each part of flake glue by weight, mix the whole to a thick mass and allow it to cool before using.

Piling Round Bar Stock

Many serious accidents have occurred by piling round shafting carelessly. The

usual practice is to lay sticks between each tier and wedge the outside lengths to prevent rolling. The wedges often become loose when removing a length of shaft and allow the whole pile to start rolling. The system of piling shown in the accompanying illustration will prevent the heaviest shafting from rolling and is simple and cheap. Cross-pieces of flat stock are bent as shown and used between successive tiers, three to four for each tier, depending on the length. The piles are arranged according to sizes and may be safely run up very high.

Embossing Wood Is Simple Operation

By HAROLD JACKSON

THE accompanying illustrations show how to make and use a simple little tool with which you can emboss very beautiful and attractive designs on furniture you are making or on any woodwork that you may happen to be doing. A design or border of some kind worked out with this tool will make your work look more finished and give it a professional appearance. Phonograph doors, six-penny nail should be used. On coarser, a sixteen or twenty-penny spike is best.

Cut the point off the nail and file two grooves in the end of the nail at right angles to each other. Use a three-cornered saw file to make these grooves. This will make four points on the nail as shown in the insert.

The desired design is lightly drawn on the work with a pencil. Be sure that your pattern outline is perfectly straight and correct before you start to emboss. The tool is used as shown. It is struck rather hard with a hammer which sends the four points down into the surface of the wood. Work up to the pencil lines, being careful not to get outside the pattern outline. The correctness of the outline is very important. Work over the entire surface within the pattern outline

ENLARGED VIEW OF NAIL END SHOWING FILED NOTCHES

DOOR-CASING DESIGN

PHONOGRAPH DOOR

TABLE TOP

Simple Tool Made from Nail Helps to Improve Appearance of Homemade Furniture

for instance, if left plain, are apt to look rather bare and unfinished, but if embossed with some appropriate design will be greatly improved. Radio cabinets, occasional table tops, etc., look better if decorated a little in some way.

The tool is made from a wire nail. The size of the nail to use depends upon the nature of the work to be done; for rather fine work, as on radio cabinets, a

in this way. Then brush the work with a stiff brush to remove any loose pieces of wood that there may be.

The embossing should be done while the wood is in the white, before any stain or varnish has been applied. Due to its roughness, the embossed parts will finish a little darker than the rest of the surface, and this gives a good contrast. It is a good idea to practice on a piece of scrap board before you start on an important job. Like everything else, a little practice will teach a great deal more than a whole lot of printed instructions. The tool is really an adaptation of the "ground" tool used by wood carvers, but, while wood carving demands a lot of practice and skill, really good work can be done with this simple method without any previous experience.

Shop Worker Reduces Fatigue and Saves Time by Using Mirror behind Dado Machine

Handy Milk-Bottle Carrier

A milk-bottle carrier for barn or emergency use can be made from a old barrel head and some tin cans. Cleat the barrel head so that it forms a solid disk. Then turn it over, with the cleats underneath, nail a barrel hoop around the rim and about three-fourths of a hoop from side to side for a handle. Cut in half as many tin cans as can be conveniently nailed to the surface of the tray to a height of about 3 in. They should be large enough to allow the milk bottles to fit inside of them. Such a tray will accommodate about ten bottles.

¶ Discarded straight petcocks with the key removed make good pipe plugs.

Mirror Helps Do Dado Work

In a woodworking plant at Wahoo, Nebr., one of the workmen has installed a small mirror on the dado machine so that, by looking into the mirror, he can tell where to strike the wood with the power-driven bit. In the photo the workman is cutting mortise-and-tenon joints in the frame for a screendoor. He claims that the mirror not only saves one-third of the time but also prevents fatigue of the neck and shoulder muscles. The device has been in use for three years and all who have worked with it have found it satisfactory. —Dale R. Van Horn, Walton, Nebr.

Extension Handle on Tap

After tapping a hole, it usually takes considerable time to screw the tap out, and the worker is likely to do this in haste and become more or less careless, which may result in a broken tap. To speed up the removal and at the same time lessen the danger of breaking off the tap, thread a 3-in. length of ¼-in. rod. Knurl it if possible although this is not necessary, and screw it into the tap, as shown. After the hole has been tapped, unscrew the tap by rolling the extension handle between the palms.

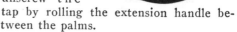

Wrecking Crane for Small Garage

By GEO. H. CAPPEL

NOWADAYS it is almost a necessity for every garage to have a wrecking crane and a good serviceable crane can readily be built by any enterprising mechanic. The drawing shows one which is made chiefly from two discarded auto frames. The dimensions given may be followed or the crane built to any suitable size. The front side bars of the frame are cut 6 ft. long and are bent at the top and bottom, as shown. The horizontal side bars, I, are from another frame. They are cut 3 ft. long, are spaced 24 in. apart and are mounted on two cross bars, H, which are 30 in. long. The method of bolting them together is shown at C. A ¾-in. hole is

¾-in. bolts and a piece of ¾ or 1-in. gas pipe, cut to fit between the inside of the channels, keep the frame from drawing together and make a tight connection when the bolts are drawn up tight. A front cross brace, N, made of ¼-in. flat stock, 2 in. wide, is used to strengthen the

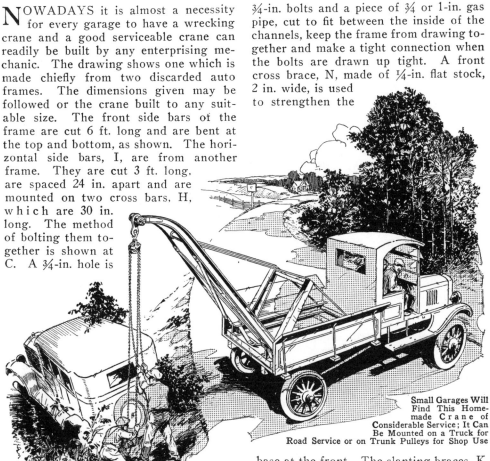

Small Garages Will Find This Home-made Crane of Considerable Service; It Can Be Mounted on a Truck for Road Service or on Trunk Pulleys for Shop Use

drilled at the ends, to permit bolting to a truck. These holes should be drilled 28½ in. center to center if the crane is to be used on a Ford truck. Long

base at the front. The slanting braces, K, which are 30 in. long, are attached to the crosspieces I, and are separated with a length of ¾ or 1-in. pipe, F, through which a long ¾ in. bolt is slipped. The braces, K, serve as a rest for the round-iron braces, E, which are attached last. The

185

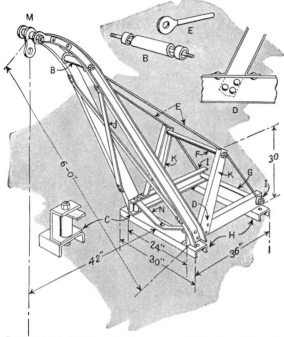

Constructional Details and Dimensions Which Show How the Crane Is Made and Assembled

main members of the crane are braced as shown with flat crosspieces, J. The crosspiece, B, like F and G, consists of a ¾-in. bolt and a ¾ or 1-in. pipe. This completes the framework of the crane except the head, M. This should extend about 3½ ft. beyond the rear crosspiece, H. An eye or hook plate is forged out of an iron bar, 6 in. long, ¾ in. thick and 3 in. wide. The lower hole is drilled to fit the hook on the differential block, while a ¾ or ⅞-in. steel bolt is slipped through the top hole and the ends of the frame. The brace rods, E, are attached after the frame is assembled so that they will have a tight fit. The detail, D, shows how the braces, K, are bent and bolted to the cross bars I.

If it is desired to use the crane also for general service in the garage, this can be done by bolting 6½-in. bars to the bottom of the crane. Large trunk pulleys are used for the front end and a caster at the rear end. In this way the crane can be used in the shop and only four bolts are needed to attach it to the pulleys. When used as a floor crane, it may be found desirable to weight the caster end. For light lifts, of course, this is unnecessary.

Sweet-Clover Stems Used for Feed

Every year I allow a part of my sweet-clover crop to seed, and then I harvest the seed. The stems of the clover then have become so large and hard that stock will eat but little of it. Running it through the threshing machine breaks up the stems so that they can be fed into a grinder made for handling ear corn, and last winter we ground about 40 bu. of clover straw. When mixed with oats or other ground feed, it is relished by stock and appears to have considerable food value.—Geo. G. McVicker, North Bend, Nebraska.

Valve-Cage Tool Adjustable for Height

To release the pressure while removing spring-washer locks from valve stems, the illustrated tool will be found useful. It consists of one piece of ¼ by 3-in. steel, 5½ in. long, and two ⅜ by 9-in. steel rods, which have been threaded 1 in. of their length at the lower ends and 3½ in. at the upper ends. Six ⅜-in. nuts are used on the rods, as shown, to properly locate the upper and lower plates. The upper plate is of ¼ by 2-in. steel and is 4¾ in. long, two holes being drilled in it, 3¼ in. center to center, and two holes drilled and tapped in the base the same distance apart. In the center of the upper plate, a ½-in. standard thread is tapped in which is fitted a 3-in. capscrew, with a piece of ⅛ by ¾-in. steel, 2¾ in. long, to form a thumbscrew handle. To the lower end of the capscrew is fitted a spring-washer release, made from 1¹⁄₁₆-in. stock, 1¼ in. long, with a ¹³⁄₁₆-in. hole drilled in the center. A cross slot, ⅝ in. wide, is cut as shown in the photo, and the piece is then joined to the capscrew by reducing

the end of the screw to ⁵⁄₁₆ in. in diameter for a distance of ⅜ in. A ⁵⁄₁₆-in. hole is drilled in the solid end of the spring-washer release and the end of the capscrew is riveted over, to prevent the washer release from coming off the screw. This makes a satisfactory cage tool as it holds the valve spring in whatever position desired and is adjustable to cages of all heights within its capacity

Homemade Tool for Straightening Steel Flanges

Straightening steel flanges is usually done with a sledge hammer, the metal being well heated to make the work easier. In a Denver steel shop, where a great deal of repair work is done, a special tool was made for this purpose. It was made from a No. 4 alligator wrench and has been found indispensable for straightening steel flanges ½ in. or less in thickness. The wrenches are heated in a forge and closed to a ¾-in. gap. A 2 or 3-ft. section of 1½-in. gas pipe is slipped well up on the handle of the wrench, hammered down and welded. With this tool a workman may straighten flanges up to ½ in. cold, without the muscle shock occasioned by the use of a sledge.—Jos. C. Coyle, Denver, Colo.

Handy Wooden Jack Facilitates Handling Railway Trucks over Tracks and in Shops

Handling Railway Trucks Easily

In rolling a pair of railway trucks it is difficult to change the course in which the wheels are rolling and to get them across tracks with the unaided hands. The jack shown in the drawing has been found very helpful in this task. A hardwood handle, resembling that of a peavey, but heavier at the lower end, has a triangular block of hardwood, 3 in. thick, spiked to the lower end. The upper end of the block, which is 4 in. wide, is curved to fit the axle of the truck. With the handle set vertically on the ground, the top of the block should be about 3 in. higher than the underside of the axle. In use, the jack is passed under the axle, and when the handle is pushed forward, the axle will be lifted and carried ahead. One man can turn or run a pair of trucks over the track with this jack.

¶When babbitt metal has been heated repeatedly, the tin and antimony are partly burned out making it unsuitable for use for bearings, etc.; oxidation is indicated by the formation of scum on the surface.

Straightening Steel Flanges Up to Half-Inch Thick without Heat with Specially Made Tool

Good Hydrant Installation

For the average farm where running water is piped to two or three outside points, the installation shown in the photo will prove satisfactory. The shut-off is set far enough underground to prevent its freezing in winter. Then this is covered with a column of 4-in. bell tile, and the stack is brought just above the ground with the bell of the last section of tile on top. A ½-gal. pail cover just fits into the bell, and a hole punched through the center of the cover will then make the installation complete.—Dale R. Van Horn, Walton, Nebr.

Emery-Wheel Stand

The emery-wheel stand shown in the drawing is made from an old piston which had been discarded from an automobile engine. It is mounted on the bench top by two long bolts, as shown. A wood block is placed between the bench and the piston to make it stand at the proper height. The wristpin bushings are left in the piston and serve as bearings for the shaft. The latter should be the right size to fit nicely in the bushings, and long enough to mount an emery wheel on one end and a pulley on the other. The end that carries the wheel can be threaded and the wheel clamped between two nuts, while the pulley is fastened with a key or a setscrew. A stand of this kind will carry a good-sized wheel, as considerable bearing

Serviceable Bench Stand for Emery Wheel Is Made from Old Piston

surface is provided by the wristpin bushings. In drilling the holes for the bolts, it is of importance to place them far enough apart so that the bolts will not interfere with the shaft.—Harold Jackson, Kankakee, Ill.

Altered Machine Tap Works Better

The machine tap will run into the work much more readily and will not break so easily if it is altered as indicated. Take any tap with four flutes and grind the threads down one-half of their depth on two opposite flutes. Whereas the ordinary tap would usually break after I had tapped about 90 holes, the altered tool tapped 450 without breakage. It is evident that this meant quite a saving where thousands of holes had to be tapped. —Arthur Whittier, Norwood, Mass.

New Use for Dictaphone

The dictaphone can be used to record orders for merchandise arriving by long-distance telephone. To do this, hold the mouthpiece of the dictaphone directly under the telephone transmitter so that you can speak into both at the same time. When the order starts coming in, each item is repeated to the customer and is thus recorded by the dictaphone. Shipping directions, terms and other information needed for the prompt and correct billing of the shipment may also be included. This method insures accuracy and at the same time saves telephone tolls as the order can be taken more quickly than if it had to be written down by hand.—M. W. Lowry, Athens, Georgia.

Improved Drill and Wire Gauge

A single drilled plate is the common form of drill and wire gauge, but a better instrument is obtained by using two plates as shown in the drawing. The difference in diameter of the drills is so slight that it requires close gauging to determine the exact number, and users of the single-plate gauge ordinarily try the next smaller hole as a check after the drill has been fitted, for, if this is not done, the drill or wire may be passed as a size larger than it is. The double-plate gauge, however, prevents mistakes of this kind and saves the time required to pull out the work and try it in the next hole. To make it, two plates were drilled together from the smallest to the largest size. After drilling, a spacing piece was pinned between the two plates and the pin riveted over on both sides. The riveting is not done until the plates are tight and is stopped when the plates are held snugly but movably on the pin. Next the back plate is moved around one hole, which brings the next smaller holes in line with the holes in the upper plate.

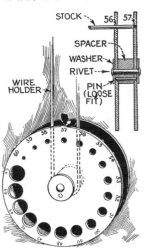

In this position a hole is drilled through both plates and the spacer, and a loose pin inserted. In use, the gauge is suspended by a wire holder from a nail or hook in the wall so that it can be spun around to bring the required hole to the most convenient position. The work is tried in the holes until it enters the one it seems to fit best. It is then pushed farther through to try it in the next smaller hole, which is in line with it in the back plate. If it fails to enter this, its size corresponds with the number of the hole it entered.

Special Frame for Holding Dump Doors Aids Riveters

Support for Dump Doors Makes Riveting Easier

The device shown here was originated at the shops of a western railroad for holding dump doors of ore cars, as well as other broad, flat steel equipment, while riveting them. It is made of 4 by 6-in. timbers, securely bolted together in an A-shape and reinforced at the bottom with steel straps, which are turned up near the end of the two timbers that form the base of the device, to keep the doors from slipping. It is 3½ ft. in height, and the base timbers are the same length, which makes it convenient for the crew to stand in an easy position while performing their task with the rivet gun and the bucking bar. —Jos. C. Coyle, Denver, Colo.

Keeping Soldering Kit Handy

The electrician, tinsmith or other mechanic, who is often compelled to work in low attics or other small spaces, will find the illustrated stunt of providing pockets on the side of the blowtorch of considerable convenience, as it serves to keep the solder, flux, tape, etc., at hand and less likely to be mislaid.

Simple Automatic Counter Attached to Frame of Roller Conveyor Is Found Dependable

Simple Counter for Roller Conveyor

The drawing shows a simple method of attaching a counter to a roller conveyor. The counter is placed on a bracket attached to the frame of the conveyor at a turn, and should be located on the outside of the curve, for the reason that there will be greater separation between the units at this point than elsewhere. The operating lever is made from light bar stock and is actuated by a spring attached to the counter arm, which can be swung out of the way instantly whenever desired. —J. S. Hagans, Chicago, Ill.

Handling Bearing Shims

While working under the car on the main bearings, it is sometimes discouraging to have the thin shims slip off the bolts and scatter on the floor. A good method of preventing this is to bend the shims in the center slightly. Shims having a single hole are bent across the hole as shown in the upper detail. Those having two holes are bent between the holes as shown in the upper detail. Those having two holes are bent between the holes as

shown below. Take care that the ends point up so that, when the bearing cap is replaced, the shim is smoothed out and the bending has no effect upon the fitting of the bearing. By replacing the heavier shims first, the thin ones will serve to hold all of them in place until the bearing cap is started over the bolts.—S. J. Gee, Montpelier, Idaho.

A Homemade Plumb Bob

Get a piece of cold-drawn steel, hexagon in shape, $4\frac{1}{4}$ in. long and $\frac{3}{4}$ in. wide. Lay out and center-punch for a $\frac{3}{16}$-in. hole near the top end, according to dimensions given in the drawing. In locating this hole allow for $\frac{1}{32}$ in. to be faced off at the end. After the hole has been drilled, set up the work in the lathe. Place it in a three-jaw universal chuck, with the drilled end of the work extending $1\frac{1}{2}$ in. Adjust it so that it runs true. Now arrange the belt for the proper spindle speed, set the lathe tool for facing and face the end. Center the end of the work with the centering tool held in the toolpost. Center-drill this end as indicated, using a center drill with a $\frac{3}{32}$-in. pilot drill, and drill a $\frac{3}{32}$-in. hole in the end to intersect the $\frac{3}{16}$-in. hole. Remove the drill chuck from the tailstock spindle, insert the hardened center and adjust the tailstock so that it will support the end of the work. Get a round-nose tool, ground to form the fillet at

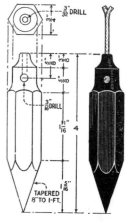

the end, and turn down to two diameters as indicated. Round the corner at the end with a file and polish the machined surfaces with a piece of emery cloth. Now turn the work around in the chuck so that it extends $1\frac{3}{4}$ in. True it as before and set the compound rest at a 108° angle, reading from the headstock side, with the handle toward the tailstock. Then turn down the work to a point and finish with emery cloth.

Keeping the Closed Car Warm

As cold weather approaches, the motorist is faced with the problem of keeping the car warm. The quantity of cold air that comes in through the floorboards and around the windows is surprising. This is especially true when the car is in motion. As the heat from the engine naturally escapes through the vents on the sides of the hood, one auto owner conserved a great deal of this heat by closing up these vents on the inside of the hood with two strips of cardboard, so that the fan blew the heated air from around the motor back against the floorboards, thus aiding in heating the inside of the car. The strips were held in place with no fastenings by simply bending the ends out through the first and last slot in the hood.

Gate Keeps Stock Safe and Ventilates Barn

To prevent the escape of stock from the barn and yet provide proper ventilation during the hot months, one farmer built a slat gate, hinged at the top as shown in the illustration. This gate is made of several 1 by 6-in. boards nailed to three vertical pieces, which are long enough to reach from the door sill to the top of the opening, where they are nailed to another horizontal piece, hinged to the top of the opening. A rope runs from the bottom of the gate over a pulley fastened to a ceiling joist at the proper distance inside, and a pull on this rope opens the gate. There is also an automatic lock, made of a 2 by 4-in. piece, 3 ft. long. This is hinged to the ceiling and has a notch, which engages with the lower edge of the gate when it is raised. The lower end of this lock is within reach.

Gate with Hinges at the Top Keeps the Stock in the Barn and Provides Plenty of Ventilation

Triangle Fitted to Be Used as T-Square

There are a great many instances where it is necessary to make rough sketches and where a little accuracy is of considerable value in future work. The drawing shows how a medium-sized triangle was made to do double duty. A short strip of heavy celluloid was

slotted to give a snug fit on the edge of the triangle so that it could be removed when not needed. The method of using the device is clearly shown in the illustration.—L. H. Georger, Buffalo, N. Y.

Protection for Stucco-Finished Houses against Water Stains

Stucco should never start closer than 8 or 10 in. to the ground line. Splashing from rains will otherwise be sure to discolor it and cover it with dirt or soot, which lies on the surface of snowbanks next to the house walls. Another blemish often seen on stucco finish is discoloration just below the windows, such as rust from screens and windows. Extra-wide sills or sills with a groove or other trough-shaped depression near each end to force the water to run off through them are the best means to prevent this trouble.—Geo. G. McVicker, North Bend, Nebr.

¶Chicks hatched in the middle of March will be early layers.

Old Hammers Drawn Out Make Good Tools for Removing Rivets

Tool for Backing Out Rivets Made from Old Hammer

In a large Denver shop old hammers which have become chipped and unsafe for use are drawn out to a ¾-in. point, as shown in the photo, and are used for backing out old rivets, after the head has been removed with an air chisel. The "backout," as it is called, may be held safely upon a rivet by one workman while it is being struck with a sledge by a second man.—Jos. C. Coyle, Denver, Colo.

Handy Mallet for Glaziers

Glaziers and others who have occasion to reglaze windows and doors will find the mallet shown in the drawing of considerable assistance in their work. It consists of a piece of flat steel, squared and polished, through which a hole is drilled from end to end to receive a length of heavy steel wire. The hole is countersunk at one end to permit the end of the wire to be clinched without projecting beyond the side of the head. The wire is bent as indicated, to form a handle, and should fit

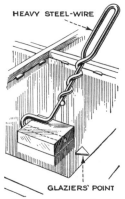

HEAVY STEEL-WIRE

GLAZIERS' POINT

rather loosely in the hole. Thus, the head of the mallet will always lie flat against the glass no matter at what angle the handle is held in driving the points. In many shops beveled chisels or other similar tools are used for this purpose, but this tool will be found much more valuable and well worth the time required to make it.—G. E. Hendrickson, Argyle, Wis.

Holder Helps in Grinding Bearing Caps

Grinding bearing caps on an emery wheel is a job that requires care in order to get the flat surface of the cap ground evenly. A simple holder, which can be made in a short time and makes the work much easier, is shown in the illustration. It consists of a length of flat steel, bent to a U-shape and having the ends ground to fit in the bolt holes of the caps. Two holes are drilled through the sides of the holder to receive a bolt, which is provided with a wingnut to tighten it so that the holder will grip the bearing securely. In this way, a comfortable grip is obtained, and at the same time the fingers are protected from the surface of the emery wheel.—G. A. Luers, Washington, D. C.

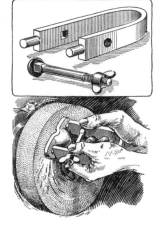

Waterproof Varnish for Wooden Trays

Wooden trays are often built for darkroom or laboratory use. To make them waterproof, yet chemically clean, is a simple matter if the following coating is applied: Melt ½ lb. of common brown rosin and add 2 oz. of yellow-wax chips, stirring the mixture until it is smooth. This will fill all cracks and pores and will render the wood absolutely non-porous. —L. B. Robbins, Harwich, Mass.

Improving Your Hot-Air Furnace

By J. TATE

ACCORDING to a well-known heating engineer, it is possible, by a few simple and inexpensive changes, to effect a saving of 20 to 30 per cent in the coal required to heat a house in severe weather, where a hot-air furnace is used for heating. "In fact," he says, "it is easy to change hot-air house heating from a system markedly inferior to steam or hot-water apparatus to a system that compares very favorably with them in nearly all respects."

It may not be possible for all readers to realize the saving mentioned above, for some of the improvements indicated later may already be incorporated in their own furnaces, but there are many installations where the full amount may really be saved.

The first simple improvement possible to make in the majority of hot-air furnaces is that of a simple apparatus for humidifying the warm air supplied to the rooms. The desirability of maintaining a reasonable amount of moisture in the air of the average home is recognized by all heating and ventilating authorities; it is, in fact, essential to health, protection of woodwork in the house and economy of fuel. Where sufficient moisture is present in the air, the temperature of

the rooms can be kept at a lower point than when the air is dry, with equal comfort to the occupants, and a lower temperature means a saving in coal to begin with. In addition to this, if the air is dry, moisture is evaporated from the woodwork of the house and the furniture, with more or less disastrous effects, and the effect on the occupants is no less bad from the standpoint of health. Fortunately, it is comparatively easy to humidify the air in a hot-air furnace, much easier than it is to do the same thing in a house heated with steam or hot water. Do not, however, rely on the cast-iron water pan fitted to many furnaces to do the work, for it will not. There is only one place to fit a humidifying pan in the average hot-air furnace, and that is on top of t h e radiator or h e a t i n g

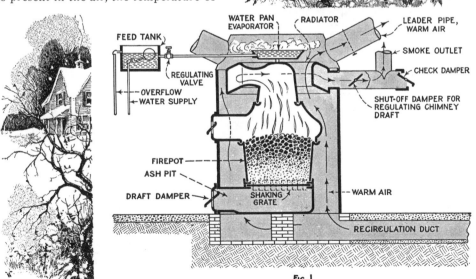

Fig. 1

The Addition of a Simple Humidifying System to the Hot-Air Furnace Not Only Adds to the Comfort of the Home Owner, but Helps Save Coal

Labels in figure: WATER PAN EVAPORATOR · RADIATOR · LEADER PIPE, WARM AIR · FEED TANK · SMOKE OUTLET · REGULATING VALVE · CHECK DAMPER · OVERFLOW · WATER SUPPLY · SHUT-OFF DAMPER FOR REGULATING CHIMNEY DRAFT · FIREPOT · ASH PIT · DRAFT DAMPER · SHAKING GRATE · WARM AIR · RECIRCULATION DUCT

drum, just beneath the bonnet of the furnace. The installation of such a pan, which should be of cast iron, is shown in Fig. 1. To make the tank function without attention, an automatic ball cock is arranged in an external tank to keep the pan in the furnace constantly supplied with water. A regulating valve is fitted in the supply line leading to the furnace pan, and an overflow pipe to the external tank. In extreme weather, when the furnace is running at full capacity, the regulating valve must be closed somewhat, in order that the air in the house may not become too saturated and the windows covered with frost. The only thing to watch in fitting such a humidifier is to keep the water level in the float tank at the same level as is required for the furnace pan.

The next thing to consider is whether the cold-air supply to the furnace is taken entirely from outdoors. If it is, that means that all the air handled by the furnace must be raised from the temperature prevailing outdoors to the temperature required for the house. In very cold or windy weather, the temperature difference is very considerable, and a lot of coal is needed to raise the temperature of the air to the higher level. This can be avoided almost entirely by the addition of a recirculation duct, through which all or a part of the air to be heated is taken from the interior of the house. Many furnaces are now fitted in this way, but many old ones are not, and it makes a considerable difference in the amount of coal burned in cold weather, and often a very appreciable difference in the comfort of the house, whether the air must be raised from zero or below to 68 or 70°, or from 50 to the same degree.

One heating engineer solved the problem in his own house by using a recirculation duct, cast right in the floor of the cellar, as indicated in Fig. 1. The main reason for using this construction was that, while it is well known that such a duct should have a cross-sectional area equal to the combined areas of all the hot-air pipes leading to the rooms, the lack of room in the ordinary cellar often makes the installation of a duct of such size impossible. The duct cast in the floor overcame this objection. The floor and walls of the duct were cast in concrete. For the top of the duct slabs of reinforced concrete were cast in open forms, about 3 in. thick, 3 ft. long and 2 ft. wide, with beveled edges. After the slabs were seasoned

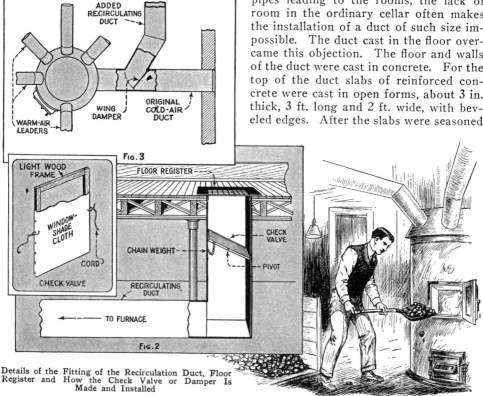

Details of the Fitting of the Recirculation Duct, Floor Register and How the Check Valve or Damper Is Made and Installed

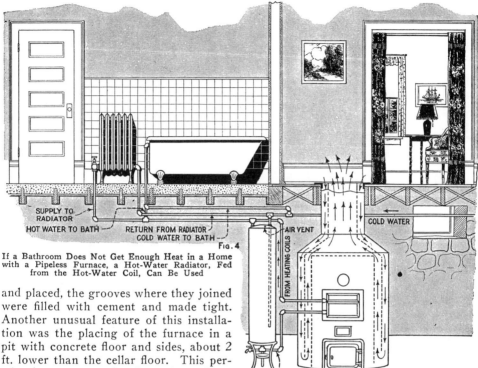

SUPPLY TO RADIATOR

HOT WATER TO BATH —

RETURN FROM RADIATOR
COLD WATER TO BATH

FIG. 4

AIR VENT

FROM HEATING COILS

COLD WATER

TO HEATING COILS

If a Bathroom Does Not Get Enough Heat in a Home with a Pipeless Furnace, a Hot-Water Radiator, Fed from the Hot-Water Coil, Can Be Used

and placed, the grooves where they joined were filled with cement and made tight. Another unusual feature of this installation was the placing of the furnace in a pit with concrete floor and sides, about 2 ft. lower than the cellar floor. This permitted easy connection from the recirculation duct to the base of the furnace, and saved labor in feeding coal to the furnace, while the extra height helped the draft in the hot-air flues, especially those leading to the first floor.

Where the floor duct cannot be installed, it is necessary to use a sheet-metal duct, proportioning this as mentioned above, or, if this is impossible, then as large as possible, at least as large as the original cold-air duct. The recirculation duct should be joined to the cold-air duct as illustrated in Fig. 3, so that a wing damper can be fitted to enable the air supply to the furnace to be taken either from outside or inside the house, or mixed in whatever proportions may be desirable, depending on the weather.

Occasionally, with a strong wind blowing into the outside cold-air duct of the installation described, more air would enter the duct than the furnace could handle. With the wing damper set, as it usually was, to take part of the supply from the inside and part from the outside, a strong current of cold air would flow around the damper and into the house through the recirculation duct and the register in

the hall. This could be stopped, of course, by closing one of the ducts by means of the wing damper, but this was often undesirable. What was needed, therefore, was a very light, almost frictionless check valve in the recirculation duct; one that would offer no resistance to the downward flow of the air from the house, but that would close against any air coming back through the duct from the outside. The valve that was finally fitted is shown in Fig. 2. This was hung in the vertical duct from the first floor in an inclined position, and was supported on cord trunnions near its center of gravity, so that it would swing closed by its own weight, but would open under the slightest suction from the furnace. In order to balance the damper accurately a very light chain was hung in a loop with one end attached to the side of the flue, and the other to the side of the damper. By altering the length of the loop, it was easy to adjust the damper, which worked perfectly.

Where a one-register or pipeless furnace is used to heat the house it is often the case that the bathroom is always more

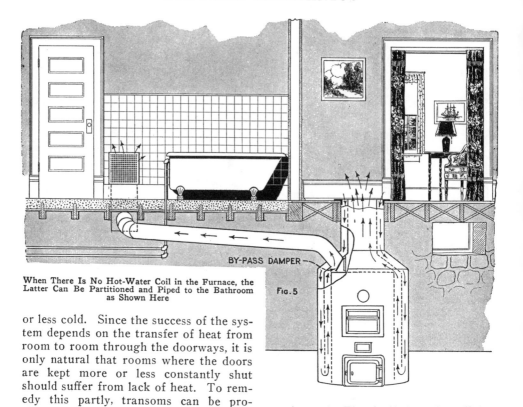

BY-PASS DAMPER

When There Is No Hot-Water Coil in the Furnace, the Latter Can Be Partitioned and Piped to the Bathroom as Shown Here   FIG. 5

or less cold. Since the success of the system depends on the transfer of heat from room to room through the doorways, it is only natural that rooms where the doors are kept more or less constantly shut should suffer from lack of heat. To remedy this partly, transoms can be provided over the doors, and these should be kept open. An opening should also be made at the bottom of the door. Another plan is to install a hot-water radiator connected to the range boiler,

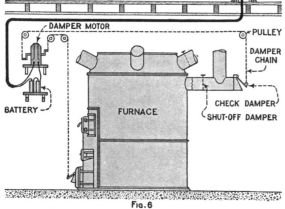

THERMOSTAT OPERATES
MOTOR TO OPEN OR CLOSE DAMPER

WIRE IN CONDUIT

DAMPER MOTOR

PULLEY

DAMPER CHAIN

CHECK DAMPER
SHUT-OFF DAMPER

BATTERY

FURNACE

FIG. 6

Reducing the Number of Trips to the Cellar in a Day, and Keeping the Temperature at a Constant Figure, a Thermostat Installation Is Well Worth While

as shown in Fig. 4; if there is sufficient space, and there is no objection to the appearance, the range boiler may be located in the bathroom and connected to a water coil in the furnace. Still another plan is shown in Fig. 5, in which a partition is fitted to the furnace, and a part of the hot air led to a register in the bathroom by a regular leader pipe. There should be a damper in the leader pipe, so that all the heat can be sent to the rest of the house when heat is not needed for the bathroom.

An automatic thermostat (Fig. 6), for controlling the furnace drafts, will not only prove of great convenience, but will be found a fuel saver. These devices consist of a thermostat in one of the living rooms, which controls a clockwork motor mounted near the furnace, and this motor, in turn, controls the ash-pit and check drafts. When adjusted and set, the thermostat will open and close the drafts all day to maintain a certain temperature, and many models can be set so as to keep the house at a lower temperature during the night, and to open the drafts to raise the temperature in the morning. These devices save fuel and frequent trips to the furnace and they also serve to keep the temperature in the house much more uniform than can be done with the infrequent manual attention usually given the fire.

However, in cases where certain kinds of soft coal are burned in the furnace, the use of a thermostat of this type is impractical, since the fire must be broken up at regular intervals, due to the caking and swelling of the coal, and, if the fire must be attended to in this manner, the dampers can be adjusted at the same time, but with the majority of coals and coke, the use of the thermostat will be attended with greater fuel efficiency and increased comfort in the house.

A Portable Hog Corral

The problem of transporting hogs from field to field by means of a portable corral was solved by two farmers as shown in the illustration. The inclosure is made of 1 by 6-in. boards and is triangular in shape, with one side hinged so that it can be used as a gate. Three wheels, two on one side and one at the apex, allow just sufficient clearance for the corral to be readily pushed over the ground. Since using this method, hogs have been easily

Portable Pen in Which Hogs Are Transported from Place to Place

moved over a plank bridge from which, with ordinary driving methods, the animals were frequently frightened into the creek and drowned.—Mel Wharton, Portland, Oreg.

By Actual Test This Sawing Outfit Has Been Found to Do the Work of Two Men

One-Man Saw Outfit

This one-man saw outfit was made in two hours at a cost of 50 cents for material. The entire frame, including the pendulum, is made of 2 by 4-in. material. The pendulum works in a slide to prevent vibration and is adjustable in length for various sizes of timber by means of the holes bored in the upper end. This saw rig, by actual test, did the work of two men with a crosscut saw. It folds up like a pocketknife and is easily moved from log to log by one man. Also, it is adjustable to uneven ground.—E. Ellsworth Claspby, Lewiston, Pa.

Fill Tractor Tank with Kerosene to Prevent Rusting

When our tractor is placed in the shed for the winter, or at other times when it is not in use for several weeks, we fill the fuel tank with kerosene. Formerly this was not done and we often had trouble with rust getting into the pipe line to the carburetor. The rust forms on the inside of the tank, drops to the bottom and, as soon as the tank is filled, it washes along into the carburetor line. — Wendell N. Mitchell, Rogers, Nebr.

Ferrotyping Prints

When ferrotyping prints it will be found that a large percentage of the surplus water can be absorbed by a large piece of

Large Piece of Oilcloth Absorbs Surplus Moisture from Ferrotyped Prints

oilcloth and the prints will then dry much more quickly. Such a piece of oilcloth is much handier to use than blotters and costs less.—Auguste Mathieu, Chicago, Ill.

Motorcycle Engine Makes Good Air Compressor

A discarded single-cylinder motorcycle engine can be readily converted into an efficient air compressor by making only a few changes in the operating mechanism. In most cases it will be found that the compression, though rather high, is not sufficient to inflate a large storage tank to 150 lb. or more, but this difficulty is easily overcome. Take the motor apart and get a plate of brass, or other similar metal, about ¼ in. thick. Cut a disk out of this a few thousandths of an inch smaller in diameter than the diameter of the cylinder, and fasten it to the piston head with machine screws that have their flat heads countersunk below the surface. This should raise the compression to the proper point, but if it does not, thicker metal must be used depending on the amount of space left between the top of the piston and the cylinder head. Remove the pushrod that operates the exhaust valve and discard it. Also remove the spring and the operating mechanism of the intake valve. Grind both valves carefully and replace the intake spring with a lighter and weaker one, which will open automatically on the suction stroke of the piston. New piston rings should be installed if necessary. Then reassemble the motor, connect the air line to the spark-plug hole and insert a check valve somewhere in the line near the compressor. Mount the engine conveniently to the power supply and, if the compressor originally was one of the belt-driven machines, the original pulley will still serve its purpose. If the engine was equipped with a sprocket, this should be removed and a flat pulley substituted. Plenty of good oil should be provided in the crankcase at all times to give lubrication, and a glass oil cup may be installed on the side to show the height of the oil.

Homemade Ratchet Wrench

A handy set of ratchet wrenches can be made up by the home mechanic. Good steel, which is capable of being oil-tempered, should be used for this purpose. The sockets are hardened, but the handle is left normal. The rollers, which take the place of the usual ratchet and pawl, are also hardened. In use, a very slight back movement will release the rollers, yet they grip firmly. —Arthman N. Capron, Athelstan, P. Q. Canada.

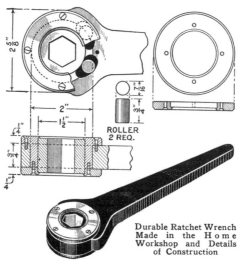

Durable Ratchet Wrench Made in the Home Workshop and Details of Construction

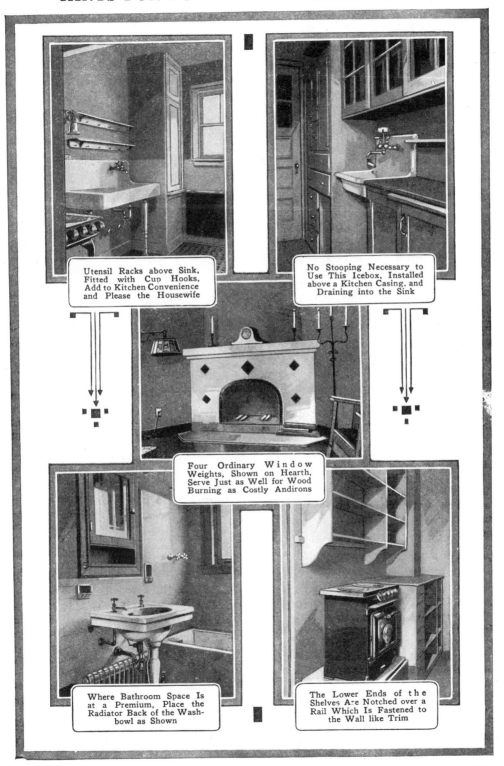

Utensil Racks above Sink, Fitted with Cup Hooks, Add to Kitchen Convenience and Please the Housewife

No Stooping Necessary to Use This Icebox, Installed above a Kitchen Casing, and Draining into the Sink

Four Ordinary Window Weights, Shown on Hearth, Serve Just as Well for Wood Burning as Costly Andirons

Where Bathroom Space Is at a Premium, Place the Radiator Back of the Washbowl as Shown

The Lower Ends of the Shelves Are Notched over a Rail Which Is Fastened to the Wall like Trim

Sliding Drain Pan for Service Station

In a new drain pit just constructed at Wahoo, Nebr., a special sliding drain pan was installed to facilitate the handling of the used oil taken from both crank-

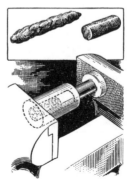

TRACKS FOR SLIDING FUNNEL

ENTRANCE TO PIT

OIL RECEIVER PIPE TO UNDERGROUND TANK

Novel Sliding Drain Pan in Oil Pit at Auto-Service Station Facilitates the Removal of Crankcase and Transmission Oil

case and transmission. Strap-iron side bars are fastened to both sides of the pit, as shown, and sliding brackets are welded to an iron ring 26 in. in diameter, which holds a large funnel-shaped receiver. This can readily be moved directly under either the crankcase or the transmission drain. The funnel fits into the elbow of a 2-in. pipe leading back into the end of the pit through another pipe, which in turn extends 8 ft. underground to a receiving tank at the bottom of the pit. The service man enters the pit through a trap at the side rather than at the end. Both trap and pit are provided with covers.—Ralph W McPherson, Wahoo, Nebr.

Imitation Marble Tiles

To prepare imitation marble finishes for decorative purposes, cut pieces of fiber wallboard into squares of the desired size and round off the edges with a sandpaper block, then coat the squares with white or colored paint and allow them to dry. A pan large enough to hold the squares is partly filled with water. On the surface of the water drop some ordinary but rather thin-mixed oil paint the color of the veining. It will be found that the paint will distribute itself over the surface of the water in all sorts of irregular shapes. Now take the squares, one at a time, and, holding them by diagonally opposite corners, just touch them to the paint-covered surface of the water. This will produce the veined effect. Remove the squares, turn them face up and allow them to dry. There is nothing to prevent a second treatment to produce veins of two or more different colors.—J. S. Hagans, Chicago, Ill.

Making Gauze Motor Brushes

Being employed in the mechanical department of a mill using a few low-voltage electric motors, which usually are equipped with copper - gauze brushes, I constructed some of these, employing a very simple device, and believe that the construction may be of interest to many. A piece of cold-rolled steel shafting of suitable diameter was obtained for the forming die. This was cut about three times the length of the brush and its ends squared. A hole of the same cross section and size as the brush was drilled entirely through this shafting. A punch was turned to make a sliding fit in this hole, its length from the shoulder to the end being made equal to that of the die minus the length of the brush. The material for the brush was flexible lamp-cord of suitable size, from which the insulation was removed. The wire was wadded up so that it could readily be forced into the die. The wad was placed in the die, the punch started, and the whole placed between the jaws of a vise and screwed up until the shoulder of the punch rested against the end of the die. The finished brush is pushed out of the die by means of a suitable drift. It is well to keep both the die and the punch well lubricated.—W. J. Edmonds, Whitehall, New York.

Wooden Pump Handle and Bracket Found Satisfactory in Emergency

Wrench Attachment for Catching Nuts

A simple device for preventing the loss of nuts when dismantling or assembling machinery is shown in the illustration. It is, of course, always undesirable to drop small pieces like these into other parts of the machine where they can hardly be extricated and may cause trouble if left. Such trouble can be prevented by the use of the wrench attachment shown in the illustration. It is made from a short length of brass tubing, first sawed nearly through at one end and flattened out; then a hole is drilled through the flat part. This hole clears the end of the bolt if it happens to project through the nut. No particular care is required when using this attachment, as the nut drops on the flattened end when released from the bolt.

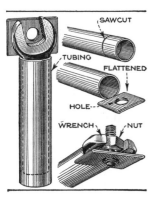

Emergency Repair for Pump Handle

When the bracket on which the pump handle was pivoted broke off, the emergency repair shown in the illustration was adopted and found entirely satisfactory. Two pieces of 1 by 4-in. boards served as a standard, on the end of which a wooden handle was pivoted. This support was braced at the bottom and fastened securely to the wooden platform of the pump. The emergency handle thus made was found just as useful and convenient as the original.—L. M. Jordan, Vredenburgh, Alabama.

Handy Basting-Thread Pick

Tailors and seamstresses will find the alteration on a thimble shown in the illustration very handy for removing basting threads. An angular cut is made through the end of a common thimble and the piece is bent outward. With the thimble worn on the middle finger, the projecting point can readily be inserted under the stitches to be removed.—G. E. Hendrickson, Argyle, Wis.

¶Graphite and oil will arrest cutting in bronze bearings when oil alone will not.

Spring-Winding Arbor

To wind an odd-shaped spring, such as shown in the illustration, is not difficult, but how to get it off the arbor is perplexing. We had

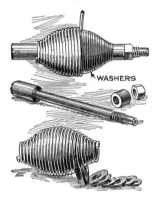

a large number of these springs to wind and the work was done in the following way: The arbor was turned down a little, as shown, in the center and 1/16-in. washers were slipped on and held by a nut. The assembly was then put in a lathe and the washers turned down to the shape desired for the coil. After a spring had been wound, the arbor was removed from the lathe and the nut unscrewed. It was then an easy matter to slip the washers out of the spring as indicated in the lower detail. For convenience in reassembling, the washers should be numbered. — Charles Kugler, Philadelphia, Pa.

Lift for Handling Auto Hood

Handling the hood of an auto while working on the engine is something of a problem to many auto mechanics since it is easily marred and, if large, difficult to handle for one man, without damaging either the hood or the fenders. Four pieces of heavy wire or light round stock, shaped as shown in the detail and each measuring about 36 in. from eye to hook, form a sling and are strung together with a strong rope, which runs over a pulley as indicated. In use, the hooks

Lifting Auto Hood Entirely Out of the Way to Prevent Marring It

are slipped under the edges of the cover and it is then pulled up and out of the way, the rope being fastened securely.— G. C. Douglas, Raleigh, N. C.

Sensitive Depth Gauge

All regular-type depth gauges have one fault; it is impossible to tell if the depth being measured is more than the setting of the gauge. This does not apply, of course, in the case of parts where the depth can be seen, nor is it a disadvantage where only one part is being measured, but

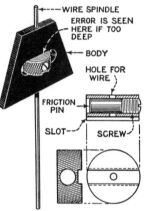

when a depth gauge is used for inspecting a number of pieces, it is set to the correct depth and, if the work is too shallow, the work is too shallow, the body of the gauge will stand clear of the work. If the body of the gauge touches the work, however, there is no means of telling how deep the part is without altering the setting of the spindle. The sensitive gauge shown is particularly adapted for inspection work, because it not only measures the depth to which it is set, but also shows if the part is deeper, and how much. The body is made of 3/16-in. flat stock and the wire spindle is 3/32 in. thick. A slot is cut in the center of the body to receive a special tightening collar, which is a knurled round piece, drilled in the center for the wire spindle, through the side for a friction pin, and is also drilled and tapped for a setscrew. The friction pin is drilled to receive the wire spindle also. The bottom of the tightening collar is slotted, to clear the width of the body about ³⁄₁₆ in. When setting the gauge to depth, the collar is turned with the slot at right angles to the body, but, in use, the slot is turned back in line. The body of the gauge will stand clear of the top surface of the work in the ordinary way if the depth is too shallow, but if the hole is too deep, the spindle will drop down and show the extent of the error between the top of the tightening collar and the slot. If the hole is correct, there is no play in the spindle and the body of the gauge rests on the work.—Harry Moore, Montreal, Can.

Tightening Storage-Battery Terminals

Storage - battery terminals m u s t be kept tight to prevent them f r o m loosening d u e t o constant vibration. When the nut cannot be s c r e w e d down any more because of the shoulder on the terminal one or more copper washers under the nut will often remedy the trouble. Another method of tightening the lug on the terminal is to drive down a small wood screw into the terminal or between the lug and the terminal, as shown in the two lower figures of the illustration. This acts as a wedge and spreads the terminal, taking up all the play between the lug and terminal. Even a nail will serve if a screw should happen not to be at hand.—G. A. Luers, Washington, D. C.

¶April is the best month of the year in which to hatch Leghorns and other light breeds of poultry.

Old Auto Casings Slipped over Large Circular Saws Offer Protection

Casing Protects Circular Saw

Old automobile casings will be found useful around woodworking plants, mills and in farm shops having large circular saws. Cut the casing as shown in the photo so that it can be slipped over the saw easily. This not only protects the saw but also prevents anyone from getting hurt while the saw is not in use.—J. B. Tate, Mokelumne Hill, Calif.

Handy Graduation for Calipers

Calipers will be found much handier if graduated as illustrated. The points are first set to the desired dimensions and lines a r e scratched on one side with the scribers. The other arm should be beveled. T h e dimensions s h o u l d be stamped or deeply etched so as not to become unreadable.— C. D. Zellar, Chicago, Ill.

Brick Cleaner from Hacksaw Blades

For cleaning the face of brick or removing paint and plaster, an excellent tool can be made from a dozen or more old hacksaw blades, mounted so that they will be spaced about ¼ in. apart, and provided with handles, as shown in the drawing. To bind the blades together, washers are placed between the ends and long threaded rods, with a nut at each end, are used to form them into a solid bundle. The handles are made up of equal lengths of ¼-in. rod, with the ends flattened, drilled and bent to the shape shown. Any brick can readily be cleaned on the face surface with this tool so that it has the appearance of being new when set into a finished wall. To hold the brick, four blocks of wood are nailed to a bench and spaced to accommodate the brick. The cleaner is rasped firmly across the face, making a clean job of resurfacing in a very few strokes.—G. A. Luers, Washington, D. C.

BLOCKS
WASHERS
HACKSAWS
¼" IRON RODS

Rubbing Down Varnish

In doing some cabinetwork, I discovered a method of saving a lot of hard work and time when rubbing down the varnish with pumice stone. I have always had a great deal of trouble to get the finely powdered stone removed from the small interstices of the wood before applying the second coat and again later on. On the last job I did, that of making a library table of black walnut, I mixed a small amount of the powdered pumice with some walnut stain. The result was highly satisfactory. The object of mixing the pumice with the stain was to fix it so that if any small amount were left in the work it would be inconspicuous.—H. F. O'Neal, Noblesville, Ind.

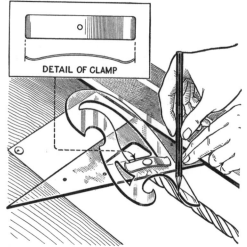

DETAIL OF CLAMP

Clamping a French Curve to a Triangle Makes It Easy to Handle

Clamp on Triangle Holds French Curve

Many an exasperating job of irregular-curve drawing can be made just as easy as the use of a triangle. A small sheet-metal clamp grips and holds the curve securely in any position by means of a thumbscrew set in one of several threaded holes in a regular triangle, and permits it to be moved along in any direction, while it is kept in perfect alinement. The same curve section can be repeated any number of times at any desired intervals and with the assurance of getting it correctly located every time. A medium-size triangle will be found preferable to serve as a base for the clamp. No tap is necessary in making the holes, as a sharp screw will cut its own thread in celluloid. Care must be taken, however, not to make the blank holes too large. They should be slightly larger than the bottom diameter of the thread. The clamp is made of ¹⁄₃₂-in. spring brass or bronze, and should be slightly bent up at the ends and sprung up in the center, as indicated. All the corners should be rounded. The thumbscrew should not be too large and must have a small stem with a fine thread similar to screws in drawing instruments. In the illustration, the arrangement is shown in laying out the flutes of a twist drill, which can be accurately done in a short time, a guide line being drawn to one side of the triangle to preserve the vertical alinement.—H. Simon, Santa Ana, Calif.

INDEX TO VOLUME 23
Shop Notes for 1926

207

Ford—continued
  cars, device for changing spring shackles on 154
  clutch, spring compressor for............. 142
  starter, assembling bendix drive on....... 150
  valve stems, shortening................ 166
Forms for concrete steps, time saving......... 30
Foul air
  in wells, handy test for.................. 162
  ridding deep well of.................... 46
Foundations, stone, eliminating air leaks in.... 175
Foundry flasks from truck wheels............ 12
Frames, window, construction of.............. 75
French curve, clamp on triangle holds........ 204
Fuels, special, metal floats for.............. 176
Funnel, handy radiator filling............... 162
Furnace, hot air, improving.................. 193
Furniture, printers' emergency.............. 157
Garage, small, wrecking crane for............. 185
Garden marker, an eight row................. 63
Garden
  marker, an eight row.................... 63
  walks and entrance, laying............... 48
Garage
  handy workbenches for................. 115
  washroom, brush for.................... 72
Gaskets, shellac and graphite replace.......... 12
Gasoline
  blowtorch, starting 127
  drum, convenient 10
  drum and oil drums, trailer for.......... 55
  lamp, blowtorch made from.............. 149
  saving 65
  washing parts in........................ 157
Gate
  for the stock corral..................... 17
  keeps stock safe and ventilates barn...... 17
Gauge
  depth for sawing........................ 123
  fixed line 131
  hinge or butt, homemade................ 102
  improved drill and wire................. 189
  never slip, aids glazier in glass cutting.... 33
  sensitive depth 202
Gauze motor brushes, making............... 200
Glass for a surface plate.................... 157
Glazier
  grooved roller for...................... 151
  never-slip gauge aids in glass cutting...... 333
Glaziers, mallet handy for.................. 192
Glazing brick walls........................ 57
Glue for cardboard........................ 182
Graduation, handy, for calipers..:.......... 203
Grain-drill tube, emergency................. 164
Graphite and shellac replace gaskets.......... 12
Grass, keeping canal banks free of........... 55
Grease cups, pouring lubricant into........... 105
Grinder
  convertible toolpost, making............. 27
  made from auto parts.................. 70
  serviceable homemade 176
Grinding
  bearing caps, holders help in............ 192
  drills for brass......................... 81
Grooved rail, bending iron on................ 85
Guard
  pulley, saves hands..................... 177
  safety, on power-line poles.............. 158
Gypsum, use of, weakens cement.............. 97
Hammer
  air, absorbing the shock of.............. 177
  handle, wax supply in, convenient for driving nails 78
  improvised soft 105
  old, tool for backing out rivets made from.. 192
Hacksaw
  blades, brick cleaner made from.......... 204
  getting service from the................. 59
Hanging windows 97
Handle, extension, on tap.................... 184
Hanger, paint-pot 4
Harvester and thresher, improving combined.... 96
Hay
  chain scatters in mow................. 142
  chute, outside 141
  curing, independent of weather air blower for 103
  shed, adjustable roof on................ 82
Heating, steam, economy in.................. 56
Heatproof paint, homemade................. 163
Hinge or butt gauge, homemade............. 102
Hints
  for the draftsman...................... 96
  lathing 147
Hitch, side, for motor truck................. 175

Hog corral, portable........................ 197
Hogs, tattooing is new marking method....... 122
Hoisting barrels, safety attachment for........ 32
Holder
  boring bar 80
  for signal lantern...................... 18
  soap, for workshop washroom............ 81
Holes
  brass, filling in....................... 63
  cutting in thin sheet copper............. 151
  drilling in edge of disk................. 35
Holster
  handy for revolver in auto.............. 141
  hip, for auto service station attendant..... 74
Honey bees, to save....................... 30
Hood, auto, lift for handling................ 202
Hook, tile, for deep trenches................ 33
Horses, clipping 65
Hose, disappearing air..................... 104
Hot air furnace, improving................... 193
Hulling and scarifying clover seed........... 160
Hydrant installation, good................. 188
Hypo, old, use for......................... 75
Ignition, substitute for dry cells for......... 147
Incubator thermometer, reading............. 36
Interior trim, installing.................... 77
Inventory, keeping perpetual................ 76
Iron
  bending on grooved rail................ 85
  from steel, test distinguishes............ 141
Irrigation canals
  keeping clean 81
  keeping moss from choking............. 47
Jack, adjustable, for repair work............ 97
Jacket, broken water, repaired without welding. 178
Jewelers, kink for........................ 85
Jig
  for center-drilling keyways.............. 177
  skate sharpening 31
  U-bolt makes good bending.............. 23
Jigs and fixtures, detachable knobs for........ 55
Jigsaw for a dollar........................ 1
Jobs, two-man, speeded up by swiveling work holder 172
Kit, soldering, keeping handy............... 189
Knob
  detachable, for jigs and fixtures......... 55
  makes acetylene tank wrench............ 131
Knurling
  in the vise........................... 140
  tool, starting the..................... 98
Labor saving snow shovel................... 34
Lacquer, using 134
Ladder
  attachment aids in hanging eaves troughs.. 57
  orchard, convenient 116
  platform on prevents cramp............. 65
  support, handy 152
Lantern chimneys, cleaning................. 61
Lanterns, large oil tanks on................ 120
Lapping bushings, quick way of.............. 130
Large clips, new use for.................... 166
Lathe
  fixture for refaces brake drums.......... 148
  graduating a six foot scale in the......... 153
  hints 147
  rigged up for use as rotary metal shears.. 152
  speed, turning bar stock on.............. 82
  tailstock, repairing 58
  work, tool setter for.................... 62
Lead
  electroplating 131
  removing from automatic pencil.......... 45
Leaks in walls, pipes and purses............. 143
Leaky steam lines, stopping................. 22
Letter box, hammered-copper 99
Letterer, window, drawing guide for.......... 103
Lighting manholes 95
Line
  fish drying 105
  gauge, fixed 131
  points, dimension, stamp for............ 134
  shaft, automatic oiler for............... 136
Link, safety, in tow chain.................. 103
Loading, permanent steps on truck aid....... 22
Locking
  cabinet drawers 4
  motor support bolts................... 128
Locknuts, brass 37
Log, sawbuck helps raise................... 132
Lubricant, pouring into grease cups........... 105
Lubricating
  rebored cylinders 60
  wagon wheels 44

NOTES

NOTES

NOTES

NOTES